S N A P

Student Notes and Problems

MATH 7
Alberta

CASTLE ROCK
RESEARCH CORP

Publisher
Gautam Rao

Contributors
Ruth Rancier
Andrea Ryan
Stephanie Vanderwielen

Rao, Gautam, 1961 –
STUDENT NOTES AND PROBLEMS – Math 7 Workbook
Alberta
(Second Edition)

1. Math – Juvenile Literature. I. Title

Published by
Castle Rock Research Corp.
2340 Manulife Place
10180 – 101 Street
Edmonton, AB T5J 3S4

1 2 3 FP 13 12 11

Dedicated to the memory of Dr. V. S. Rao

STUDENT NOTES AND PROBLEMS WORKBOOKS

Student Notes and Problems (SNAP) workbooks are a series of support resources in mathematics for students in grades 3 to 12 and in science for students in grades 9 to 12. SNAP workbooks are 100% aligned with curriculum. The resources are designed to support classroom instructions and provide students with additional examples, practice exercises, and tests. SNAP workbooks are ideal for use all year long at school and at home.

The following is a summary of the key features of all SNAP workbooks.

UNIT OPENER PAGE

- summarizes the curriculum outcomes addressed in the unit in age-appropriate language
- identifies the lessons by title
- lists the prerequisite knowledge and skills the student should know prior to beginning the unit

LESSONS

- provide essential teaching pieces and explanations of the concepts
- include example problems and questions with complete, detailed solutions that demonstrate the problem-solving process

NOTES BARS

- contain key definitions, formulas, reminders, and important steps or procedures
- provide space for students to add their own notes and helpful reminders

PRACTICE EXERCISES

- include questions that relate to each of the curriculum outcomes for the unit
- provide practice in applying the lesson concepts

REVIEW SUMMARY

- provides a succinct review of the key concepts in the unit

PRACTICE TEST

- assesses student learning of the unit concepts

ANSWERS AND SOLUTIONS

- demonstrate the step-by-step process or problem-solving method used to arrive at the correct answer

Answers and solutions for the odd-numbered questions are provided in each student workbook. A *SNAP Solutions Manual* that contains answers and complete solutions for all questions is also available.

CONTENTS

Working with Percents

Fractional Operations

The Cartesian Plane

Patterns

Expressions and Equations

Geometric Constructions

Circles

Area

Probability

Data Analysis

Answers and Solutions

OPERATIONS WITH DECIMAL NUMBERS

When you are finished this unit, you will be able to…
- solve a given problem involving the addition and subtraction of decimal numbers
- solve a given problem involving the multiplication or division of decimal numbers
- check the reasonableness of solutions using estimation
- solve a given problem that involves operations on decimals (limited to thousandths) by considering the order of operations

PREREQUISITE SKILLS AND KNOWLEDGE

Prior to starting this unit, you should be able to…
- read and write numbers to the thousandths place value
- round numbers up to the hundredths place value
- use arithmetic to solve problems involving decimal numbers
- use front-end estimation

Lesson 1   USING FRONT-END ESTIMATION

Estimating calculations involves making a reasonable guess as to what the final answer will be. You use numbers close to the original numbers so you can work with them easily.

You should estimate in these situations:
- When an exact answer is not needed.
- When the problem can be solved by knowing about how much.
- When you want to check if an answer is reasonable.

There are many methods for estimating. **Front-end estimation** is a useful strategy that involves calculations with the first digit of each number. All the other digits of the number get replaced with a zero.

ESTIMATING SUMS

A **sum** is the result of two or more numbers being added together.

Example

Using front-end estimation, determine the approximate sum of $237 + 596$.

Solution

Step 1

Keep the first digit. Replace the other digits with zeros.

$$237 \rightarrow 200$$
$$+596 \rightarrow +500$$

Step 2

Perform the operation indicated in the question.
In this case, it is addition.

$$\begin{array}{r} 200 \\ +500 \\ \hline 700 \end{array}$$

The estimate is less than the actual answer because each number was decreased in value when the remaining digits were changed to zeros. Because of this, the estimate is not always as accurate as needed.

2

Your Turn 1

a) Use front-end estimation to calculate the approximate sum of $372 + 315$.

600

b) Explain why the estimate will be higher or lower than the actual answer.

Example

Use front-end estimation to calculate the approximate sum of $2\ 335.45 + 43.99 + 159.76 + 32.23$.

Solution

Step 1

Keep the first digit of the numbers, and make all the other digits zero. Notice digits after the decimal point are left off completely.

$$
\begin{array}{rcl}
\mathbf{2}\ 335.45 & \rightarrow & 2\ 000 \\
43.99 & \rightarrow & 40 \\
159.76 & \rightarrow & 100 \\
+\ \ 32.23 & \rightarrow & +\ \ 30 \\
\end{array}
$$

Step 2

Perform the operation indicated in the question.

In this case, it is addition.

$$
\begin{array}{r}
2\ 000 \\
40 \\
100 \\
+\ 30 \\
\hline
2\ 170 \\
\end{array}
$$

Your Turn 2

a) Use front-end estimation to calculate the approximate sum of $5\ 389.12 + 459.28 + 9\ 112.94 + 783.8$.

b) Explain why the estimate will be higher or lower than the actual answer.

NOTES

The subtrahend is the amount being subtracted.

ESTIMATING DIFFERENCES

A **difference** is the result of two or more numbers being subtracted from one another.

Example

Use front-end estimation to calculate the approximate difference of 5 490.892 – 345.67.

Solution

Step 1

Keep the first digit of the numbers, and make all the other digits zero.

$$\begin{array}{rcl} \mathbf{5}\ 490.892 & \rightarrow & 5\ 000 \\ -\ \ \ 345.670 & \rightarrow & -\ 300 \end{array}$$

Step 2

Perform the operation indicated in the question.
In this case, it is subtraction.

$$\begin{array}{r} 5\ 000 \\ -\ \ \ 300 \\ \hline 4\ 700 \end{array}$$

The difference of 5 490.892 – 345.67 is approximately 4 700.

Your Turn 3

a) Use front-end estimation to calculate the approximate difference of 8 962.45 – 545.17.

$$\begin{array}{r} 8\ 000 \\ -\ 500 \\ \hline 7\ 500 \end{array}$$

b) Explain why the estimate will be higher or lower than the actual answer.

ESTIMATING PRODUCTS

A product is the result of two or more numbers being multiplied together.

Example

Use front-end estimation to calculate the approximate product of
$1\,491.67 \times 51.03$.

Solution

Step 1

Keep the first digit. Make all the other digits zero.

$$1\,491.67 \rightarrow 1\,000$$
$$\times \quad 51.03 \rightarrow \times \quad 50$$

Step 2

Perform the operation indicated in the question.
In this case, it is multiplication.

$$
\begin{array}{r}
1000 \\
\times \quad 50 \\
\hline
50\,000
\end{array}
$$

The product of $1\,491.67 \times 51.03$ is approximately 50 000.

The estimate is less than the actual answer because both factors were decreased in value. The greater the decrease, the less accurate the answer.

Your Turn 4

Use front-end estimation to calculate the approximate product of
$2\,745.82 \times 45.72$.

NOTES

ESTIMATING QUOTIENTS

A quotient is the result of one number being divided by another number.

Example

Use front-end estimation to calculate the approximate quotient of $173.42 \div 21.36$.

Solution

Step 1

Keep the first digit. Make all the other digits zero. Drop the digits after the decimal.

$$21.36 \rightarrow \quad 20\overline{)100}$$
$$\uparrow$$
$$173.42$$

Step 2

Perform the operation indicated in the question.
In this case, it is division.

$$20\overline{)100}^{\;5}$$

The quotient of $173.42 \div 21.36$ is approximately 5.

Your Turn 5

Use front-end estimation to calculate the approximate quotient of $972.981 \div 32.43$.

APPLICATIONS OF FRONT-END ESTIMATION

In everyday life, quick estimates are required to determine an approximate solution to a problem. For example, you may estimate the cost of two CDs and one DVD to see if you have enough money to buy all three. Your parents may estimate if there is enough gas in the car to get them where they are going. A party organizer might estimate how many people are going to attend their event in order to determine how much food to order.

When given mathematical problems, there are clues that let you know if an estimated answer or actual calculation is required. Some words that indicate estimation are *about*, *around*, *approximately*, *almost*, *close to*, and *roughly*.

Example

John collected bottles four weeks in a row to earn some extra cash for a purchase he is saving up for. He put the money in a jar on his dresser. The amounts he put in the jar were $31.75, $21.75, $12.80, and $37.26. The purchase is $89.99. Is John close to having enough money?

Solution

Step 1

Use front-end estimation.

$$
\begin{array}{rcr}
31.75 & \rightarrow & 30 \\
21.75 & \rightarrow & 20 \\
12.80 & \rightarrow & 10 \\
+37.25 & \rightarrow & +30 \\
\end{array}
$$

Step 2

Perform the operation indicated in the problem.
In this case, it is addition.

$$
\begin{array}{r}
30 \\
20 \\
10 \\
+30 \\
\hline
90 \\
\end{array}
$$

The estimate is $90.00. John knows the actual calculation is more than that. John has more than $90.00 saved up, which is enough for his purchase.

Your Turn 6

Janet committed to making 100 cookies for a fundraiser at the school. She baked 32 cookies in the morning. In the afternoon, she baked another 43 cookies. Finally, in the evening, she baked 22 more cookies. Did she come close to the amount she committed to?

PRACTICE EXERCISES

Use front-end estimation to calculate the approximate sum of the following expressions.

1. $43.781 + 28.3$

2. $9.718 + 0.726$

Use front-end estimation to calculate the approximate difference of the following expressions.

3. $85.96 - 34.5$

4. $970.52 - 433.28$

Use front-end estimation to calculate the approximate product of the following expressions.

5. 64.8×36.2

6. $1\ 132.73 \times 28.64$

Use front-end estimation to calculate the approximate quotient of the expressions.

7. $92.7 \div 9.4$

8. $2\ 484.72 \div 64.26$

9. A party planner needs to arrange 32 flower vases for a reception. She has 317 long stem roses and 91 stems of baby's-breath to work with. Approximately how many stems of each type of flower can she put evenly in each vase?

10. A book store manager ordered 23 cases of the latest bestseller. There were 32 books in each case. The store had 602 customers preorder a copy of the book. Using front-end estimation, determine whether the manager ordered enough books.

Lesson 2   ADDING DECIMALS

The addition equation is *addend + addend = sum*.

If you decide to buy a scarf for $12.99 and mittens for $5.99, how much money do you owe?

The problem is asking you to add the prices and find the sum of the two items.

Three strategies that can be used for adding decimals numbers are using base ten blocks, place value tables, and paper and pencil.

USING BASE TEN BLOCKS

Base ten blocks visually represent numbers. When representing decimal numbers, the value of the cube becomes 1. The blocks that follow become one-tenth smaller for each increment.

Number Value	Base Ten Block	Decimal Number Value
cube = 1 000 (thousands)		cube = 1 (ones)
flat = 100 (hundreds)		flat = 0.1 (tenths)
rod = 10 (tens)		rod = 0.01 (hundredths)
unit = 1 (ones)		unit = 0.001 (thousandths)

Example
Model the decimal number 3.142.

Solution

Step 1
Identify the base ten blocks required.
There are 3 ones, so you will need three cubes.
There is 1 tenth; you will need one flat.
There are 4 hundredths; you will need four rods.
There are 2 thousandths; you will need two units.

NOTES

Step 2

Model the decimal number.

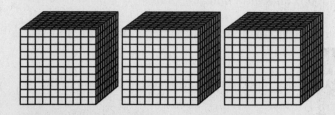

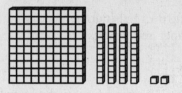

Your Turn 1

Model the decimal number 1.32.

ADDING DECIMALS WITH BASE TEN BLOCKS

To add decimal numbers using base ten blocks, follow these steps:
1. Model each addend.
2. Combine like blocks together, and regroup the blocks for the most efficient set in each place value.

Example

Use base ten blocks to solve $1.73 + 2.45$.

Solution

Step 1
Model each addend.
Model 1.73.

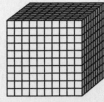

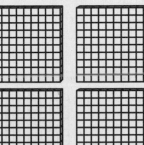

Model 2.45.

NOTES

Step 2
Combine like blocks together.

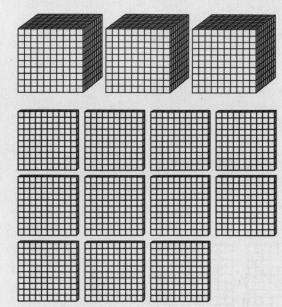

Regroup the blocks for the most efficient set in each place value.
Regroup 10 of the 11 flat blocks as a cube leaving 1 flat.

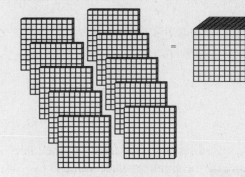

The final set becomes

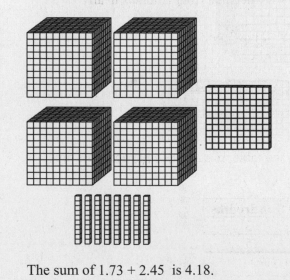

The sum of 1.73 + 2.45 is 4.18.

Your Turn 2

Use base ten blocks to solve $1.285 + 2.834$.

USING PLACE VALUE TABLES

To add decimal numbers using place value tables, follow these steps:
1. Determine the number of columns necessary, and construct the table.
2. Enter the numbers into the table. Put place holders of 0 where there are no digits.
3. Beginning from the right, add the column of numbers.

Example

Use a place value table to solve $1.73 + 2.45$.

Solution

Step 1

Determine the number of columns necessary, and construct the table. The largest place value is ones, and the smallest place value is hundredths. Make a place value table that includes all three place values and a column for the decimal (four columns in all).

Ones	.	Tenths	Hundredths
	.		
	.		
	.		

Step 2

Enter the numbers into the table, making sure the decimals are lined up.

Ones	.	Tenths	Hundredths
1	.	7	3
2	.	4	5
	.		

Step 3
Beginning at the right, add the digits in each column.

Ones	.	Tenths	Hundredths
1	.	7	3
2	.	4	5
4	.	1	8

The sum of 1.73 + 2.45 is 4.18.

Your Turn 3
Use a place value table to solve 0.43 + 76 + 19.42 + 63.2 + 9.52.

USING PAPER AND PENCIL
To add decimal numbers with pencil and paper, follow these steps:
1. Align decimal numbers in a vertical column so the digits of the same place value and decimals form a straight line.
2. Starting at the far right, add the digits in each vertical column; carry tens over to the next column. Bring down the decimal point, and align it directly below the other decimal points.

Example
Solve the expression 38.76 + 2.07 + 43.45 + 479.21.

Solution

Step 1
Write the numbers one on top of the other, lining up the decimal points.

```
  38.76
   2.07
  43.45
+479.21
```

Step 2
Start at the far right, and add all the numbers in the column. Bring down the decimal point, and align it directly below the other decimal points.

```
 1 2 1  1
  38.76
   2.07
  43.45
 1
+479.21
 563.49
```

The sum of 38.76 + 2.07 + 43.45 + 479.21 is 563.49.

Missing spaces to the right of the decimal may be filled in with zeros as place holders.

Your Turn 4

Solve the expression $41.47 + 9.04 + 385.82 + 111.71$.

APPLICATIONS OF ADDITION

You encounter decimal numbers in everyday situations such as shopping, measuring, weather, and time.

When solving decimal problems that involve addition, look for keywords such as *sum*, *in addition to*, *change*, *increased by*, *more than*, *plus*, *altogether*, *in total*, and *in all*.

Example

Penny goes to a ski store that is having a "Get Ready for Winter Sale." Everything in the store has no GST. The price of a scarf is $7.49, mittens are $14.99, and toques are $12.49.

a) If Penny decides to buy the scarf and toque, about how much will she spend?

Solution

Add the prices of the two items.
Often, when people shop, they will estimate the total of a purchase to make sure they have enough money when they get to the cashier.
In this case, a rough estimate is sufficient.

Use front-end estimation.

$$
\begin{array}{rcr}
12.49 & \rightarrow & 12 \\
+7.49 & \rightarrow & +\ 7 \\
\hline
& & 19
\end{array}
$$

The estimated values are lower than the actual values. Penny needs more than $19.00 to purchase the toque and scarf.

b) If Penny decides to buy the scarf and toque, exactly how much will she spend?

Solution

Write the numbers one on top of the other, lining up the decimal. Start at the far right, and add all the numbers in the column.

$$
\begin{array}{r}
\overset{1}{1}2.49 \\
+\ 7.49 \\
\hline
19.98
\end{array}
$$

Penny will spend $19.98 purchasing the scarf and toque.

Your Turn 5

a) Estimate and then calculate how much Penny will spend if she buys the scarf and mittens.

b) Estimate and then calculate how much Penny will spend if she buys the mittens and toque.

PRACTICE EXERCISES

Model each of the following decimal numbers using base ten blocks.

1. 0.243

2. 0.104

3. 2.321

4. 2.435

Use base ten blocks to solve the following expressions.

5. $1.362 + 3.135$

6. $2.471 + 1.692$

Calculate the sums of the following expressions using paper and pencil.

7. $1.278 + 2.510$

8. $5.137 + 2.841$

Use place value tables to solve the given expressions.

9. $42.36 + 8.14 + 267.22 + 331.63$

10. $3.19 + 42.85 + 119.03 + 614.10$

11. Compare adding decimal numbers to adding whole numbers. How is adding decimals the same as adding whole numbers? How is adding decimals different from adding whole numbers?

Lesson 3 SUBTRACTING DECIMALS

Think:
Subtrahend is the **S**econd number in **S**ubtraction.
Minuend **M**ust be first.

The subtraction equation is *minuend – subtrahend = difference*.

You decide to buy the scarf and mittens. When you get to the cash register, you hand the cashier $30.00. How much change will you get back?

This problem asks you to find the difference between what you owe and how much you gave to the cashier.

Three strategies for subtracting decimals numbers are using base ten blocks, place value tables, and paper and pencil.

USING BASE TEN BLOCKS

To subtract decimal numbers using base ten blocks, follow these steps:
1. Model the minuend, and cross out the blocks representing the subtrahend.
2. Identify the quantity of the remaining base ten blocks. This value represents the difference.

Example

Use base ten blocks to solve $2.64 - 1.43$.

Solution
Step 1
Model the minuend.
Model 2.64.

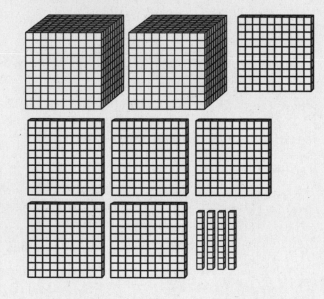

20

Cross out the blocks representing the subtrahend (1.43).
Start with the smallest place value, and work to the largest place value.

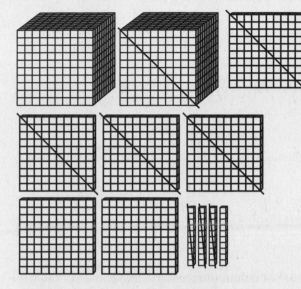

Step 2

Identify the quantity of the remaining base ten blocks.

The value of the expression $2.64 - 1.43$ is 1.21.

Your Turn 1

Use base ten blocks to solve $2.34 - 1.12$.

NOTES

USING PLACE VALUE TABLES
To subtract decimal numbers using place value tables follow these steps:

Step 1
Determine the number of columns and construct the table.

Step 2
Enter the numbers into the table. Put place holders of 0 where there are no digits.

Step 3
Beginning from the right and work to the left. Regroup when necessary.

Example
Use a place value table to solve $2.64 - 1.43$.

Solution
Step 1
Determine the number of columns necessary, and construct the table. The largest place value is ones, and the smallest place value is hundredths. Make a place value table that includes all three place values and a column for the decimal (four columns in all).

Ones	.	Tenths	Hundredths
	.		
	.		
	.		

Step 2
Enter the numbers into the table, making sure the decimals are lined up.

Ones	.	Tenths	Hundredths
2	.	6	4
1	.	4	3
	.		

Step 3
Beginning at the right, subtract the digits in each column.

Ones	.	Tenths	Hundredths
2	.	6	4
1	.	4	3
1	.	2	1

The value of the expression $2.64 - 1.43$ is 1.21.

Your Turn 2

Use a place value table to solve $19.623 - 15.42$.

USING PAPER AND PENCIL

To subtract decimal numbers with pencil and paper, follow these steps:
1. Align the minuend above the subtrahend in a vertical column so the digits of the same place value and decimals form a straight line.
2. Starting at the far right, subtract the digits in each vertical column; borrow from the left column if necessary. Bring down the decimal point, and align it directly below the other decimal points.

Example

Solve the expression $479.21 - 43.45$.

Solution
Step 1
Write the numbers one on top of the other, lining up the decimal points.

```
  479.21
-  43.45
```

Step 2
Start at the far right, and subtract all the numbers in the column. Bring down the decimal point, and align it directly below the other decimal points.

```
      8  11 11
  47 9. 2 1
-  43. 4 5
  435. 7 6
```

The difference of $479.21 - 43.45$ is 435.76.

Your Turn 3

Solve the expression $3\,185.82 - 116.73$.

APPLICATIONS OF SUBTRACTION

When solving problems that involve subtraction, look for keywords such as *difference*, *left over*, *change*, *decreased by*, *less than*, *minus*, *how much more*, *take away*, and *how much less*.

Example

John bought a computer for $2 346.79. Three years later, he sold it for $725.00.

a) About how much money did he lose in the sale of his computer?

Solution
Use front-end estimation.
Subtract the prices of the two items.

$$
\begin{array}{r}
2\ 346.79 \rightarrow 2\ 000 \\
-725 \rightarrow -700 \\
\hline
1\ 300
\end{array}
$$

Since both numbers were decreased, the exact calculation will be greater than $1 300.

b) Calculate exactly how much money John lost.

Solution
Write the minuend on top of the subtrahend, lining up the decimal points.

$$
\begin{array}{r}
2\ 346.79 \\
-725.00 \\
\hline
\end{array}
$$

Start at the far right, and subtract the lower digit from the upper digit in each column.

$$
\begin{array}{r}
{}^{1}{}^{13} \\
2\ 346.79 \\
-725.00 \\
\hline
1\ 621.79
\end{array}
$$

John lost $1 621.79 from the original purchase price.

Your Turn 4

Albert's mass is 46.5 kg, and Michael's mass is 62.8 kg. Estimate and then calculate the difference in mass between the two boys.

24

PRACTICE EXERCISES

Use base ten blocks to solve the following expressions.

1. $3.443 - 1.21$

2. $2.421 - 1.32$

3. $1.748 - 0.542$

Calculate the differences of the following expressions using paper and pencil.

4. 6.439 − 2.045

5. 34.05 − 12.39

6. 54.892 − 13.67

Use place value tables to solve the given expressions.

7. 95.87 − 6.25

8. 152.1 − 74.3

9. 85.261 − 52.14

10. A tailor has a piece of cloth that is 16.43 m long. If he cuts 7.89 m from the piece, how much cloth is left?

Lesson 4 MULTIPLYING DECIMALS

The multiplication equation is as follows:
multiplicand (factor 1) × *multiplier* (factor 2) = *product*

When multiplying decimal numbers, follow the same process as multiplying whole numbers.

To determine where to put the decimal point in the answer, count how many digits in total are after the decimal points in the factors being multiplied. Then starting from the right, count the same number of places as the total and place the decimal point in the answer.

Place the decimal point into the answer after all the multiplication steps are completed.

Example

What is the solution to 3.5 × 2.8?

Solution

```
    3.5   (1 digit behind the decimal)
  × 2.8   (1 digit behind the decimal)
   ───
   280
  +700
   ───
   980   ──move decimal 2 places──→ 9.8
              to the left
```

Check the reasonableness of the solution with estimation.

```
   3.5   →    3.5
  ×2.8       ×  3
            ─────
             10.5
```

Your Turn 1

What is the solution to 4.23×1.62 ?

NOTES

For multiplying larger decimal numbers, it is easiest to use a calculator. Enter the values into the calculator along with the correct mathematical operation.

Example

Solve the expression 42.25×1.36 using a calculator.

Solution

Enter the expression into your calculator.

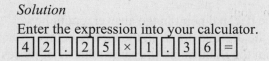

The answer that appears on the screen will be 57.46.

Your Turn 2

a) Use a calculator to find the product of the expression 325.18×32.11.

b) Use a calculator to find the product of the expression 760.38×29.8.

APPLICATIONS OF MULTIPLYING DECIMALS

When solving problems involving the multiplication of decimals, look for keywords such as *of*, *product*, *doubled*, and *tripled*.

Systematically work through each of the steps:
Step 1
Identify the given information.

Step 2
Decide on the strategy or operation to use.

Step 3
Apply the strategy.

Step 4
Check the solution.

Example

Marie bought five books as birthday presents for five cousins. Each book cost $10.95. She left the store with $10.25. How much money did Marie start with?

There is no GST on produce items in a grocery store

Solution

Step 1
Identify the given information.

Each of the five books cost $10.95.
Marie left the store with $10.25.

Step 2
Decide on the strategy or operation to use.

To determine the amount she started with, add the cost of five books and the amount she had when she left the store.

The cost of five books can be determined by multiplying the cost of one book by 5.

Step 3
Apply the strategy.
She spent $10.95 \times 5 = \$54.75$ to buy the books.

10.95 (2 digit behind decimal)
$\times$ 5 (0 digits behind decimal)
5475 $\xrightarrow{\text{move decimal 2 places to the left}}$ 54.75

The cost of the books was $54.75.

If Marie left with $10.25 in her pocket, she had $10.25 plus the total cost of the books to begin with.
$10.25 + \$54.75 = \$65.00$

Step 4
Check the solution.
$65 - 54.75 = 10.25$

Marie started with $65.00

Your Turn 3

How much will it cost to buy 4.25 kg of apples if they are $2.20/kg?

PRACTICE EXERCISES

Find the product for each of the following problems.

1. 12×3.4

2. 7.5×3.2

3. 125.2×0.42

4. 32.07×14.6

5. 0.36×0.81

6. 9.34×14.6

7. Use a calculator to find the answer to 2.2×4.1.

8. Use a calculator to find the answer to 10.45×6.7.

9. Jill wants to buy 3 digital cameras for her school. Each camera costs \$138.50. How much money does Jill need to buy the cameras?

10. What is the total cost of 65 CDs if each CD costs \$17.99?

30

Lesson 5   DIVIDING DECIMALS

The division equation is *dividend ÷ divisor = quotient*.

Paige is running low on painting supplies. She visits the local art store because they are having a sale with no GST on any product. If paintbrushes cost 2 for $4.98 and watercolours cost $0.75, how many water colours can she buy with the $6.00 in her pocket?

The problem asks Paige how many $0.75 groups are in $6.00. When a number is broken into smaller parts, the operation is called division.

When dividing decimal numbers, follow these steps:

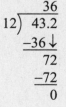

- Step 1
- If the divisor is a decimal number, move the decimal point to the right until the decimal is at the end of the divisor; move the decimal point in the dividend the same number of places.

-

- Step 2
- Divide as normal using long division until the answer either terminates or repeats.

-

- Step 3
- Place the decimal point in the answer directly over the decimal point in the dividend.

Example

What is the solution to $4.32 \div 1.2$?

Solution

Step 1

Move the decimal over one place in the divisor and dividend to get a whole number divisor.

$$1.2\overline{)4.32} \;\rightarrow\; 12\overline{)43.2}$$

Step 2

Divide using long division.

$$
\begin{array}{r}
36 \\
12\overline{)\;43.2} \\
-36\downarrow \\
\hline
72 \\
-72 \\
\hline
0
\end{array}
$$

Step 3

Place a decimal point directly above the decimal point in the dividend.

```
        3.6
  12) 43.2
      −36↓
        72
       −72
         0
```

Therefore, $4.32 \div 1.2 = 3.6$.

Your Turn 1

What is the solution to $6.24 \div 2.6$?

For dividing larger decimal numbers, it is easiest to use a calculator. Enter the values into a calculator along with the correct mathematical operation.

Example

Calculate the answer to $327.18 \div 4.1$ using your calculator.

Solution

Enter the expression into your calculator.

3 2 7 . 1 8 ÷ 4 . 1 =

The answer that will appear on the screen is 79.8.

Your Turn 2

Calculate the answer to $68.1 \div 3.2$ using a calculator.

APPLICATIONS OF DIVIDING DECIMALS

When solving problems involving the division of decimals, look for keywords such as *quotient*, *how many times*, *per*, *average*, and *each*.

Systematically work through each of the steps when solving a mathematical problem.

Example

If it costs $1.20/min to use a computer at an Internet café, how many complete minutes could Alton use the computer if he has $10.00?

Solution

Step 1
Identify the given information.
The computer use is $1.20/min.
Alton has $10.00.

Step 2
Decide on the strategy or operation to use.
Divide the total cash by 1.2.

Step 3
Apply the strategy or operation.
Make the decimal divisor a whole number before dividing.
The decimal must move the same number of places to the right in the dividend as the divisor. Add place holders to keep the decimal in its new spot if needed. Then, follow the same process you would use to divide whole numbers.

```
        8.33
  12)100.00
      96
      40
      36
      40
      36
       4
```

Since the remainder 4 repeats the quotient is $8.3\overline{3}$.

Step 4
Check the answer.
$8.\overline{3}$ is a repeating decimal. Take to the nearest tenth.
Doing the inverse operation is a good way to check.
$100 \div 8.3 = 12.04$
$8.3 \times 12 = 99.6$

Since a partial minute cannot be purchased, the total number of minutes that Alton can buy is 8.

Alton can use the computer for 8 minutes.

Your Turn 3

A box of artist pencils is on sale for $8.50. There are 12 pencils in each box. The boxes usually sell for $9.99. What is the regular price and sale price of each pencil?

PRACTICE EXERCISES

Find the quotient for each of the following problems. Show work.

1. $126 \div 4.2$

2. $15.4 \div 8$

3. $103.23 \div 18$

4. $24 \div 0.12$

5. $6.25 \div 0.5$

6. $4.28 \div 0.16$

7. Use a calculator to find the answer to $254.2 \div 4.1$

8. Use a calculator to find the answer to $3.42 \div 0.36$.

Estimate and then solve the given expressions using a calculator.

9. $33.99 \div 2.5$

10. $\dfrac{48.59}{4.3}$

Lesson 6 USING ORDER OF OPERATIONS WITH DECIMAL NUMBERS

NOTES

When solving mathematical expressions or equations with more than one operation, a set of rules called **order of operations** is followed. The operations are performed in a specific order to get the correct answer. The specific order used is called BEDMAS.

Brackets	Carry out all operations inside of the brackets first.
Exponents	Evaluate the exponents.
Division Multiplication	Carry out operations in the order they appear from left to right (reading order).
Addition Subtraction	Carry out operations in the order they appear, from left to right (reading order).

Example

Evaluate the expression $15.5 \div 2(6.1 - 2.3)$ following the order of operations.

Solution

Complete the operations inside the brackets. Within the brackets, follow the order of operations.

$15.5 \div 2(\underline{6.1 - 2.3})$
$= 15.5 \div 2(3.8)$

Complete the multiplication and division in order from left to right.
$\underline{15.5 \div 2}(3.8)$
$= \underline{7.75(3.8)}$
$= 29.45$

An equal sign is placed in front of each line of the expression as the calculations progress to show that the expression that follows is equal to the expression above it.

Your Turn 1

Evaluate the expression $86.8 \div (5.6 \times 6.2) - 1.7$ following the order of operations.

APPLICATION OF ORDER OF OPERATIONS

The order of operations is followed when making calculations in everyday life.

Example

Josh bought supper for his friends. He ordered one salad at $3.99, three cheeseburger combos at $5.49 each, eight ice cream sundaes at $1.29 each, and four chicken combos at $5.99 each.

a) Using the correct order of operations, write an expression for the total cost of the burgers Josh bought.

Solution

Read the problem from the beginning, and write down each number and operation as it appears in the question.
- one salad at $3.99 = 1×3.99
- three cheeseburger combos at $5.49 each = 3×5.49
- eight ice cream sundaes at $1.29 each = 8×1.29
- four chicken combos at $5.99 each = 4×5.99

Each of these individual calculations are added together to get the total bill. The expression is $3.99 + 3 \times 5.49 + 8 \times 1.29 + 4 \times 5.99$.

b) Calculate the total cost before taxes.

Solution

Follow the order of operations.
Multiply or divide in order from left to right.
$3.99 + \underline{3 \times 5.49} + 8 \times 1.29 + 4 \times 5.99$
$= 3.99 + 16.47 + \underline{8 \times 1.29} + 4 \times 5.99$
$= 3.99 + 16.47 + 10.32 + \underline{4 \times 5.99}$
$= 3.99 + 16.47 + 10.32 + 23.96$

Add and subtract in order from left to right.
$\underline{3.99 + 16.47} + 10.32 + 23.96$
$= \underline{20.46 + 10.32} + 23.96$
$= \underline{30.78 + 23.96}$
$= 54.74$

The total food bill was $54.74.

At is a keyword for multiply.

NOTES

Your Turn 2

Nicholas went to the store to pick up a few clothing supplies.
He purchased two pairs of socks at $3.99/pair, five shirts at $15.99 each, and three pairs of jeans at $52.99.

a) Using the correct order of operations, write an expression for the total cost of the clothing items Nicholas bought before taxes.

b) Calculate the total cost before taxes.

PRACTICE EXERCISES

Evaluate the given expressions following the order of operations. Show all work.

1. $12.35 \div 1.3 \times 2.6 + (6.8 - 1.2)$

2. $5.1 - (6 - 3.2) \times 2.6 + 4.1$

3. $4.5 - 7.6 \div 2 + 5.6 \times (12.2 - 2.2)$

Use the following information to answer the next two questions.

> Susan decided to raise money for three local charities by selling apples. She talked to the neighbourhood grocery store manager who said he would give her a reduced price on the apples she wanted to sell. She bought the apples for $220 and sold them all for a total of $550.

4. Using the correct order of operations, write an expression that will determine how much money Susan is going to give to each charity.

5. Calculate how much each charity will receive.

Use the following information to answer the next two questions.

> Anna has $645 saved up in the bank. She needs to earn $1 800 before she can buy a computer. She earns $231 each week babysitting after school.

6. Using the correct order of operations, write an expression that will determine how many weeks Anna still needs to babysit.

7. Calculate how many more weeks Anna must babysit until she has enough money to buy a computer.

8. Solve $12.6 \div 2.1 + 12 \div 4$.

9. Solve $64.8 \div 8 - 2.5$.

10. Solve $6.2 + (24.7 - 15.7) \times 3.6$.

REVIEW SUMMARY

- Reading and writing numbers correctly requires a thorough understanding of place value. Decimal numbers are named according to the place value of the last digit.
- Front-end estimation uses the first digit of each number to determine an approximate answer.
- When adding and subtracting decimals without using a calculator, it is very important to line up the decimal points of each decimal number. Then add or subtract as you would for whole numbers.
- When multiplying numbers, the product will have the same number of digits to the right of the decimal point as the total number of decimal places in the numbers being multiplied together.
- When dividing decimals, move the decimal point in the divisor to the right until the decimal is at the end of it; move the decimal point in the dividend the same number of places. Then divide as normal using long division until the answer either terminates or repeats. Place the decimal point in the answer directly over the decimal point in the dividend.
- To perform questions with more than one mathematical operation, use the acronym BEDMAS. It means that operations in Brackets are done first, followed by Exponents, then Division and Multiplication in order from left to right, followed by Addition and Subtraction in order from left to right.

PRACTICE TEST

Evaluate each of the following expressions. Show all work.

1. $\begin{array}{r} 6.428 \\ +12.596 \\ \hline \end{array}$

    19.024

2. $\begin{array}{r} 48.02 \\ -9.451 \\ \hline \end{array}$

    59 ?

3. $215+6.02+49.47+109.5$ 379.99

4. 42×5.3

    $\begin{array}{r} 42 \\ \times 53 \\ \hline 126 \\ 210 \\ \hline 2226 \end{array}$

5. 17.04×6.1

    $\begin{array}{r} 17.04 \\ \times 6.1 \\ \hline 1704 \\ 10224 \\ \hline 103.944 \end{array}$

42

6. $52 \div 1.3$ ~~40~~

Estimate the answers to each of the following questions using front-end estimation.

7. $48.96 \div 5.1$ 9R3

8. 4.2×10.5 40

Evaluate each of the following expressions using the order of operations.

9. $5.7 + 4.9 \times 2.1$ 5.7 + 10.29 = 15.99

$$\begin{array}{r} 14.3 \\ -\ 8.6 \\ \hline 7.7 \end{array}$$

10. $8.2 \times (14.3 - 8.6) + 2.5$ 8.2 × 7.7

11. Use a place value table to evaluate $39.423 - 21.63$.

12. Dania bought six pencils priced at $0.78 each and four pens at $1.29 each. The GST was $0.49. What was the total cost of the stationery purchase?

13. Evaluate the expression $5\ 832 \div 10.8$ using a calculator.

44

OPERATIONS WITH INTEGERS

When you are finished this unit, you will be able to…

- explain using concrete materials, such as integer tiles and diagrams, that the sum of opposite integers is zero
- using a number line, illustrate the results of adding or subtracting negative and positive integers
- add two given integers using concrete materials or pictorial representations, and record the process symbolically
- subtract two given integers using concrete materials or pictorial representations, and record the process symbolically
- solve problems involving the addition and subtraction of integers

PREREQUISITE SKILLS AND KNOWLEDGE

Prior to starting this unit, you should be able to…

- read and write numbers to the thousandths place value
- explain what integers are and their applications
- use arithmetic to solve problems
- use number lines

Lesson 1   INTRODUCTION TO INTEGERS

A **set** refers to a group of numbers, such as natural numbers, whole numbers, or integers. Braces { } are placed around the elements in the set.

Other examples of integers are golf scores and counting down a launch lift-off.

The arrows at the ends of a number line mean that the number line continues infinitely in both directions.

To remember whether numbers to the left or right on a number line are larger, think **l**eft is **l**ess.

The set of **integers** contains all the positive whole numbers, negative whole numbers, and zero.

$$\{...-3, \ -2, \ -1, \ 0, \ +1, \ +2, \ +3...\}$$

An integer uses a positive (+) sign or a negative (–) sign to indicate its value. If a number does not have a sign in front of it, it is assumed to be positive. These signs represent the value of the integer. Brackets are placed around the integers to separate the integer and its sign from the operators. For example, $(+3)-(-4)$ is read as "positive three minus negative four."

Integers represent a variety of values. For example, temperature can be +20°C or –20°C, depending on the season.

The following are some other examples of integer numbers:
- Elevation—1 000 m below sea level (–1 000 m) or 1 000 m above sea level (+1 000 m).
- Money—a profit of $10 (+$10) or a debt of $10 (–$10).

NUMBER LINES

Number lines visually represent integers. An arrow above the number line shows the value of an integer.

The number of steps the arrow moves from zero determines the integer's value. The direction the arrow moves indicates the sign of the integer:
- A move to the right indicates a positive integer.
- A move to the left indicates a negative integer.

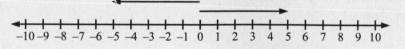

The arrow moving five steps to the right represents +5. The arrow moving five steps to the left represents –5.

Numbers to the right on a number line have larger values than numbers on the left, so +5 is greater than –5.

Example

Use a number line to compare the numbers +3 and +5. Then, insert a >, <, or = sign to make a true statement.

Solution

+3 is to the left of +5.
+3 is less than +5, or +5 is greater than +3.

+3 < +5

Example

Use a number line to compare the numbers +3 and –5. Then, insert a >, <, or = sign to make a true statement.

Solution

+3 is to the right of –5.
+3 is greater than –5, or –5 is less than +3.

+3 > –5

Your Turn 1

a) Use a number line to compare the numbers –3 and –5. Then, insert a >, <, or = sign to make a true statement.

b) Use a number line to compare the numbers –3 and +5. Then, insert a >, <, or = sign to make a true statement.

INTEGER TILES

Integer tiles can be used to represent integers. The colour of the tile indicates a positive or negative value of the integer.

Shaded tiles represent positive integers.

Unshaded tiles represent negative integers.

□

The number of tiles determines the integer's value.

Example

Represent the integer +2 with integer tiles.

Solution
Shaded tiles represent positive integers.
Draw two shaded tiles.

Example

Represent the integer –3 with integer tiles.

Solution
Unshaded tiles represent negative integers.
Draw three unshaded tiles.

□□□

Your Turn 2

a) Represent the integer –6 with integer tiles.

b) Represent the integer +5 with integer tiles.

OPPOSITE INTEGERS

Two integers that are the same distance but opposite directions from zero on a number line are **opposite integers**.

Example

Use a number line to illustrate the opposite integer for –4.

Solution

Since –4 is four steps to the left of zero, the opposite integer must have the same value and be four steps to the right of zero

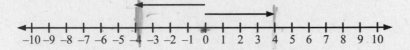

The opposite of –4 is +4 because both numbers are four steps away from 0.

Your Turn 3

Use a number line to illustrate the opposite integer for –8.

![number line from -10 to 10]

ZERO PRINCIPLE

For every integer, there is always an opposite integer. The **zero principle** states that the sum of two opposite integers is always zero. For example, $(-3)+(+3)=0$.

Number lines can model the zero principle.

Example

Use a number line to show that $(+4)+(-4)=0$.

Solution

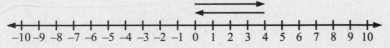

The top arrow represents the first term in the equation. It starts at the origin and moves four steps to the right: +4. The bottom arrow starts where the first arrow left off and moves four steps to the left: –4.

Sum is the answer from adding two numbers together.

A move in one direction combined with an equal move in the opposite direction results in an answer of zero because there is no change in position. The arrow ends exactly where it started.

Your Turn 4

Use a number line to show that $(-6) + (+6) = 0$.

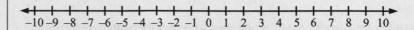

Integer tiles can model the zero principle. When a shaded tile is paired with an unshaded tile, they cancel each other out.

These are called **zero pairs**.

Example

Use integer tiles to show that $(-4) + (+4) = 0$.

Solution

Four negative integer tiles are placed first. Then, four positive integer tiles are placed beside or below them. There is one negative tile for every positive tile or four zero pairs. The tiles cancel each other out. There are no leftover tiles, meaning the sum is zero.

Your Turn 5

Use integer tiles to show that $(-2) + (+2) = 0$.

PRACTICE EXERCISES

1. Explain how positive and negative signs are different from plus and minus signs.

2. List some real-life examples where negative numbers are used.

Write the integer that the following four questions represent.

3.

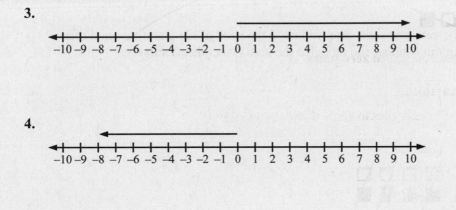

4.

5.

☐ ☐ ☐

6.

■ ■ ■ ■ ■

7. Use the number line to compare the numbers –3 and –6. Then, insert a > or < sign to make a true statement.

State the opposite integer of the following integers.

8. +3

9. −18

10. 34

11. Ms. Dean wanted to model the zero principle. She walked to the back of her classroom and then walked back to the front. Explain whether she modeled the zero principle effectively.

Lesson 2   ADDING INTEGERS

To add integers, there are three methods to use:

- Integer tiles
- Number lines
- Calculations using paper and pencil

USING INTEGER TILES

Example

Use integer tiles to evaluate $(+4)+(-3)$.

Evaluate means to find the answer.

Solution

The first term is +4. Draw four shaded tiles.

The second term is –3. Draw three unshaded tiles. Notice the tiles are lined up opposite to each other. This makes it easy to see the zero pairs.

There are three zero pairs. One positive tile remains.

$(+4)+(-3)=(+1)$

Your Turn 1

Use integer tiles to evaluate $(+12)+(-6)$.

To add integers using a number line, follow these steps:

Step 1

Draw a number line.

Step 2

Place the pencil at the value of the first term.

Move the arrow to the left if the integer is negative or to the right if the integer is positive.

Step 3

Move the pencil the number of places indicated by the value of the second term. The answer to the question is located where the pencil stops.

USING NUMBER LINES

Example

Use a number line to evaluate $(+4)+(-5)$.

Solution

Step 1

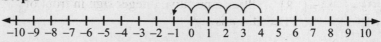

Step 2

Position your pencil on the first integer (+4).

Step 3

Move your pencil five places to the left of (+4). The pencil lands on (–1).

$$(+4)+(-5)=(+1)$$

Your Turn 2

Use a number line to evaluate $(+3)+(-6)$.

USING CALCULATIONS

When adding integers using paper and pencil, there are two rules to follow:

Rule 1: If the signs are the same on the integers, add the numerical values and keep the same sign.

Example

Solve $(+3)+(+5)$.

Solution

$3+5=8$	Add the numerical values.
$(+3)+(+5)=(+8)$	Place a positive integer sign in front of the answer.

Example

Solve $(-3)+(-5)$.

Solution

$3+5=8$	Add the numerical values.
$(-3)+(-5)=(-8)$	Place a negative integer sign in front of the answer.

Your Turn 3

a) Solve $(+14)+(+36)$.

b) Solve $(-12)+(-57)$.

Rule 2: If the signs are different on the integers, subtract the smaller numerical value from the larger numerical value. Then, place the sign of the larger numerical value in front of the answer.

Example

Solve $(-8)+(+3)$.

Solution

$8-3=5$	The numerical value of –8 is 8. The numerical value of +3 is 3. Subtract 3 from 8.
–5	Since 8 is the larger numerical value, place a negative integer sign in front of the answer.
$(-8)+(+3)=(-5)$	Complete the equation.

NOTES

Example

Solve $(+6)+(-4)$.

Solution

$6-4=2$	The numerical value of +6 is 6. The numerical value of –4 is 4. Subtract 4 from 6.
$+2$	Since +6 is a larger numerical value, place a positive integer sign in front of the answer.
$(+6)+(-4)=(+2)$	Complete the equation.

Your Turn 4

a) Solve $(+12)+(-30)$.

b) Solve $(+61)+(-21)$.

56

PRACTICE EXERCISES

Solve the following equations.

1. $(+31)+(-19)$

2. $(-25)+(+10)$

3. $(+13)+(+40)$

Add the following integers using integer tiles.

4. $(-7)+(-13)$

5. $(-4)+(+9)$

Add the following integers using a number line.

6. $(-8)+(+12)$

7. $(+9)+(-11)$

8. Write the addition expression represented by the given integer tiles.

Determine if each of the following diagrams match their addition statement. If they do not, explain why and make the corrections to the diagram.

9.

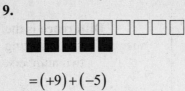

$$= (+9) + (-5)$$

10.

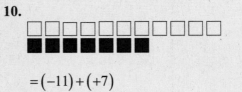

$$= (-11) + (+7)$$

Lesson 3   SUBTRACTING INTEGERS

To subtract integers, there are three methods to use:
- Integer tiles
- Number lines
- Calculations using paper and pencil

USING INTEGER TILES

When the integer signs are the same and the numerical value of the second term is smaller than the first term, follow these steps:

Step 1
Draw integer tiles to represent the first term.

Step 2
Subtract the number of tiles equal to the second term. The tiles that remain are the difference.

Example

Use integer tiles to solve the expression $(+4)-(+3)$.

Solution
Step 1
Draw four shaded tiles to represent +4.

■■■■

Step 2
Subtract the number of tiles to equal the second term.

The second term is +3. Take away three shaded tiles.

■

There is one tile left over.

$(+4)-(+3)=(+1)$

Your Turn 1

Use integer tiles to solve the expression $(-7)-(-4)$.

NOTES

For all other subtraction questions, follow these steps:

Step 1

Draw integer tiles to represent the first term.

Step 2

Add zero pairs until there are enough tiles to represent the second term.

Step 3

Subtract the tiles that represent the second term. The tiles that remain are the difference.

Example

Use integer tiles to solve the expression $(-3)-(-5)$.

Solution

In this expression, the signs are the same, but the absolute value of the second term is larger than the absolute value of the first term.

Step 1

Draw integer tiles to represent the first term.
Draw three unshaded tiles to represent –3.

Step 2

In this case there are not enough unshaded tiles to represent –5.
Add zero pairs until there are enough tiles to represent the second term.
Add two zero pairs. Now there are five unshaded tiles to represent –5.

Step 3

Subtract the tiles that represent the second term.
The second term is –5. Take away five unshaded tiles.

There are two positive tiles left over. The answer is +2.
$(-3)-(-5)=(+2)$

Your Turn 2

Use integer tiles to solve the expression $(+1)-(+6)$.

60

USING NUMBER LINES

To subtract using a number line, follow these steps:

Step 1
Place a pencil at the point representing the second term in the question.

Step 2
Move the pencil to the point representing the first term.

Step 3
Determine the length and direction of the movement. The length of the movement gives the numerical value of the answer. Movement to the right gives a positive answer, while movement to the left gives a negative answer.

Example

Use a number line to solve the expression $(+4)-(+3)$.

Solution

Step 1
Place a pencil on the second term, +3.

Step 2
Move the pencil to the point representing the first term, +4.

Step 3
Determine the length and direction of the movement.
The pencil moved one step to the right. This gives an answer of +1.
$$(+4)-(+3)=(+1)$$

Your Turn 3

Use a number line to solve the expression $(-2)-(+9)$.

USING CALCULATIONS

When subtracting integers using paper and pencil, change the subtraction expression into an addition expression by following these rules:
1. Change the subtraction sign to an addition sign.
2. Change the integer sign on the number that *follows the subtraction sign* to its opposite.

Once the subtraction expression has been changed into an addition expression, follow the same procedure as for adding integers.

Example

Change the following subtraction expressions into addition expressions.

a) $(+4)-(+2)$

Solution

$(+4)-(+2)$ $\downarrow$ $(+4)+(-2)$	Change the subtraction sign to an addition sign.
	Change the integer sign on the number that follows the subtraction sign to its opposite. The opposite of +2 is –2.

b) $(+4)-(-2)$

Solution

$(+4)-(-2)$ $\downarrow$ $(+4)+(+2)$	Change the subtraction sign to an addition sign.
	Change the integer sign on the number that follows the subtraction sign to its opposite. The opposite of –2 is +2.

c) $(-4)-(+2)$

Solution

$(-4)-(+2)$ $\downarrow$ $(-4)+(-2)$	Change the subtraction sign to an addition sign.
	Change the integer sign on the number that follows the subtraction sign to its opposite. The opposite of +2 is –2.

62

d) $(-4)-(-2)$

Solution

$(-4)-(-2)$	Change the subtraction sign to an addition sign.
$\downarrow$ $(-4)+(+2)$	Change the integer sign on the number that follows the subtraction sign to its opposite. The opposite of −2 is +2.

Your Turn 4

Rewrite the following subtraction expressions as addition expressions.

a) $(+8)-(-4)$

b) $(+6)-(+4)$

c) $(-5)-(-3)$

d) $(-7)-(+3)$

PRACTICE EXERCISES

1. Solve $(+1)-(-4)$ using integer tiles.

Subtract the following integers using a number line.

2. $(+1)-(+6)$

3. $(-5)-(+2)$

Use the following diagram to answer the next question.

4. Determine one of the subtraction expressions that the given diagram represents.

Change the following subtraction expressions into addition expressions.

5. $(-45)-(+3)$

6. $(+32)-(-20)$

7. $(-3)-(-5)$

Subtract the following integers by first changing each subtraction expression into an addition expression.

8. $(+9)-(-24)$

9. $(+35)-(+27)$

10. $(-12)-(-23)$

Lesson 4 PROBLEM SOLVING WITH INTEGERS

To translate mathematical word problems into expressions or equations, break the problem up into smaller sections and look for keywords that determine the value of all the integers in the problem. A few examples include the following:

- Positive keywords (+): above, gain, increase, up, over, more than, profit, add, greater than, larger
- Negative keywords (–): below, loss, decrease, down, under, less than, debt, minus, reduce, diminish

To solve an integer problem, follow these steps:

Step 1
Identify integer and operation keywords.

Step 2
Write an expression representing the problem.

Step 3
Solve.

Example
Lyla was given $20 and spent $11 of it. Write an addition expression that represents the statement.

Solution
Step 1
Identify integer and operation keywords.

Integer keywords: *given* indicates positive, and *spends* indicates negative.

Given $20 → (+$20)
Spends $11 → (–$11)

Step 2
Write an expression representing the problem.
$($20$) + (-$11$)$

Your Turn 1
Write a subtraction expression that represents Lyla's statement.

The last sentence of the problem will often indicate whether the integers should be added or subtracted. A few examples include the following:

- Addition keywords: sum, altogether, total, plus, increased by, in all, up
- Subtraction keywords: difference, change, less, decreased by, down

Example

A submarine was at a depth of 65 m when it ascends 21 m. What is the final depth of the submarine?

Solution

Step 1

Identify integer and operation keywords.

Integer keywords: *depth* indicates negative (–65), *ascends* indicates positive (+21).

Operation keyword: *up* indicates addition.

Step 2

Write an expression representing the problem.

The expression is $(-65)+(+21)$.

Step 3

Solve.

$$(-65)+(+21)=(-44)$$

The submarine is now at a depth of –44 m, which means 44 m below the surface of the water.

Your Turn 2

The melting point of oxygen is –218°C. Its boiling point is 35°C higher. Determine the boiling point of oxygen.

There are other strategies used to solve integer problems. Sometimes, you will need to work backward from a given amount.

Example

Janet invested in a beverage company. In the first week, her investment went up $10, then down $3, up $8, up again $4, and down $3. If she had $30 in her stock portfolio by the end of the first week, how much money did she originally invest?

Solution

Work backward by starting at $30. Do operations in reverse, adding where the stock went down and subtracting where the stock went up.
$30 + $3 − $4 − $8 + $3 − $10 = $14

Janet originally invested $14 in the beverage company.

Your Turn 3

On Monday morning, the value of a particular stock was worth $250. By Friday, it was only worth $120. What is the difference in the value of the stock from Monday to Friday?

Some problems involve adding or subtracting complex integer equations.

Example

Calculate $(-15)+(+25)+(+38)+(-23)+(-10)$.

Solution

Strategy 1
Add the positive integers $(+25) + (+38) = + 63$

Add the negative integers
$(-15) + (-23) + (-10) = -48$.

Add sums together
$(+63) + (-48) = + 15$

The sum of $(+63)$ and (-48) is +15.

Strategy 2

Pair up integers with other integers where their sum equals 0, cancel, and then add up the remaining integers.

$$(-15)+(-10)=(-25)$$

This will cancel with +25.

$$(-15) + (+25) + (+38) + (-23) + (-10) = ?$$
$$(+38)+(-23)=(+15)$$

or

$$(-15)+(-23)=(-38)$$

This will cancel with +38.

$$(-15) + (+25) + (+38) + (-23) + (-10) = ?$$
$$(+25)+(-10)=(+15)$$

Your Turn 4

Use both strategies described to calculate
$(-12)+(+33)+(-20)+(-13)+(+25)$.

PRACTICE EXERCISES

Identify the keyword and what it indicates. Write an integer to represent the statement.

1. Four over par in golf.

2. A loss of 5 kg.

3. A win of 10 points.

4. Thirty degrees Celsius below zero.

5. A submarine was situated 242 m below sea level. If it ascends 75 m, what is its final position?

Use the following information to answer the next question.

The base of a mountain is 5 245 m below the surface of the ocean. Its peak is 3 159 m above the surface of the ocean.

6. What is the total height of the mountain?

Use the following information to answer the next question.

To get to his office, Jimmy took an elevator 17 floors above street level. After work, he took the elevator down to where his car was parked, which was 5 floors below street level.

7. How many floors did Jimmy ride down?

Use the following information to answer the next question.

The lowest temperature recorded in Alberta was –54°C. The highest temperature was 46°C.

8. What is the difference between the lowest and the highest temperatures?

Use the following information to answer the next question.

Jinny went shopping one morning. She bought a $20 DVD and then bought lunch for $9. After lunch, she bought a gift for her mother for $10. When she got home, she realized she still had $30 in her purse.

9. How much money did Jinny have to begin with?

Use the following information to answer the next question.

Two integers have a sum of –12 and a difference of +6.

10. Identify the two integers.

REVIEW SUMMARY

- The sum of opposite integers is zero.
- A number line can model the addition or subtraction of integers: the length of the arrow indicates the integers value, whereas the arrows direction indicates the sign of the integer.
- When adding integers, the second arrow will move to the *right* if the second integer is positive and to the *left* if it is negative
- When subtracting integers, the second arrow will move to the *right* if the first integer is positive and to the *left* if it is negative
- Integer tiles can model the addition and subtraction of integers. The number of tiles that remain is the value of the integer, whereas the colour to of the tiles indicates the sign of the integer.
- Zero pairs are pairs of opposite coloured integer tiles that have sum of zero.
- When problem solving with integers, use a strategy to help simplify the question, and make the calculations easier.

PRACTICE TEST

1. Match the following expressions with the sign or operation that best fits.

    a) (-3) _____ plus

    b) $(+3)$ _____ minus

    c) $(+3)+(3)$ _____ positive

    d) $(-3)-(-3)$ _____ negative

Use a number line to compare the following numbers. Then, insert a >, <, or = sign to make each of the following statements true.

2. -3 and $+2$

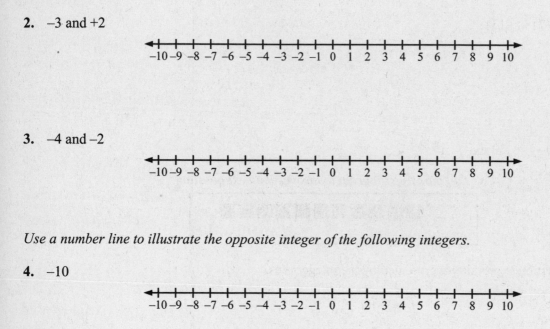

3. -4 and -2

Use a number line to illustrate the opposite integer of the following integers.

4. -10

5. $+4$

Solve the following expressions.

6. $(+14)+(+36)$ 7. $(-12)+(-57)$

What integer do the given diagrams represent?

8.

9.

▪▪▪▪▪

10. Calculate $(-7)+(-13)$.

Use the following diagram to answer the next question.

11. Write an addition expression represented by the integer tiles.

Subtract the given integers by changing each expression to an addition expression.

12. $(-16)-(+31)$

13. $(-45)-(-54)$

14. $(-42)-(+21)$

Use the following information to answer the next question.

On Monday morning, the value of a particular stock was worth \$320. By Friday, it was only worth \$185.

15. What is the difference in the value of the stock from Monday to Friday?

WORKING WITH DECIMALS AND FRACTIONS

When you are finished this unit, you will be able to...
• use divisibility rules to determine if a number is divisible by 2, 3, 4, 5, 6, 9, and 10
• read and write numbers to any number of decimal places
• describe equivalent mixed numbers and improper fractions
• compare and order improper fractions, mixed numbers, and decimals to the thousandths place value
• convert all fractions and mixed numbers to decimal form
• convert from terminating decimals to fractions

Lesson	Page	Completed on
1. Divisibility Rules	78	
2. Using Divisibility Rules	87	
3. Converting Fractions into Decimals	95	
4. Converting Decimals into Fractions	102	
5. Equivalent Fractions	108	
6. Comparing and Ordering Numbers	116	
Review Summary	126	
Practice Test	127	
Answers and Solutions	at the back of the book	

PREREQUISITE SKILLS AND KNOWLEDGE

Prior to starting this unit, you should be able to...
• read and write numbers to the thousandths place value
• know what improper fractions and mixed numbers are
• compare and order numbers

Lesson 1 DIVISIBILITY RULES

Divisible means a number can be divided by another number evenly.

Divisibility rules allow you to identify if one number is divisible by another number quickly without the use of a calculator.

Divisibility rules are presented in groups because the groups of numbers have similar rules. This will help you remember the rules for the first ten numbers.

RULES FOR 2, 5, AND 10
The divisibility rules for 2, 5, and 10 are as follows:

- 2—a number is divisible by 2 if the number ends in an even digit (0, 2, 4, 6, or 8)
- 5—a number is divisible by 5 if the number ends in a 0 or 5
- 10—a number is divisible by 10 if the number ends in zero

Factors are numbers that are multiplied to form another number (2 and 4 are factors of 8).

Example

Determine if 2, 5, or 10 are factors of the number 45 672 978.

Solution
The last digit is even, so the number is divisible by 2.
The last digit is not 0 or 5, so the number is not divisible by 5 and 10.

Of the numbers 2, 5 and 10, only 2 is a factor of 45 672 978.

Example

Determine if 2, 5, and 10 are factors of the number 812 938 275.

Solution
The last digit is odd, so the number is not divisible by 2.
The last digit is 5, so the number is divisible by 5.
The last digit is not 0, so the number is not divisible by 10.

Of the numbers 2, 5, or 10, only 5 is a factor of 812 938 275.

Example

Determine if 2, 5, or 10 are factors of the number 839 729 384 190.

Solution
The last digit is even, so the number is divisible by 2.
The last digit is 0, so the number is divisible by 5 and 10.

Therefore, 2, 5, and 10 are factors of 839 729 384 190.

Your Turn 1

a) Considering the factors 2, 5 and 10, what observation can be made about numbers ending with the digit 2, 4, 6, or 8?

b) Considering the factors 2, 5 and 10, what observation can be made about numbers ending with the digit 5?

c) What observation can be made about numbers ending with the digit 0?

RULES FOR 3 AND 9

The divisibility rules for 3 and 9 are as follows:

- 3—the sum of the digits is divisible by 3
- 9—the sum of the digits is divisible by 9

Example

Determine whether the number 876 453 is divisible by 3 or 9.

Solution

$8 + 7 + 6 + 4 + 5 + 3 = 33$	Add the digits in the number.
$3 + 3 = 6$	Add the digits of the sum again until it becomes a one digit number.
$6 \div 3 = 2$	Determine if 3 is a factor of the sum.
6 is not divisible by 9	Determine if 9 is a factor of the sum.

The number 876 453 is divisible by 3 but not 9.

NOTES

Example

Determine whether the number 462 893 112 is divisible by 3 or 9.

Solution

$4 + 6 + 2 + 8 + 9 + 3 + 1 + 1 + 2 = 36$	Add the digits in the number.
$3 + 6 = 9$	Add the digits of the sum.
$9 \div 3 = 3$	Determine if 3 is a factor of the sum.
$9 \div 3 = 1$	Determine if 9 is a factor of the sum.

The number 462 893 112 is divisible by 3 and 9.

Your Turn 2

Determine whether 478 374 297 is divisible by 3 or 9.

RULE FOR 6

The divisibility rule for 6 is the number is divisible by both 2 *and* 3.

Example

Determine whether the number 876 453 is divisible by 6.

Solution

The last digit is not even, so the number is not divisible by 2.

$8 + 7 + 6 + 4 + 5 + 3 = 33$
Since 3 is a factor of 33, the number is divisible by 3.

Therefore, 6 is not a factor of 876 453 because 2 is not a factor.

Example

Determine whether the number 839 729 384 192 is divisible by 6.

Solution
The last digit is even, so the number is divisible by 2.

$8 + 3 + 9 + 7 + 2 + 9 + 3 + 8 + 4 + 1 + 9 + 2 = 65$
$6 + 5 = 11$
Since 3 is not a factor of 11 the number is not divisible by 3.

Therefore, 6 is not a factor of 839 729 384 192 because 3 is not a factor.

Example

Determine whether the number 45 672 978 is divisible by 6.

Solution
The last digit is even, so the number is divisible by 2.

$4 + 5 + 6 + 7 + 2 + 9 + 7 + 8 = 48$
$4 + 8 = 12$
Since 3 is a factor of 12 the number is divisible by 3.

Therefore, 6 is a factor of 45 672 978 because 2 and 3 are factors.

Your Turn 3

Why do 2 and 3 have to be factors for the number to be divisible by 6?

RULES FOR 4 AND 8

The divisibility rules for 4 and 8 are as follows:
- 4—a number is divisible by 4 if the last two digits are divisible by 4.
- 8—a number is divisible by 8 if the last three digits are divisible by 8.

Example

Determine whether the number 823 136 947 452 is divisible by 4 or 8.

Solution
The last two digits are 52.
$52 \div 4 = 13$

The last three digits are 452
$452 \div 8 = 56.5$

The number 823 136 947 452 is divisible by 4 but not 8.

Example

Determine whether the number 839 283 017 402 846 256 is divisible by 4 or 8.

Solution
The last two digits are 56.
$56 \div 4 = 14$

The last three digits are 256
$256 \div 8 = 32$

Therefore, 4 and 8 are factors of 839 283 017 402 846 256.

Your Turn 4

a) If a number is divisible by 8, is it also divisible by 4?

b) Because 2 is a factor of 4 and 8, what conclusions can be made about the end digit to determine if the number is divisible by 4 or 8?

DIVIDING BY ZERO

Division by zero is an operation that has no answer. To understand this, look at the relationship between division and multiplication.

Example

Show the expression $12 \div 2$ using base ten blocks.

Solution
Draw twelve units.
□□□□□□□□□□□□

To divide, break up the units into groups of 2.

🮕🮕🮕🮕🮕🮕

Since 6 groups are the result, $12 \div 2 = 6$.
Now, to show the expression $12 \div 0$ using base ten blocks, draw twelve units.
□□□□□□□□□□□□

To divide, break up the units into groups of 0. Since you cannot make zero groups, division by zero is undefined. **Undefined** means there is no answer. It is impossible to divide any number by 0.

82

APPLICATION OF DIVISIBILITY RULES

There are plenty of examples in everyday life when you have a total amount of something and you have to decide if it can be evenly divided.

Example

There is a shipment of water colour pencils to a school.

128 red	88 green	25 yellow
293 blue	66 orange	63 purple

a) Which pencils can be divided into groups of 2?

Solution

Any number that ends with an even digit can be divided into groups of 2.

128 red → 8 is even.	66 orange → 6 is even.
293 blue → 3 is odd.	25 yellow → 5 is odd.
88 green → 8 is even.	63 purple → 3 is odd.

The red, green, and orange pencils can be divided into groups of 2.

b) Which pencils can be divided into groups of 3?

Solution

Add the digits of the number. If the sum is a multiple of 3, then the number is divisible by 3.

red: $1 + 2 + 8 = 11$	orange: $6 + 6 = 12$
blue: $2 + 9 + 3 = 14$	yellow: $2 + 5 = 7$
green: $8 + 8 = 16$	purple: $6 + 3 = 9$

The orange and purple pencils can be divided into groups of 3.

c) Which pencils can be divided into groups of 6?

Solution

If the number is divisible by 2 and 3, it will be divisible by 6 as well. The orange pencils are divisible by 2 and 3, so they are divisible by 6 as well.

Your Turn 5

Kiana bought 360 L of dirt for planting up pots.

a) Could she use up all the dirt if she bought 4 L pots?

b) Could she use up all the dirt if she bought 5 L pots?

PRACTICE EXERCISES

1. Explain whether the number 239 is divisible by 2.

2. Explain whether the number 12 837 is divisible by 3.

3. Explain whether the number 72 is divisible by 4.

4. Explain whether the number 2 345 is divisible by 5.

5. Explain whether the number 3 330 is divisible by 5.

6. Explain whether the number 186 is divisible by 6.

7. Explain whether the number 283 945 is divisible by 6.

Explain why the given number is or is not divisible by 8.

8. 281 832

9. 17 921 930

Explain why the given number is or is not divisible by 9.

10. 79

11. 1 872

Lesson 2   USING DIVISIBILITY RULES

The divisibility rules make sorting numbers, determining factors, and writing fractions in lowest terms much easier.

SORTING NUMBERS

Venn diagrams are visual organizers made up of at least two circles that intersect.

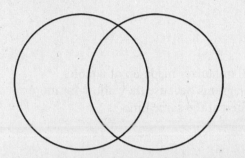

Use Venn diagrams to compare and sort information into categories based on their characteristics. If there is something that shares both characteristics, it is placed in the centre where the two circles overlap.
If an item does not match any of the characteristics, it is placed outside of the Venn diagram.

Example

830, 4 837, 8 356, 847 240, 938 285, 8 372 045

Using a Venn diagram, sort the numbers that are divisible by 5 and 2.

Solution
Place the numbers that are divisible by 5, but in the left part of the circle: 938 285 and 8 372 045.

Place the number that is divisible by 2, but in the right part of the circle:
8 356.

Place the numbers that are divisible by both 5 and 2 in the centre where the circles overlap: 830 and 847 240.

Place 4837 outside the circles because it is not divisible by 5 or 2.

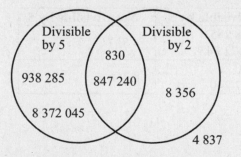

Your Turn 1

Given 9, 10, 18, 32, 42, 51, 54, 56, 57, 62, and 63, sort the numbers into a Venn diagram based on divisibility by 2 and divisibility by 3.

Carroll diagrams are another visual organizer made up of a table. They are more detailed than Venn diagrams because they allow for more than two characteristics to be compared at the same time.

Example

Given 830, 4 837, 8 356, 847 240, 938 285, and 8 372 045, sort the numbers that are divisible by 5 and 2.

Solution

Determine if each number is divisible by 2 or 5.

830 → divisible by 2 and 5 because the last digit is 0.

4 837 → not divisible by 2 or 5 because the last digit is odd.

8 356 → divisible by 2 because the last digit is even, and not divisible by 5 because the last digit is not a 0 or 5.

847 240 → divisible by 2 and 5 because the last digit is 0.

938 285 → not divisible by 2 because the last digit is odd, and divisible by 5 because the last digit is 5.

8 372 045 → not divisible by 2 because the last digit is odd, and divisible by 5 because the last digit is 5.

List the characteristics on the top and side of the table. Read the characteristics that are adjacent to each cell. Place the numbers within the cell that agrees with both characteristics.

	Divisible by 5	Not Divisible by 5
Not divisible by 2	938 285 8 372 045	4 837
Divisible by 2	830 847 240	8 356

Your Turn 2

Sort the numbers 10, 12, 18, 20, 30, and 36 into this Carroll diagram.

	Divisible by 4	Not divisible by 4
Divisible by 6		
Not Divisible by 6		

DETERMINING FACTORS

Factors are numbers that are multiplied together to form another number. A number can have many factors. For example, the factors of 12 are 1, 2, 3, 4, 6, and 12. The smallest factor of any number is 1. The largest factor of any number is the number itself. Divisibility rules make finding factors quick.

Example

Determine the factors of 24.

Solution

All numbers have 1 and the number as factors.

$2 \rightarrow$ the number is even, so 24 is divisible by 2: $24 \div 2 = 12$.

$3 \rightarrow$ the digits add up to a multiple of 3: $2 + 4 = 6$. The number is divisible by 3. $24 \div 8 = 3$

$4 \rightarrow$ 24 is divisible by 4: $24 \div 4 = 6$.

$5 \rightarrow$ the number does not end in a 0 or 5, so 24 is not divisible by 5.

$6 \rightarrow$ the number is divisible by 2 and 3, so it is divisible by 6: $24 \div 6 = 4$.

6 was also determined to be a factor when looking at divisibility of 4.

$8 \rightarrow$ 24 is divisible by 8: $24 \div 8 = 3$.
8 was determined to be a factor when looking at divisibility of 3.

$9 \rightarrow$ the sum of the digits is not a multiple of 9, so 24 is not divisible by 9.

The factors of 24 are 1, 2, 3, 4, 6, 8, 12, and 24.

NOTES

Your Turn 3

Show the process for determining the factors of 36.

The greatest common factor is written as GCF.

When working with fractions, common factors are found between numbers. **Common factors** are factors that are the same in all the numbers. For example, 2 is a common factor that 4, 8, and 12 share. Some numbers share more than one common factor. For example 4, 8, and 12 have 2 and 4 as common factors. The 4 is the **greatest common factor** (GCF) because it is the largest factor that all three numbers share.

Venn and Carroll diagrams are useful for sorting the factors to find common factors and the greatest common factor.

Example

Determine the greatest common factor of 18 and 24.

Solution

Use divisibility rules to determine the factors of each number.
Factors of 18 are 1, 2, 3, 6, 9, and 18.
Factors of 24 are 1, 2, 3, 4, 6, 8, 12, and 24.

Draw the Carroll or Venn diagram and place the factors into the correct circle or cell.

	Factors of 18	Not Factors of 18
Factors of 24	1, 2, 3, 6	4, 8, 12, 24
Not Factors of 24	9, 18	

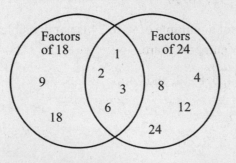

The common factors of 18 and 24 are 1, 2, 3, and 6. The greatest common factor is 6.

Your Turn 4

Determine the greatest common factor of 28 and 32.

WRITING FRACTIONS IN LOWEST TERMS

Fractions are always written in lowest terms. A **term** is a number that is separated by an operator. Remember the line separating the numerator from the denominator is also a division sign. **Lowest terms** means the terms (numerator and denominator) have no other common factors beside 1.

To write a fraction in lowest terms, follow these steps:

Step 1
List the factors of both numbers.

Step 2
Determine the GCF that both numbers share.

Step 3
Divide both terms by the GCF.

Example

Write $\dfrac{24}{36}$ in lowest terms.

Solution

Step 1
List the factors of both numbers.
Factors of 24: 1, 2, 3, 4, 6, 8, 12, 24
Factors of 36: 1, 2, 3, 4, 6, 9, 12, 18, 36

Step 2
Determine the GCF that both numbers share.
12 is the greatest common factor.

Step 3
Divide both terms by the GCF.

$$\frac{24 \div 12}{36 \div 12} = \frac{2}{3}$$

Written in lowest terms, $\dfrac{24}{36}$ is $\dfrac{2}{3}$.

Your Turn 5

Write $\dfrac{32}{48}$ in lowest terms.

PRACTICE EXERCISES

Show the process for determining the factors of the given number.

1. 48

2. 30

3. Determine the greatest common factor of 16 and 24.

4. Draw a Carroll or Venn diagram, and place the factors of 16 and 24 into the correct circle or cell.

Write the given fractions in lowest terms.

5. $\dfrac{18}{30}$

6. $\dfrac{24}{42}$

7. $\dfrac{28}{36}$

8. $\dfrac{20}{40}$

9. Use a Venn diagram to determine the greatest common factor of 24 and 28.

10. Sort the numbers 12, 18, 27, 30, 36, 42, and 47 into a Carroll diagram based on divisibility by 6 and divisibility by 9.

Lesson 3   CONVERTING FRACTIONS INTO DECIMALS

Numbers are presented as decimals and fractions. To do calculations or compare the values, all the numbers in the problem must be in the same form. Changing fractions into decimals and decimals into fractions is a valuable skill.

CONVERTING FRACTIONS

Fractions can be thought of as parts of a whole. Fractions are also operations. The line dividing the numerator from the denominator is a division operator. To convert a fraction into a decimal, divide the numerator (dividend) by the denominator (divisor).

Terminating decimals are decimal numbers that come to an end. All the digits are written down. Some examples include 0.174, 3.24, and 9.819 02.

Example

Write $\dfrac{2}{5}$ as a decimal.

Solution

Method 1
Written calculation

$$5\overline{)20}$$

with quotient 0.4, and 20 subtracted leaving 0.

Method 2
Calculator
Type in $\boxed{2}\ \boxed{\div}\ \boxed{5}\ \boxed{=}$
The answer on the screen is 0.4.

Repeating decimals are decimal numbers where the numbers continue on forever, with one or more digits repeating. If one digit after the decimal repeats, it is referred to as a single-digit repeating decimal. Some examples include 0.999… and 6.634 222 22….

If more than one digit repeats, it is referred to as a multi-digit repeating decimal. Some examples include 4.125 125… and 17.080 808…

Since writing the same number or numbers over and over again is not practical or efficient, a bar is placed over the repeating digits. This is referred to as bar notation. For example, 6.634 222 22 is written $6.634\overline{2}$ and 17.080 808… is written $17.\overline{08}$.

NOTES

Because repeating decimals never end, the calculator screen only shows as many places as the screen allow for.
If the repeating digit is 5 or greater, the calculator will often round the last digit. For example
$3.\overline{6}$ would display as
3.666 666 67

Example

Write $\dfrac{2}{9}$ as a decimal.

Solution

Method 1

Written calculation

$$
\begin{array}{r}
0.222 \\
9\overline{)2000} \\
18\downarrow \\
\overline{20} \\
18\downarrow \\
\overline{20} \\
18 \\
\overline{2}
\end{array}
$$

Method 2

Calculator

Type in $\boxed{2}\ \boxed{\div}\ \boxed{9}\ \boxed{=}$.
The answer on the screen is 0.222 222 222 2.

$\dfrac{2}{9}$ written as a decimal is $0.\overline{2}$.

Your Turn 1

a) Write $\dfrac{23}{25}$ as a decimal.

b) Write $\dfrac{18}{27}$ as a decimal.

IDENTIFYING TERMINATING OR REPEATING DECIMALS

To determine whether a fraction is equivalent to a terminating decimal or repeating decimal, look at the denominator.

The equivalent decimal terminates in these cases:
- The denominator is the prime number 2 or 5.
- The denominator is not divisible by 3.

The equivalent decimal repeats in these cases:
- The denominator is a prime number *other than* 2 or 5.
- The denominator is divisible by 3.

Example

Is $\dfrac{7}{32}$ equivalent to a terminating decimal or repeating decimal?

Solution

Use the divisibility rules to determine if 3 is a factor of 32.
$3 + 2 = 5$
32 is not divisible by 3.

Because 3 is not a factor of 32, $\dfrac{7}{32}$ is equivalent to a terminating decimal.

$$\frac{7}{32} = 7 \div 32$$
$$= 0.218\,75$$

Example

Is $\dfrac{14}{24}$ equivalent to a terminating decimal or repeating decimal?

Solution

Use the divisibility rules to determine if 3 is a factor of 24.
$2 + 4 = 6$

24 is divisible by 3.

Because 3 is a factor of 24, $\dfrac{14}{24}$ is equivalent to a repeating decimal.

$$\frac{14}{24} = 14 \div 24$$
$$= 0.58\overline{3}$$

NOTES

Prime numbers have 1
and itself as factors

Example

Is $\dfrac{8}{11}$ equivalent to a terminating decimal or repeating decimal?

Solution

The denominator is a prime number; only 1 and 11 are factors of 11.

Because the denominator is a prime number other than 2 or 5, $\dfrac{8}{11}$ is equivalent to a repeating decimal.

$$\dfrac{8}{11} = 8 \div 11$$
$$= 0.\overline{72}$$

Your Turn 2

Determine whether the given fractions are equivalent to a terminating or repeating decimal.

a) $\dfrac{22}{45}$

b) $\dfrac{17}{20}$

PATTERNS WITH REPEATING DECIMALS

Fractions with denominators of 3, 9, and 11 are easy to convert into decimals using mental math if you understand the patterns.

Example

Use the fraction $\dfrac{1}{11}$ to answer the following questions.

a) Describe the pattern of the repeating decimal when the numerator is increased by one.

Solution

Convert the first few fractions into their decimal equivalents.

$$\dfrac{1}{11} = 1 \div 11 \qquad\qquad \dfrac{2}{11} = 2 \div 11 \qquad\qquad \dfrac{3}{11} = 3 \div 11$$
$$\phantom{\dfrac{1}{11}} = 0.\overline{09} \qquad\qquad\qquad = 0.\overline{18} \qquad\qquad\qquad = 0.\overline{27}$$

The pattern is that as the numerator increases by 1, the decimal increases by nine hundredths repeating.

b) Predict what the decimal equivalent will be for $\dfrac{6}{11}$.

Solution

Multiply the numerator by $0.\overline{09}$.
When doing the multiplication, multiply the numbers as if there were no repeating bar. Then, place the bar over the product.
$6 \times 0.\overline{09} = 0.\overline{54}$

The decimal equivalent of $\dfrac{6}{11}$ is $0.\overline{54}$.

c) Predict what the repeating decimal equivalent will be for $\dfrac{1}{111\,111}$.

Solution

The smallest place value in the denominator is millionths. Multiply $\overline{9}$ by the place value.
$\overline{9} \times 0.000\,001 = 0.\overline{000\,009}$

The decimal equivalent of $\dfrac{1}{111\,111}$ is $0.\overline{000\,009}$.

Your Turn 3

Use the fraction $\frac{1}{9}$ to answer the following questions.

a) Describe the pattern of the repeating decimal when the numerator is increased by one.

b) Predict what the decimal equivalent will be for $\frac{8}{9}$.

c) Describe the pattern of the repeating decimal when the denominator is multiplied by a tenth.

d) Predict what the repeating decimal equivalent will be for $\frac{1}{99\ 999}$.

PRACTICE EXERCISES

Write the given fractions as decimals. Use a calculator.

1. $\dfrac{36}{40}$ 0.9

2. $\dfrac{9}{15}$ 0.6

3. $\dfrac{18}{33}$ 0.54

4. Determine whether the fraction $\dfrac{9}{11}$ is equivalent to a terminating or repeating decimal.

Write each of the following fractions in decimal form. Use a calculator.

5. $\dfrac{12}{50}$ 0.24

6. $\dfrac{32}{128}$ = 0.25

Write each of the following improper fractions in decimal form. Use a calculator.

7. $\dfrac{13}{5}$ 2.6

8. $\dfrac{24}{5}$ 4.8

Write each of the following mixed numbers in decimal form. Use a calculator.

9. $1\dfrac{3}{8}$ 1.375

10. $3\dfrac{7}{8}$ 3.875

Lesson 4   *CONVERTING DECIMALS INTO FRACTIONS*

Terminating and repeating decimals can be converted into proper fractions.

CONVERTING TERMINATING DECIMALS TO FRACTIONS

To represent a terminating decimal as a fraction, follow these steps:

Step 1
Determine the denominator, using the place value of the last digit.

Step 2
Determine the numerator by removing the decimal point.

Step 3
Reduce the fraction to lowest terms.

Example

Change 0.375 to a fraction in lowest terms.

Solution

Step 1
Determine the denominator, using the place value of the last digit.
Use the place value of the last digit in 0.375 as the denominator of the fraction.

Since the 5 is in the thousandths position, the denominator is 1 000.

$$\frac{}{1\,000}$$

Step 2
Determine the numerator, by removing the decimal point.
Remove the decimal point. The number becomes 375.

$$\frac{375}{1\,000}$$

Step 3
Reduce the fraction to lowest terms by dividing the numerator and denominator by the GCF.

$$\frac{375}{1\,000} = \frac{375 \div 125}{1\,000 \div 125}$$
$$= \frac{3}{8}$$

Written as a fraction in lowest terms, 0.375 is $\frac{3}{8}$.

Your Turn 1

a) Express 0.761 as a fraction in lowest terms.

b) Express 0.98 as a fraction in lowest terms.

c) Explain how a decimal number is used to determine the numerator and the denominator of a fraction.

CONVERTING REPEATING DECIMALS TO FRACTIONS

To represent a single-digit repeating decimal as a fraction, follow these steps:

Step 1
Determine the denominator, using the number of repeating digits.

Step 2
Determine the numerator, by removing the decimal point and bar.

Step 3
Reduce the fraction to lowest terms.

Example

Express $0.\overline{6}$ as a fraction in lowest terms.

Solution

Step 1
Determine the denominator, using the number of repeating digits.

One digit repeats in $0.\overline{6}$, so the denominator is 9.

$$\frac{?}{9}$$

Step 2
Determine the numerator, by removing the decimal point and bar.
The numerator becomes 6.

$$\frac{6}{9}$$

NOTES

Step 3
Reduce the fraction to lowest terms by dividing the numerator and denominator by the GCF.

$$\frac{6 \div 3}{9 \div 3} = \frac{2}{3}$$

Expressed as a fraction in lowest terms, $0.\overline{6}$ is $\frac{2}{3}$.

Your Turn 2

Express $0.\overline{3}$ ... as a fraction in lowest terms.

Example

Express $0.\overline{87}$ as a fraction in lowest terms.

Solution
Step 1
Determine the denominator, using the number of repeating digits.
Two digits repeat in $0.\overline{87}$, so the denominator is 99.

$$\frac{?}{99}$$

Step 2
Determine the numerator, by removing the decimal point and bar.
The number becomes 87.

$$\frac{87}{99}$$

Step 3
Reduce the fraction to lowest terms by dividing the numerator and denominator by the same GCF.

$$\frac{87 \div 3}{99 \div 3} = \frac{29}{33}$$

Expressed as a fraction in lowest terms, $0.\overline{87}$ is $\frac{29}{33}$.

Your Turn 3

Express $0.\overline{24}$ as a fraction in lowest terms.

Example

Express $0.\overline{972}$ as a fraction in lowest terms.

Solution

Step 1

Determine the denominator.

Three digits repeats in $0.\overline{972}$, so the denominator is 999.

$$\frac{?}{999}$$

Step 2

Determine the numerator.

Remove the decimal point and bar. The number becomes 972.

$$\frac{972 \div 27}{999 \div 27} = \frac{36}{37}$$

Step 3

Expressed as a fraction in lowest terms, $0.\overline{972}$ is $\frac{36}{37}$.

If you cannot see the larger factor that both numbers share, use the largest factor you see and keep reducing. For example, the previous fraction could be reduced like this:

$$\frac{972 \div 9}{999 \div 9} = \frac{108 \div 3}{111 \div 3}$$
$$= \frac{36}{37}$$

Your Turn 4

Express $0.\overline{321}\ldots$ as a fraction in lowest terms.

When the single digit that repeats is the number 9 $\left(0.\overline{9}\right)$, the resulting

fraction is $\frac{9}{9} = 1$.

The answer is 1 because the number that separates $0.\overline{9}$ from 1 is represented by a decimal point followed by an infinite number of zeros, followed by a one. Since that number is impossibly small, there is no practical difference between the numbers. The accepted way of expressing the value is 1.

PRACTICE EXERCISES

1. Change 0.437 into a fraction in lowest terms.

2. Calculate the fraction for 0.7777 in lowest terms.

Identify whether the following decimal numbers are terminating or repeating.

3. 3.4 T

4. $5.\overline{3}$ R

5. $0.\overline{69}$ R

Change the following decimals to fractions in lowest terms.

6. 0.45 $\frac{45}{100} = \frac{9}{20}$

7. 0.275 $\frac{275}{100.0}$

8. 1.7 $1\frac{7}{10}$

9. Dylan's mass is about 1.4 times as much as Lauren's mass. Express this decimal as a fraction.

    $1\frac{2}{5}$

10. Write 1.64 as a fraction in lowest terms.

    $1\frac{32}{50} = 1\frac{16}{25}$

Lesson 5   EQUIVALENT FRACTIONS

Adam has $\frac{2}{3}$ of a pizza. Samantha has $\frac{3}{4}$ of a pizza. Who has the bigger amount?

To answer the question, the fractions have to be part of the same whole. In other words, both fractions need the same denominator. To do this, make equivalent fractions.

Look at the following two diagrams. In diagram 1, two of the three rows are shaded. In diagram 2, six of nine squares are shaded. Each drawing shows the same amount shaded.

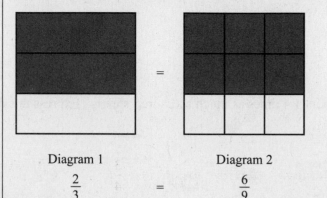

Diagram 1   Diagram 2

$\frac{2}{3}$ = $\frac{6}{9}$

Example

Use division to create two equivalent fractions for $\frac{8}{12}$.

Solution

If the numbers are not prime, check to see if the numerator and denominator can be divided by the *same* number.

Step 1
Use divisibility rules to find factors that divide evenly into the numerator and denominator.
Factors of 8: 1, 2, 4, 8
Factors of 12: 1, 2, 3, 4, 6, 12

Step 2
Choose a common factor to divide both numbers by.
$$\frac{8 \div 2}{12 \div 2} = \frac{4}{6}$$

To make an equivalent fraction, it does not have to be the GCF. Only when reducing to lowest terms does the GCF have to be used.

Step 3
Choose another common factor to divide both numbers by.

$$\frac{8 \div 4}{12 \div 4} = \frac{2}{3}$$

The fractions $\frac{2}{3}$ and $\frac{4}{6}$ are equivalent to $\frac{8}{12}$.

Your Turn 1

Use division to create two equivalent fractions for $\frac{12}{16}$.

Example

Use multiplication to create two equivalent fractions for $\frac{3}{4}$.

Solution
Choose any number to be the factor. Multiply the numerator and denominator by the factor.
$$\frac{3 \times 3}{4 \times 3} = \frac{9}{12}$$

Multiply the numerator and denominator by another factor.
$$\frac{3 \times 4}{4 \times 4} = \frac{12}{16}$$

The fractions $\frac{9}{12}$ and $\frac{12}{16}$ are equivalent to $\frac{3}{4}$.

Your Turn 2

Use multiplication to create two equivalent fractions for $\frac{1}{3}$.

The GCF is 4. The fraction $\frac{2}{3}$ is an equivalent fraction in lowest terms.

COMPARING USING EQUIVALENT FRACTIONS

To make equivalent fractions with two or more fractions, follow these steps:

Step 1
Find the lowest common denominator (LCD) of both fractions.

Step 2
Multiply or divide the numerator and denominator by the same factor.

Step 3
Compare the numerators.

Example

$$\frac{2}{3} \bigcirc \frac{3}{4}$$

Insert a >, <, or = sign to make the statement true.

Solution
Before comparing the fractions, they have to be rewritten as equivalent fractions with the same denominator.

Step 1
Find the LCD.

List the multiples of both denominators until a common multiple appears.
3: 3, 6, 9, <u>12</u>
4: 4, 8, <u>12</u>

The LCD of 3 and 4 is 12.

Step 2
Multiply the numerator and denominator of the first fraction by 4 to create an equivalent fraction with a denominator of 12.

$$\frac{2 \times 4}{3 \times 4} = \frac{8}{12}$$

Multiply the numerator and denominator of the second fraction by 3 to create an equivalent fraction with a denominator of 12.

$$\frac{3 \times 3}{4 \times 3} = \frac{9}{12}$$

Step 3
Compare the numerators to determine the larger fraction.

$$\frac{8}{12} < \frac{9}{12}$$

Since 8 is smaller than 9, $\frac{2}{3} < \frac{3}{4}$.

Link the equivalent fraction to its original fraction.

Your Turn 3

$$\frac{5}{6} \bigcirc \frac{7}{8}$$

Insert a >, <, or = sign to make the statement true.

The divisibility rules can be used to determine whether the denominator of one fraction is a multiple of the other fraction.

Example

$$\frac{2}{4} \bigcirc \frac{3}{8}$$

Insert a >, <, or = sign to make the statement true.

Solution
Step 1
Find the LCD.

Use divisibility rules to determine if the smaller denominator (4) is a factor of the larger denominator (8).

8 is divisible by 4.

Step 2
Because 4 is a factor of 8, multiply the numerator and denominator of $\frac{2}{4}$, by 2 to create an equivalent fraction with a denominator of 8.

$$\frac{2 \times 2}{4 \times 2} = \frac{4}{8}$$

Step 3
Compare the numerators.

$$\frac{4}{8} > \frac{3}{8}$$

Since 4 is larger than 3, $\frac{2}{4} > \frac{3}{8}$.

Your Turn 4

$$\frac{7}{15} \bigcirc \frac{3}{5}$$

Insert a >, <, or = sign to make the statement true.

To compare the value of mixed numbers, look at the whole number first. If the whole numbers of the mixed numbers are *different*, compare their values to determine the larger or smaller mixed number.

Example

$$3\frac{2}{3} \bigcirc 5\frac{1}{2}$$

Insert a >, <, or = sign to make the statement true.

Solution
The whole numbers are different (3 and 5). Since 5 is the larger value,

$$3\frac{2}{3} < 5\frac{1}{2}.$$

Your Turn 5

$$5\frac{7}{8} \bigcirc 4\frac{8}{9}$$

Insert a >, <, or = sign to make the statement true.

If the whole numbers are the *same*, make equivalent fractions of the fraction part of the mixed number.

Example

$$5\frac{2}{5} \bigcirc 5\frac{2}{4}$$

Insert a >, <, or = sign to make the statement true.

Solution
The whole numbers are the same. Make equivalent fractions of the fraction part of the mixed number.

Step 1
Find the LCD.
List the multiples of both denominators until a common multiple appears.
5: 5, 10, 15, <u>20</u>
4: 4, 8, 12, 16, <u>20</u>

The LCD of 5 and 4 is 20.

Step 2
Multiply the numerator and denominator of the first fraction by 4 to create an equivalent fraction with a denominator of 20.

$$\frac{2\times4}{5\times4}=\frac{8}{20}$$

Multiply the numerator and denominator by 5 to create an equivalent fraction with a denominator of 20.

$$\frac{2\times5}{4\times5}=\frac{10}{20}$$

Step 3
Compare the numerators to determine the larger fraction.

$$\frac{8}{20}<\frac{10}{20}$$

Since 8 is smaller than 10, $5\frac{2}{5}<5\frac{2}{4}$.

Your Turn 6

$2\frac{2}{3}\;\bigcirc\;2\frac{4}{7}$

Insert a >, <, or = sign to make the statement true.

APPLICATION OF EQUIVALENT FRACTIONS

There are times when quantities are given in fraction form with different denominators.

Example

Jimmy, Priya, and Ali were all working on homework assignments.

Jimmy completed $\frac{5}{6}$ of his homework assignment, Priya completed $\frac{2}{3}$ of her assignment, and Ali completed $\frac{3}{5}$ of his assignment. Who completed the **most** homework?

Solution
Step 1
Determine what the problem is asking.

The problem is asking for the person who completed the most homework.

Step 2
Determine the given information.

Jimmy completed $\dfrac{5}{6}$.

Priya completed $\dfrac{2}{3}$.

Ali completed $\dfrac{3}{5}$.

Step 3
Identify the strategy or operation to use.

Strategy: equivalent fractions

Step 4
Apply the strategy or operation.

Multiples of 6: 6, 12, 18, 24, <u>30</u>
Multiples of 3: 3, 6, 9, 12, 15, 18, 21, 24, 27, <u>30</u>
Multiples of 5: 5, 10, 15, 20, 25, <u>30</u>

$$\dfrac{5\times5}{6\times5}=\dfrac{25}{30} \qquad \dfrac{2\times10}{3\times10}=\dfrac{20}{30} \qquad \dfrac{3\times6}{5\times6}=\dfrac{18}{30}$$

The largest numerator is 25. $\dfrac{25}{30}=\dfrac{5}{6}$ is the biggest faction.

Jimmy completed the most homework.

Your Turn 7

Isabella was reading the nutrition label on various packages to compare the daily amount of vitamin C in each serving. Label A said it contained $\dfrac{2}{4}$ of the daily amount. Label B said it contained $\dfrac{2}{6}$ of the daily amount.

Label C said it contained $\dfrac{3}{8}$. Which label has the **least** daily amount of vitamin C?

114

PRACTICE EXERCISES

Use division to create two equivalent fractions.

1. $\dfrac{15}{30}$

2. $\dfrac{18}{24}$

Use multiplication to create two equivalent fractions.

3. $\dfrac{4}{6}$

4. $\dfrac{5}{7}$

Insert a >, <, or = sign to make each of the following statements true.

5. $\dfrac{2}{6}\bigcirc\dfrac{3}{18}$

6. $1\dfrac{3}{4}\bigcirc 1\dfrac{2}{6}$

7. $\dfrac{4}{5}\bigcirc\dfrac{5}{6}$

Order the numbers from smallest to largest.

8. $\dfrac{1}{3},\dfrac{2}{4},\dfrac{3}{8},\dfrac{4}{5}$

9. $\dfrac{4}{3},\dfrac{6}{4},\dfrac{7}{2},\dfrac{8}{5}$

10. $\dfrac{20}{6},\dfrac{6}{6},\dfrac{12}{6},\dfrac{4}{6}$

Lesson 6 COMPARING AND ORDERING NUMBERS

The following are three strategies used to compare fractions, decimals, and whole numbers:
• Benchmarks
• Place value tables
• Equivalent fractions

USING BENCHMARKS

A benchmark is a reference point used to judge the location of another value on a number line.

Divisions in the number line can include fractions. Four commonly used benchmark fractions are $\frac{1}{10}$, $\frac{1}{4}$, $\frac{1}{2}$, and $\frac{3}{4}$.

Memorizing the benchmark fractions and their decimal equivalents allows you to compare fractions and decimals without converting their formats.

Fraction	Decimal
$\frac{1}{10}$	0.10
$\frac{1}{4}$	0.25
$\frac{1}{2}$	0.50
$\frac{3}{4}$	0.75

To order numbers using benchmarks, first order the numbers greater than 1 and then order the numbers less than 1.

Example

0.3, $\frac{5}{2}$, $1\frac{1}{4}$, $\frac{1}{5}$, $\frac{3}{9}$, 2.25, $\frac{2}{5}$, $\frac{3}{12}$

Descending means from largest to smallest.

Using benchmarks on a number line, order the set of numbers in descending order.

Solution

Start with the numbers greater than 1: $\frac{5}{2}$, $1\frac{1}{4}$, and 2.25.

Convert the improper fraction $\frac{5}{2}$ to a mixed number.

$5 \div 2 = 2 \text{ R1}$

$\qquad = 2\frac{1}{2}$

The three numbers greater than 1 are $2\frac{1}{2}$, $1\frac{1}{4}$, and 2.25.

Compare the whole numbers. The number 1 is smaller than the other two whole numbers. The fraction falls on a benchmark.

Look at the decimal and fraction of the two remaining numbers: $2\frac{1}{2}$ and 2.25. The benchmark equivalents show that $0.25 = \frac{1}{4}$ is less than $\frac{1}{2} = 0.50$.

The remaining numbers are 0.3, $\frac{1}{5}$, $\frac{3}{9}$, $\frac{2}{5}$, and $\frac{3}{12}$.

Look for fractions that can be reduced to lowest terms. The fractions $\frac{3}{9}$ and $\frac{3}{12}$ can both be reduced.

$$\frac{3 \div 3}{9 \div 3} = \frac{1}{3} \qquad \frac{3 \div 3}{12 \div 3} = \frac{1}{4}$$

When the numerators are the same, the fraction with the *smallest* denominator is the *largest*. Using the reduced fractions, there are three fractions with the same numerator: $\frac{1}{5}$, $\frac{1}{3}$, and $\frac{1}{4}$. Evaluate them based on their denominators and their position relative to the benchmark.

The fraction $\frac{1}{4}$ is a benchmark and placed automatically.

The denominator 3 is smaller than the denominator 4, so $\frac{1}{3}$ is larger than $\frac{1}{4}$.

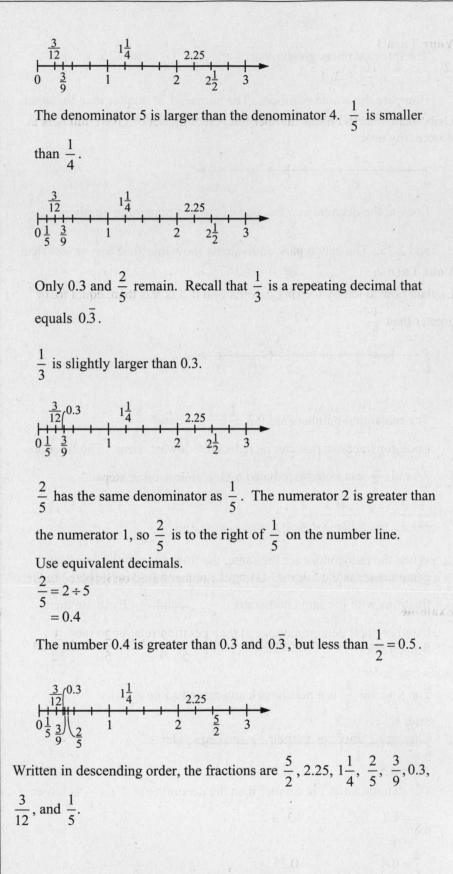

The denominator 5 is larger than the denominator 4. $\frac{1}{5}$ is smaller than $\frac{1}{4}$.

Only 0.3 and $\frac{2}{5}$ remain. Recall that $\frac{1}{3}$ is a repeating decimal that equals $0.\overline{3}$.

$\frac{1}{3}$ is slightly larger than 0.3.

$\frac{2}{5}$ has the same denominator as $\frac{1}{5}$. The numerator 2 is greater than the numerator 1, so $\frac{2}{5}$ is to the right of $\frac{1}{5}$ on the number line.

Use equivalent decimals.

$$\frac{2}{5} = 2 \div 5$$
$$= 0.4$$

The number 0.4 is greater than 0.3 and $0.\overline{3}$, but less than $\frac{1}{2} = 0.5$.

Written in descending order, the fractions are $\frac{5}{2}$, 2.25, $1\frac{1}{4}$, $\frac{2}{5}$, $\frac{3}{9}$, 0.3, $\frac{3}{12}$, and $\frac{1}{5}$.

Your Turn 1

$\dfrac{2}{9}$, 1.7, $\dfrac{8}{18}$, $\dfrac{16}{9}$, 0.2, $1\dfrac{3}{4}$

Using benchmarks on this number line, order the set of given numbers in descending order.

Your Turn 2

Explain how to tell by looking at a fraction if it is less than, equal to, or greater than $\dfrac{1}{2}$.

USING PLACE VALUE TABLES

To order numbers using place value tables, follow these steps:

Step 1
Change all fractions to their decimal equivalents.

Step 2
In a place value table, rank each decimal number based on its place value.

Example

Use a place value table to order 0.3, $\dfrac{5}{2}$, $1\dfrac{1}{4}$, $\dfrac{1}{5}$, $\dfrac{3}{9}$, 2.25, $\dfrac{2}{5}$, and $\dfrac{3}{12}$ in ascending order.

Solution

Step 1
Change all fractions to their decimal equivalents.

$\dfrac{5}{2} = 2.5$	$1\dfrac{1}{4} = 1.25$
$\dfrac{1}{5} = 0.2$	$\dfrac{3}{9} = 0.\overline{3}$
$\dfrac{2}{5} = 0.4$	$\dfrac{3}{12} = 0.25$

Step 2

In a place value table, rank each decimal number based on its place value.

Ones	.	Tenths	Hundredths	Thousandths	Rank
0	.	3	0	0	
2	.	5	0	0	
1	.	2	5	0	
0	.	2	0	0	
0	.	3	3	3	
2	.	2	5	0	
0	.	4	0	0	
0	.	2	5	0	

Start by evaluating the numbers less than 1. Look at the numbers with a 0 in the ones place. Compare the tenths place.

The smallest value is 2 tenths. There are two numbers with a 2 in the tenths place. Move to the hundredths position. Since 0 is smaller than 5, 0.2 is smaller than 0.25.

Ones	.	Tenths	Hundredths	Thousandths	Rank
0	.	3	0	0	
2	.	5	0	0	
1	.	2	5	0	
0	.	2	0	0	1
0	.	3	3	3	
2	.	2	5	0	
0	.	4	0	0	
0	.	2	5	0	2

There are two numbers with 3 in the tenths place. Move to the hundredths place. Since 0 is smaller than 3, 0.3 is smaller than $0.\overline{3}$.

Ones	.	Tenths	Hundredths	Thousandths	Rank
0	.	3	0	0	3
2	.	5	0	0	
1	.	2	5	0	
0	.	2	0	0	1
0	.	3	3	3	4
2	.	2	5	0	
0	.	4	0	0	
0	.	2	5	0	2

There is only one more number less than 1.

Ones	.	Tenths	Hundredths	Thousandths	Rank
0	.	3	0	0	3
2	.	5	0	0	
1	.	2	5	0	
0	.	2	0	0	1
0	.	3	3	3	4
2	.	2	5	0	
0	.	4	0	0	5
0	.	2	5	0	2

Look at the ones place. Since 1 is smaller than 2, 1.25 is the next smallest number.

Ones	.	Tenths	Hundredths	Thousandths	Rank
0	.	3	0	0	3
2	.	5	0	0	
1	.	2	5	0	6
0	.	2	0	0	1
0	.	3	3	3	4
2	.	2	5	0	
0	.	4	0	0	5
0	.	2	5	0	2

There are two numbers with 2 in the ones places. Move to the tenths place. Since 2 is less than 5, 2.25 is smaller than 2.5.

Ones	.	Tenths	Hundredths	Thousandths	Rank
0	.	3	0	0	3
2	.	5	0	0	8
1	.	2	5	0	6
0	.	2	0	0	1
0	.	3	3	3	4
2	.	2	5	0	7
0	.	4	0	0	5
0	.	2	5	0	2

Written in ascending order, the numbers are $\frac{1}{5}$, $\frac{3}{12}$, 0.3, $\frac{3}{9}$, $\frac{2}{5}$, $1\frac{1}{4}$, 2.25, and $\frac{5}{2}$.

Your Turn 3

Use a place value table to order 3.45, $3\frac{1}{2}$, 0.4, $3\frac{3}{9}$, and $\frac{4}{16}$ from least to greatest.

Your Turn 4

When is the place value table a good strategy to use for ordering numbers?

USING EQUIVALENT FRACTIONS

If most of the denominators are the same, it is easiest to make equivalent fractions with the ones that have different denominators.

Example

Using equivalent fractions, order 0.8, $\frac{12}{5}$, $1\frac{1}{5}$, $\frac{3}{5}$, 2.2, $\frac{2}{5}$, and $\frac{2}{10}$

from largest to smallest.

Solution

Step 1

Convert the decimals to fractions in lowest terms.

$$2.2 = 2\frac{2}{10}$$

$$0.8 = \frac{8 \div 2}{10 \div 2} \qquad = \frac{2 \times 10 + 2}{10}$$

$$= \frac{4}{5} \qquad = \frac{22 \div 2}{10 \div 2}$$

$$= \frac{11}{5}$$

Step 2

Change mixed numbers into improper fractions.

$$1\frac{1}{5} = \frac{1 \times 5 + 1}{5}$$

$$= \frac{6}{5}$$

Step 3

Make equivalent fractions of those without a denominator of 5.

$$\frac{2}{10} = \frac{2 \div 2}{10 \div 5}$$

$$= \frac{1}{5}$$

Step 4

Compare the numerators.

$$\frac{4}{5}, \frac{12}{5}, \frac{6}{5}, \frac{3}{5}, \frac{11}{5}, \frac{2}{5}, \frac{1}{5}$$

The numbers from largest to smallest are $\frac{12}{5}$, 2.2, $1\frac{1}{5}$, 0.8, $\frac{3}{5}$, $\frac{2}{5}$, and $\frac{2}{10}$.

Your Turn 5

Using equivalent fractions, order $\frac{4}{10}$, $1\frac{2}{10}$, $\frac{3}{5}$, $1\frac{2}{5}$, and 0.3, from smallest to largest.

PRACTICE EXERCISES

Compare the following fractions.

1. $\dfrac{4}{5}$ and $\dfrac{1}{5}$

2. $3\dfrac{1}{2}$ and $2\dfrac{8}{9}$

Order the following numbers from largest to smallest.

3. $\dfrac{3}{7}$, 0.45, $\dfrac{7}{16}$

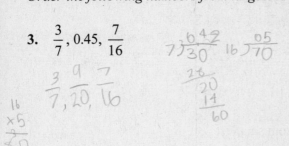

Use the following information to answer the next question.

> Rose, Pam, and Ben were all working on homework assignments. Rose completed $\dfrac{7}{8}$ of her homework assignment, Pam completed $\dfrac{2}{3}$ of her assignment, and Ben completed $\dfrac{4}{5}$ of his assignment.

4. Order these fractions from smallest to largest.

5. Which fraction is larger: $\frac{7}{8}$ or $\frac{8}{9}$?

6. Order the numbers $\frac{3}{5}$, 1.25, $\frac{12}{5}$, 0.675, $1\frac{3}{8}$, and $\frac{5}{6}$ from smallest to largest.

$8\overline{)\begin{array}{c}0.375\\30\\24\\\overline{60}\\96\end{array}}$

$\frac{3}{5}, 1\frac{1}{4}, \frac{12}{5}, \frac{675}{1000}, 1\frac{3}{8}, \frac{5}{6}$

$6\overline{)\begin{array}{c}0.8\overline{3}\\50\\48\end{array}}$

$6\overline{)60}$

0.6, 1.25, 2.4, 0.675, 0.375, 0.83

0.6, 0.675, 0.83, 1.25, 1.375, 2.4

7. Order the numbers $\frac{35}{28}$, $\frac{6}{5}$, and $\frac{4}{3}$ from largest to smallest.

$\frac{25}{28}, \frac{6}{5}, \frac{4}{3}$

REVIEW SUMMARY

- A number is divisible by
  - 2 if the number ends in an even digit (0, 2, 4, 6, or 8)
  - 3 if the sum of the digits is divisible by 3
  - 4 if the last two digits are divisible by 4
  - 5 if the number ends in a 0 or 5
  - 6 if the number is divisible by 2 and 3
  - 8 if the last three digits are divisible by 8
  - 9 if the sum of the digits is divisible by 9
  - 10 if the number ends in zero
- Division by zero is an operation that has no answer.
- Venn diagrams are used to compare and sort information into categories based on their characteristics. If there is something that shares both characteristics, it is placed in the centre where the two circles overlap. If an item does not match any of the characteristics, it is placed outside of the Venn diagram.
- Carroll diagrams are more detailed than Venn diagrams because they allow for more than two characteristics to be compared at the same time.
- Common factors are factors that are the same in all the numbers being compared. The greatest common factor (GCF) is the largest factor that all the numbers being compared share.
- To convert a fraction to a decimal, divide the numerator (dividend) by the denominator (divisor).
- A benchmark is a reference point used to judge the location of another number on a number line. Divisions in the number line can include whole numbers or fractions.

PRACTICE TEST

State the divisibility rule used to determine if a number is divisible by the following numbers.

1. 6

2. 4

3. 5

Determine whether the following numbers are divisible by 3.

4. 57

5. 129

6. 1 862

7. 12 837

8. 85 294 913

9. 54 930

Determine whether the numbers below are divisible by 9.

10. 79

11. 369

12. 77 923

13. 18 72

14. 991 037

15. 48 230 023

Change each decimal below to a fraction in lowest terms.

16. 0.32 $\dfrac{8}{25}$

17. 0.8 $\dfrac{4}{5}$

18. 0.5 $\dfrac{1}{2}$

19. 1.7 $1\dfrac{7}{10}$

20. 2.005 $2\dfrac{1}{200}$

21. 10.25 $10\dfrac{1}{4}$

Express each of the following fractions as a decimal.

22. $\dfrac{6}{10}$ 0.6

$$9\overline{)40} \quad \begin{array}{r} 0.44 \\ \hline 40 \\ 36 \\ \hline 40 \end{array}$$

23. $\dfrac{12}{50}$ 0.24

$$128\overline{)320} \quad \begin{array}{r} 0.25 \\ \hline 256 \\ 640 \end{array}$$

24. $\dfrac{32}{128}$ 0.25

25. $\dfrac{4}{9}$ $0.4\bar{4}$

26. $\dfrac{5}{6}$ 0.83

55⟌50 0.8

27. $\dfrac{45}{55}$ 0.8

Compare the following fractions.

28. $\dfrac{5}{7}$ and $\dfrac{7}{9}$

29. $\dfrac{15}{4}$ and $\dfrac{28}{9}$

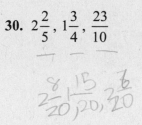

Order from largest to smallest.

30. $2\dfrac{2}{5}$, $1\dfrac{3}{4}$, $\dfrac{23}{10}$

$2\dfrac{8}{20}$, $1\dfrac{15}{20}$, $2\dfrac{6}{20}$

NOTES

WORKING WITH PERCENTS

When you are finished this unit, you will be able to…
- estimate and calculate percentages
- convert between fractions, decimals, and percentages
- estimate the answer to problems that involve whole numbers and decimals

PREREQUISITE SKILLS AND KNOWLEDGE

Prior to starting this unit, you should be able to…
- read and write numbers to the thousandths place value
- know what percent is
- round numbers up to the hundredths place value
- demonstrate your understanding of decimals and their place value

Lesson 1   EXPRESSING PERCENTAGES AS FRACTIONS AND DECIMALS

NOTES

Percent means *"for every 100."*

Percents are written using the percent symbol, %.

40% means *for every 40 out of 100.*

Percents can be expressed as fractions and decimals.

CONVERTING PERCENTAGES INTO FRACTIONS

Fractions are comprised of a numerator that represents the part and a denominator that represents the whole.

A percentage represents a part of a whole, where the whole is 100.

Because a percentage is a number out of 100, they can be expressed as fractions where the denominator is 100.

For example, $85\% = \dfrac{85}{100} \rightarrow 85$ out of 100

Example

Convert 25% into a fraction.

Solution

Step 1

Write the percentage over a denominator of 100.

25% means 25 out of 100, so it can be written as $\dfrac{25}{100}$.

Step 2

Simplify the fraction.

Divide the numerator and the denominator by 25.

$$\frac{25 \div 25}{100 \div 25} = \frac{1}{4}$$

Therefore, 25% can be written as $\dfrac{1}{4}$.

Your Turn 1

Convert 40% into a fraction.

CONVERTING PERCENTAGES INTO DECIMAL NUMBERS

A percentage can also be converted into a decimal number. To change a percent into a decimal, move the decimal point in the percentage two places to the left and remove the percent symbol.

Example

Change 25% into a decimal.

> *Solution*
> Move the decimal point two places to the left and remove the percent symbol.
> $25\% \rightarrow 25. \rightarrow 0.25$

Therefore, 25% can be written as 0.25.

Your Turn 2

Change 40% into a decimal.

PROBLEM SOLVING WITH PERCENTAGES

When solving problems involving finding percentages, you could be required to identify a fraction or decimal before you can calculate the percentage.

To calculate the percentage, follow these steps:

Step 1
Identify the fraction.

Step 2
Calculate the decimal equivalent of the fraction.

Step 3
Write the percentage.

Unless otherwise stated, round the percentage to the nearest whole number.

Example

Harvey has a monthly salary of $3 600. He spends $580 per month on food. What percentage of his monthly salary does he spend on food?

> *Solution*
> **Step 1**
> Identify the fraction.
> The amount spent on food represents the part which is 580.
> The entire monthly salary represents the whole which is 3 600.
>
> The fraction is $\dfrac{580}{3\ 600}$.

Step 2
Calculate the decimal equivalent of the fraction.
Divide the numerator by the denominator.
$580 \div 3\,600 \doteq 0.16$

Step 3
Write the percentage.
Multiply the result by 100, and place a percent symbol after the answer.
$0.16 \times 100 = 16\%$

Harvey spends approximately 16% of his monthly salary on food.

Your Turn 3

Chen got 16 out of 22 questions correct on his math quiz. What percentage of the questions did he get correct?

Sometimes when you go shopping, there are signs indicating a bonus on some items. For example, you may see a bottle of shampoo with a label saying "100 mL for free." It is helpful to know the percentage increase or decrease so you can determine if it is a good deal.

Use the same steps to calculate the percentage.

Example

The original price of a shirt was $50, and it was put on sale for $30.
The original price of another shirt was $75 and is now on sale for $50.
Which shirt is the better deal?

Solution
Step 1
Determine the fraction.
The decrease in price is the numerator, and the original price is the denominator.
The decrease in price of the first shirt is $50 - 30 = 20$.
The original price of the first shirt was $50.

The fraction is $\dfrac{20}{50}$.

The decrease in the price of the second shirt is $75 - 50 = 25$.
The original price of the second shirt was $75.

The fraction is $\dfrac{25}{75}$.

Step 2
Calculate the decimal equivalent of the fractions.
Divide the numerator by the denominator.
First shirt: $20 \div 50 = 0.40$
Second shirt: $25 \div 75 \doteq 0.33$

Step 3
Write the percentage.
Multiply the result by 100, and place a percent sign after the answer.
First shirt: $0.40 \times 100 = 40\%$
Second shirt: $0.33 \times 100 = 33\%$

The first shirt has the greater percentage of decrease, which means it is the better deal.

Your Turn 4

Michelle is buying shampoo and sees two containers. One has 500 mL offering an additional bonus of 250 mL in it. Another brand has 650 mL and is offering an additional 100 mL bonus. Which shampoo bottle is the better buy?

PRACTICE EXERCISES

1. Write $\dfrac{3}{25}$ as a percentage.

2. Write $\dfrac{6}{10}$ as a percentage.

3. Write 24 out of 52 as a percentage.

4. Write 13 out of 60 as a percentage.

5. Write 50% as a decimal.

6. Write 23% as a decimal.

7. Cesar bought a pair of jeans for $75.00 and paid $4.50 in taxes. What percentage was the sales tax?

8. Danny owns a grocery store. His food costs are $3 500, while his total food sales are $10 600. What percentage of his food sales do the food costs represent?

9. A particular movie theatre holds 250 people. On one Wednesday evening, only 150 of the seats are full. Calculate the percentage of seats that are full in the theatre on Wednesday evening.

10. Ruby planted a garden in her backyard. She planted 14 roses, 8 tulips, and 20 gerbera daisies. Determine the percentage of her garden devoted to roses.

Lesson 2 PERCENT OF A NUMBER

A sign in the department store says shoes are 20% off the regular price. If the shoes are regularly $120.00, what is the discount?

The question is asking you to calculate the percent, or part of, a number. What is 20% of 120?

The two methods used to find the percent of a number are: equivalent fractions and multiplying by a decimal.

USING EQUIVALENT FRACTIONS

To calculate the percent of a number using equivalent fractions, follow these steps:

Step 1
Set up equivalent fractions with the percentage being the first fraction.

Step 2
Determine how the equivalent denominator was created.

Step 3
Multiply or divide the numerator by the same number.

Example

Using equivalent fractions, find 18% of 200.

Solution
Step 1
Set up equivalent fractions.

Write the percentage as the first fraction. The numerator of the second fraction is represented with a variable (a letter or symbol used to represent a value). The denominator is the given number.

$$\frac{18}{100} = \frac{x}{200}$$

Step 2
Determine the number used to create the equivalent denominator.

The denominator is multiplied by 2 to get 200.
$$100 \times 2 = 200$$

Step 3
Multiply the numerator by the same number.
$$\frac{18 \times 2}{100 \times 2} = \frac{36}{200}$$

18% of 200 is 36.

Your Turn 1

What is 18% of 50?

MULTIPLYING BY A DECIMAL

To calculate the percent of a number by multiplying by a decimal, follow these steps:

Step 1

Convert the percentage into a decimal.

Step 2

Multiply the decimal number by the given number.

Example

Calculate 18% of 200.

Solution

Step 1

Convert the percentage to a decimal.

$18\% = 0.18$

Step 2

Multiply the decimal number by the given number.

$0.18 \times 200 = 36$

18% of 200 is 36.

Your Turn 2

Calculate 45% of 400.

FINDING THE VALUE OF THE UNKNOWN NUMBER

Sometimes, the denominator is the unknown value. In this case, only the equivalent fraction strategy will allow you to calculate the unknown value.

Example

5 is 25% of what number?

Solution

Step 1

Set up equivalent fractions.
The percent is written as the first fraction.
Since 5 represents the part, it will go in the numerator of the second fraction.

$$\frac{25}{100} = \frac{5}{x}$$

Step 2

Determine the number used to create the equivalent numerator.
The numerator is divided by 5 to get 5.

$$25 \div 5 = 5$$

Step 3

Divide the denominator by the same divisor.

$$\frac{25 \div 5}{100 \div 5} = \frac{5}{20}$$

5 is 25% of 20.

Your Turn 3

45 is 15% of what number?

PRACTICE EXERCISES

1. Use two strategies to determine 42% of 300.

2. Use two strategies to determine 16% of 25.

3. 60 is 20% of what number?

4. 7 is 35% of what number?

5. A DVD is regularly priced at $29.95. It is on sale for 15% off. How much will the discounted DVD cost?

6. The original price of an MP3 player was $200.00. It is advertised on sale for $130.00. What is the percentage discount?

7. A CD costs $19.99. Calculate the total cost after 5% GST is added.

8. What is 25% of 800?

9. Calculate 20% of 420.

10. Sarah spent 55% of her allowance on clothes, 10% on candy, and 20% on a movie. She saved the rest.

a) What percentage of her money did Sarah spend?

b) What percentage of her money did she save?

c) If Sarah receives a $50 allowance per month, how much money did she spend this month?

REVIEW SUMMARY

- Percent means out of 100. The percent sign (%) behind a number is used to indicate that the number is a percentage.
- To convert a percentage into a fraction, place the percent as the numerator and 100 as the denominator.
- To convert a percentage into a decimal number, move the decimal in the percent two places to the left and remove the percent symbol.
- To calculate a percent of a number use equivalent fractions.
- To calculate a percent of a number, convert the percentage to a decimal and multiply by the decimal.

PRACTICE TEST

1. Write the fraction $\frac{12}{40}$ as a percentage.

2. Calculate 25% of 900.

3. Write 30% as a decimal.

4. Write 20% as a fraction in lowest terms.

5. Write the fraction $\frac{3}{8}$ as a percentage.

6. Write 59% as a decimal.

7. Change 42% to a decimal.

8. Change 82% to a fraction in lowest terms.

9. Write 78% as a fraction in lowest terms.

10. At LollyPop Daycare, 20 children are under the age of five. If there are 25 children registered at the daycare, what percentage of the children are under the age of five?

11. A jacket is regularly priced at $149.95. It is on sale for 20% off, and there are no taxes. Using the two methods of solving, how much will the jacket cost on sale?

12. Approximately 13.5 million people, or 42% of the population, voted in the last federal election. Roughly how many voters were eligible to vote?

13. Harry works at a furniture store and earns 6% commission on all the sales he makes in a month. If Harry sold $18 700 worth of furniture in November, how much commission did he earn?

14. If Dave bought a shirt for $89.00 and paid $5.34 in taxes, what percentage of tax did he pay for his shirt?

    A. 4%   **B.** 5%

    C. 6%   **D.** 7%

15. The original cost of a car is $8 000. The tax on the cost of the car is 12%. What is the total purchase price of the car including tax?

FRACTION OPERATIONS

When you are finished this unit, you will be able to…
- determine the common denominator of a given set of positive fractions or mixed numbers
- simplify a given positive fraction or mixed number by identifying the common factor between the numerator and denominator
- determine the sum of two given positive fractions with like and unlike denominators
- determine the difference of two given positive fractions with like and unlike denominators
- determine the sum of two mixed numbers with like and unlike denominators
- determine the difference of two mixed numbers with like and unlike denominators
- model addition and subtraction of a given positive fraction or given mixed number
- solve a given problem involving the addition or subtraction of positive fractions or mixed numbers and determine if the solution is reasonable

PREREQUISITE SKILLS AND KNOWLEDGE

Prior to starting this unit, you should be able to…
- recognize improper fractions and mixed numbers
- change improper fractions to proper fractions and vice versa

Lesson 1   ADDING AND SUBTRACTING FRACTIONS WITH LIKE AND UNLIKE DENOMINATORS

ADDING FRACTIONS WITH LIKE DENOMINATORS PICTORALLY

Fractions compare parts of an object to the whole. The numerator represents the number of parts while the denominator represents the whole. For example, a pizza is cut into 8 slices. John eats 2 pieces and his sister eats 3 pieces of the pizza. The fraction representing the pieces of pizza John ate is $\frac{2}{8}$. The fraction representing the pieces of pizza John's sister ate is $\frac{3}{8}$. Together, they ate $\frac{5}{8}$ of the pizza.

Because the fractions have the same denominator, the numerators can be added. You can also show this operation using diagrams.

To add fractions with like denominators using diagrams, follow these steps:

Step 1
Draw a grid based on the factors of the denominator.

Step 2
Colour the parts of the grid that are equivalent to each numerator.

Step 3
Add the total number of coloured parts.

Example

Draw a diagram to solve $\frac{4}{9} + \frac{2}{9}$.

Solution
Step 1
Draw a grid based on the factors of the denominator.
The factors of the denominator are 1, 3, and 9. Use 3×3.

Step 2
Colour the parts of the grid that are equivalent to each numerator.
The numerators are 4 and 2. Use a different colour for each numerator.

Step 3
Count the total number of coloured parts.
You have 6 coloured squares in total.

$$\frac{4}{9} + \frac{2}{9} = \frac{6}{9}$$

Notice that 2 of the 3 columns are shaded. The fraction $\frac{6}{9}$ can be

reduced to $\frac{2}{3}$.

$$\frac{4}{9} + \frac{2}{9} = \frac{2}{3}$$

Your Turn 1

Draw a diagram to solve $\frac{4}{8} + \frac{3}{8}$.

ADDING FRACTIONS WITH LIKE DENOMINATORS NUMERICALLY

To add fractions with like denominators numerically, follow these steps:

Step 1
Add the numerators of the fractions while keeping the denominators
the same.

Step 2
Reduce the resulting fraction to lowest terms by dividing
the numerator and denominator by the greatest common factor (GCF)
if required.

Example

Add $\dfrac{4}{9}$ and $\dfrac{2}{9}$.

Solution

Step 1

Add the numerators of the fractions while keeping the denominators the same.

$$\dfrac{4}{9} + \dfrac{2}{9} = \dfrac{4+2}{9}$$

$$= \dfrac{6}{9}$$

Step 2

Reduce the resulting fraction to lowest terms by dividing the numerator and denominator by the GCF.

The GCF is 3.

$$\dfrac{6 \div 3}{9 \div 3} = \dfrac{2}{3}$$

The sum of $\dfrac{4}{9} + \dfrac{2}{9} = \dfrac{2}{3}$.

Your Turn 2

Add $\dfrac{2}{6}$ and $\dfrac{1}{6}$.

SUBTRACTING FRACTIONS WITH LIKE DENOMINATORS PICTORALLY

Fractions with like denominators can also be subtracted. For example, a pizza is cut into 8 slices. John eats 2 pieces and his sister eats 3 pieces.

The fraction representing the pieces of pizza John ate is $\dfrac{2}{8}$.

The fraction representing the pieces of pizza John's sister ate is $\dfrac{3}{8}$.

Together, they ate $\dfrac{5}{8}$ of the pizza so only $\dfrac{3}{8}$ of the pizza is left.

Because the fractions have the same denominator, the numerators can be subtracted. You can also show this operation using diagrams.

148

To subtract fractions with like denominators using diagrams, follow these steps:

Step 1
Draw a grid based on the factors of the denominator.

Step 2
Shade in the parts of the grid that are equivalent to the first numerator.

Step 3
Cross out the shaded parts equivalent to the second numerator.

Step 4
Count the total number of remaining shaded parts.

Example

Draw a diagram to solve $\dfrac{4}{9} - \dfrac{1}{9}$.

Solution

Step 1
Draw a grid based on the factors of the denominator.
The factors of the denominator are 1, 3, and 9. Use 3×3.

Step 2
Shade in the parts of the grid that are equivalent to the first numerator.
The first numerator is 4.

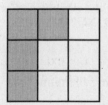

Step 3
Cross out the shaded parts equivalent to the second numerator.
The second numerator is 1.

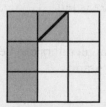

Step 4

Count the total number of remaining shaded parts.
There are 3 shaded squares left.

$$\frac{4}{9} - \frac{1}{9} = \frac{3}{9}$$

Notice that 1 column is left shaded. The fraction $\frac{3}{9}$ can be reduced

to $\frac{1}{3}$.

The difference of $\frac{4}{9} - \frac{1}{9} = \frac{1}{3}$.

Your Turn 3

Draw a diagram to solve $\frac{4}{8} - \frac{3}{8}$.

SUBTRACTING FRACTIONS WITH LIKE DENOMINATORS NUMERICALLY

To subtract fractions with like denominators numerically, follow
these steps:

Step 1

Subtract the numerators of the fractions while keeping the denominators
the same.

Step 2

Reduce the resulting fraction to lowest terms by dividing the numerator
and denominator by the GCF if required.

Your Turn 4

Subtract $\frac{1}{5}$ and $\frac{3}{5}$.

Your Turn 5

Subtract $\frac{3}{8}$ from $\frac{7}{8}$.

ADDING FRACTIONS WITH UNLIKE DENOMINATORS

To add fractions with unlike denominators, follow these steps:

Step 1
Rewrite the fractions using the lowest common denominator (LCD).

Step 2
Add the numerators of the fractions while keeping the denominators the same.

Step 3
Reduce the resulting fraction to lowest terms by dividing the numerator and denominator by the GCF if required.

Example

Add $\frac{1}{4}$ and $\frac{2}{3}$.

Solution

Step 1
Rewrite the fractions using the LCD.

Write the multiples of each denominator until a common one appears.
Multiples of 3: 3, 6, 9, **12**, 15…
Multiples of 4: 4, 8, **12**, 16, 20…
The lowest common denominator of 3 and 4 is 12.

Multiply the numerator and the denominator of each fraction by the same factor.

$$\frac{1 \times 3}{4 \times 3} = \frac{3}{12} \qquad\qquad \frac{2 \times 4}{3 \times 4} = \frac{8}{12}$$

NOTES

Step 2

Add the numerators of the fractions while keeping the denominators the same.

$$\frac{3}{12} + \frac{8}{12} = \frac{3+8}{12}$$
$$= \frac{11}{12}$$

Step 3

Reduce the resulting fraction to lowest terms.

The fraction is in lowest terms.

$$\frac{1}{4} + \frac{2}{3} = \frac{11}{12}$$

Your Turn 6

Add $\frac{1}{3}$ and $\frac{2}{5}$.

SUBTRACTING FRACTIONS WITH UNLIKE DENOMINATORS

To subtract fractions with unlike denominators, follow these steps:

Step 1

Rewrite the fractions using the LCD.

Step 2

Subtract the numerators of the fractions while keeping the denominators the same.

Step 3

Reduce the resulting fraction to lowest terms by dividing the numerator and denominator by the GCF if required.

Example

Subtract $\dfrac{1}{4}$ from $\dfrac{2}{3}$.

Solution

Step 1

Rewrite the fractions using the LCD.

Write the multiples of each denominator until a common one appears.
Multiples of 3: 3, 6, 9, **12**, 15…
Multiples of 4: 4, 8, **12**, 16, 20…
The lowest common denominator of 3 and 4 is 12.

Multiply the numerator and the denominator of each fraction by the same factor.

$$\frac{2 \times 4}{3 \times 4} = \frac{8}{12} \qquad \frac{1 \times 3}{4 \times 3} = \frac{3}{12}$$

Step 2

Subtract the numerators of the fractions while keeping the denominators the same.

$$\frac{8}{12} - \frac{3}{12} = \frac{8-3}{12} = \frac{5}{12}$$

Step 3

Reduce the resulting fraction to lowest terms.

The fraction is in lowest terms.

$$\frac{2}{3} - \frac{1}{4} = \frac{5}{12}$$

Your Turn 7

Subtract $\dfrac{1}{3}$ from $\dfrac{2}{5}$.

PRACTICE EXERCISES

1. Use a diagram to solve $\dfrac{4}{6}+\dfrac{1}{6}$.

$\dfrac{5}{6}$

2. Use a diagram to solve $\dfrac{4}{6}-\dfrac{2}{6}$.

$\dfrac{2}{6}$

Calculate the sum or difference in each of the following expressions.

3. $\dfrac{23}{65}+\dfrac{32}{65}$ $= \dfrac{55}{65}$

4. $\dfrac{20}{24}-\dfrac{12}{24}$ $\dfrac{8}{24}$

5. $\frac{1}{4} + \frac{1}{2} = \frac{3}{4}$

6. $\frac{5}{7} + \frac{1}{5} = \frac{25}{35} + \frac{7}{35} = \frac{32}{35}$

7. $\frac{5}{6} - \frac{2}{3} = \frac{1}{6}$

8. $\frac{4}{7} - \frac{6}{11} = \frac{44}{77} - \frac{42}{77} = \frac{2}{77}$

9. $\frac{5}{6} - \frac{3}{12} = \frac{10}{12} - \frac{3}{12} = \frac{7}{12}$

10. $\frac{5}{7} - \frac{2}{5} = \frac{25}{35} - \frac{14}{35} = \frac{11}{35}$

Lesson 2   MIXED NUMBERS

A **mixed number** is made up of two parts: a whole number and a fraction.

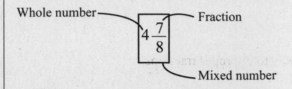

For example, Albert picked up 5 pizzas. Each pizza was cut into 8 slices. On the way home, he ate one piece. The amount of pizza remaining is 4 whole pizzas and $\frac{7}{8}$ of the fifth pizza. The mixed number $4\frac{7}{8}$ represents the amount of pizza left.

ADDING MIXED NUMBERS WITH LIKE DENOMINATORS

You can use one of two methods to add mixed numbers with the same denominators.

Method 1

Step 1

Change the mixed numbers to improper fractions using the following formula:

$$a\frac{b}{c} \rightarrow \frac{a \times c + b}{c}$$

Step 2

Add the numerators of the fractions while keeping the denominators the same.

Step 3

Reduce the resulting improper fraction to lowest terms if required.

Step 4

Change the improper fraction to a mixed number using the following formula:

$$\text{numerator} \div \text{denominator} = \text{quotient} + \frac{\text{remainder}}{\text{denominator}}$$

156

Example

Calculate $2\dfrac{1}{6}+3\dfrac{3}{6}$.

Solution

Step 1

Change the mixed numbers to improper fractions.

$$2\frac{1}{6}=\frac{2\times 6+1}{6} \qquad\qquad 3\frac{3}{6}=\frac{3\times 6+3}{6}$$

$$\phantom{2\frac{1}{6}}=\frac{13}{6} \qquad\qquad\qquad \phantom{3\frac{3}{6}}=\frac{21}{6}$$

Step 2

Add the numerators of the fractions while keeping the denominators the same.

$$\frac{13}{6}+\frac{21}{6}=\frac{13+21}{6}$$

$$\phantom{\frac{13}{6}+\frac{21}{6}}=\frac{34}{6}$$

Step 3

Reduce the resulting improper fraction to lowest terms.

Divide the numerator and denominator by the GCF (2).

$$\frac{34\div 2}{6\div 2}=\frac{17}{3}$$

Step 4

Change the improper fraction to a mixed number.

$17\div 3=5\text{ R}2$

$$\frac{17}{3}=5\frac{2}{3}$$

$$2\frac{1}{6}+3\frac{3}{6}=5\frac{2}{3}$$

Your Turn 1

Calculate $2\dfrac{1}{8}+3\dfrac{5}{8}$.

Method 2

Step 1
Add the whole numbers together.

Step 2
Add the fractions.

Step 3
Combine the whole number and fraction.

Step 4
Reduce the mixed number to lowest terms.

Example

Calculate $2\frac{1}{6}+4\frac{3}{6}$.

Solution
Step 1
Add the whole numbers.
$2+4=6$

Step 2
Add the fractions.
$\frac{1}{6}+\frac{3}{6}=\frac{4}{6}$

Step 3
Combine the whole numbers and fractions.
$6+\frac{4}{6}=6\frac{4}{6}$

Reduce the mixed number to lowest terms.
$$6\frac{4}{6}=6\frac{4\div 2}{6\div 2}$$
$$=6\frac{2}{3}$$

$$2\frac{1}{6}+4\frac{3}{6}=6\frac{2}{3}$$

Your Turn 2

Calculate $1\frac{1}{4}+3\frac{2}{4}$.

ADDING MIXED NUMBERS WITH UNLIKE DENOMINATORS

Method 1
To add mixed numbers with unlike denominators, follow these steps:

Step 1
Change the mixed numbers to improper fractions.

Step 2
Rewrite the fractions with the LCD.

Step 3
Add the numerators of the equivalent fractions while keeping the denominators the same.

Step 4
Reduce the resulting fraction to lowest terms if required.

Step 5
Change the improper fraction to a mixed number using the following formula:

$$\text{numerator} \div \text{demoninator} = \text{quotient} + \frac{\text{remainder}}{\text{denominator}}$$

Example

Calculate $2\frac{1}{4} + 1\frac{2}{3}$.

Solution

Step 1
Change the mixed numbers to improper fractions.

$$2\frac{1}{4} = \frac{2 \times 4 + 1}{4} \qquad\qquad 1\frac{2}{3} = \frac{1 \times 3 + 2}{3}$$
$$= \frac{9}{4} \qquad\qquad\qquad\qquad = \frac{5}{3}$$

Step 2
Rewrite the fractions with the LCD.

Write the multiples of each denominator until a common one appears.
Multiples of 3: 3, 6, 9, **12**, 15…
Multiples of 4: 4, 8, **12**, 16, and 20…
The lowest common denominator of 3 and 4 is 12.

Multiply the numerator and the denominator of each fraction by the same factor.

$$\frac{9 \times 3}{4 \times 3} = \frac{27}{12} \qquad\qquad \frac{5 \times 4}{3 \times 4} = \frac{20}{12}$$

Step 3
Add the numerators of the fractions while keeping the denominators the same.

$$\frac{27}{12}+\frac{20}{12}=\frac{27+20}{12}$$
$$=\frac{47}{12}$$

Step 4
Change the improper fraction to a mixed number.
$47\div12=3$ remainder 11

$$\frac{47}{12}=3\frac{11}{12}$$

The sum of $2\frac{1}{4}+1\frac{2}{3}=3\frac{11}{12}$.

Your Turn 3

Calculate $3\frac{1}{4}+2\frac{2}{3}$.

SUBTRACTING MIXED NUMBERS WITH LIKE DENOMINATORS

Use one of two methods to subtract mixed numbers with the same denominators.

Method 1

Step 1
Change the mixed numbers to improper fractions using the following formula:

$$a\frac{b}{c}\rightarrow\frac{a\times c+b}{c}$$

Step 2
Subtract the numerators of the fractions while keeping the denominators the same.

Step 3
Reduce the resulting improper fraction to lowest terms if required.

Step 4

Change the improper fraction to a mixed number using the following formula:

$$\text{numerator} \div \text{demoninator} = \text{quotient} + \frac{\text{remainder}}{\text{denominator}}$$

Example

Calculate $3\frac{3}{6} - 2\frac{1}{6}$.

Solution

Step 1

Change the mixed number to an improper fraction.

$$3\frac{3}{6} = \frac{3 \times 6 + 3}{6} \qquad\qquad 2\frac{1}{6} = \frac{2 \times 6 + 1}{6}$$

$$= \frac{21}{6} \qquad\qquad\qquad\qquad = \frac{13}{6}$$

Step 2

Subtract the numerators of the fractions while keeping the denominators the same.

$$\frac{21}{6} - \frac{13}{6} = \frac{21 - 13}{6}$$

$$= \frac{8}{6}$$

Step 3

Reduce the resulting improper fraction to lowest terms.

The GCF of 8 and 6 is 2. Divide both the numerator and denominator by 2.

$$\frac{8 \div 2}{6 \div 2} = \frac{4}{3}$$

Step 4

Change the reduced improper fraction to a mixed number.

$$4 \div 3 = 1 \text{ R}1$$

$$\frac{4}{3} = 1\frac{1}{3}$$

$$3\frac{3}{6} - 2\frac{1}{6} = 1\frac{1}{3}$$

Your Turn 4

Calculate $3\frac{5}{8} - 2\frac{1}{8}$.

NOTES

Method 2

Step 1
Subtract the whole numbers.

Step 2
Subtract the fractions.

Step 3
Combine the whole numbers and fractions and reduce the mixed number to lowest terms.

Example

Calculate $2\dfrac{4}{6} - 1\dfrac{2}{6}$.

Solution

Step 1
Subtract the whole numbers.
$2 - 1 = 1$

Step 2
Subtract the numerators of the fractions while keeping the denominators the same.

$$\frac{4}{6} - \frac{2}{6} = \frac{4-2}{6}$$
$$= \frac{2}{6}$$

Step 3
Add the whole number and the fraction.

$$1 + \frac{2}{6} = 1\frac{2}{6}$$

Reduce the fraction into lowest terms.

$$1\frac{2}{6} = 1\frac{2 \div 2}{6 \div 2}$$
$$= 1\frac{1}{3}$$

$$2\frac{4}{6} - 1\frac{2}{6} = 1\frac{1}{3}.$$

Your Turn 5

Calculate $4\dfrac{3}{4} - 1\dfrac{1}{4}$

SUBTRACTING MIXED NUMBERS WITH UNLIKE DENOMINATORS

To subtract mixed numbers with unlike denominators, follow these steps:

Step 1

Change the mixed numbers to improper fractions using the following formula:

$$a\frac{b}{c} \rightarrow \frac{a \times c + b}{c}$$

Step 2

Rewrite the fractions using the LCD.

Step 3

Subtract the numerators of the equivalent fractions while keeping the denominators the same.

Step 4

Reduce the resulting improper fraction to lowest terms if required.

Step 5

Change the improper fraction to a mixed number using the following formula:

$$\text{numerator} \div \text{denominator} = \text{quotient} + \frac{\text{remainder}}{\text{denominator}}$$

Example

Calculate $2\frac{3}{4} - 1\frac{1}{3}$.

Solution

Step 1

Change the mixed numbers to improper fractions.

$$2\frac{3}{4} = \frac{2 \times 4 + 3}{4} \qquad\qquad 1\frac{1}{3} = \frac{1 \times 3 + 1}{3}$$

$$= \frac{11}{4} \qquad\qquad\qquad\qquad = \frac{4}{3}$$

Step 2

Rewrite the fractions using the LCD.

Write the multiples of each denominator until a common one appears.
Multiples of 3: 3, 6, 9, **12**, 15...
Multiples of 4: 4, 8, **12**, 16, 20…
The lowest common denominator of 3 and 4 is 12.

Multiply the numerator and the denominator of each fraction by the same factor.

$$\frac{11 \times 3}{4 \times 3} = \frac{33}{12} \qquad\qquad \frac{4 \times 4}{3 \times 4} = \frac{16}{12}$$

Step 3

Subtract the numerators of the fractions while keeping the denominators the same.

$$\frac{33}{12} - \frac{16}{12} = \frac{33-16}{12}$$
$$= \frac{17}{12}$$

Step 4

Change the reduced improper fraction to a mixed number.

$17 \div 12 = 1$ remainder 5

$$\frac{17}{12} = 1\frac{5}{12}$$
$$2\frac{3}{4} - 1\frac{1}{3} = 1\frac{5}{12}$$

Your Turn 6

Calculate $3\frac{4}{5} - 2\frac{1}{3}$.

PRACTICE EXERCISES

Calculate the sum or difference in each of the following expressions.

1. $1\frac{1}{3} + 2\frac{1}{3}$ $3\frac{2}{3}$

2. $3 + 4\frac{1}{2}$ $7\frac{1}{2}$

3. $2\frac{1}{2} + 2\frac{3}{6}$ $2\frac{6}{6}$

4. $3\frac{2}{6} + 4\frac{8}{12}$ $7\frac{12}{12} = 8$

5. $5\frac{5}{8} + 2\frac{1}{8}$ $7\frac{6}{8}$

6. $1\frac{3}{7} + \frac{6}{7}$ $1\frac{9}{7} = 2\frac{2}{7}$

7. $2\frac{1}{2} - 2\frac{1}{6}$ $\frac{2}{6}$

8. $4\frac{8}{12} - 3\frac{2}{6}$ $4\frac{8}{12} - 3\frac{5}{12} = 1\frac{3}{12} = 1\frac{1}{4}$

9. $1\frac{2}{3} - \frac{6}{7}$ $1\frac{14}{21} - \frac{18}{21} = \frac{35}{21} - \frac{18}{21} = \frac{17}{21}$

10. $4\frac{1}{2} - 3\frac{8}{10} = 4\frac{5}{10} - 3\frac{8}{10} = 3\frac{15}{10} - 3\frac{8}{10} = \frac{7}{10}$

Lesson 3   PROBLEM SOLVING WITH FRACTIONS

You have to follow an order of operations when solving problems involving more than one operation to get the correct answer. Use the acronym **BEDMAS** to help remember the order of operations.

- **Brackets**—complete all operations inside a set of brackets. When brackets occur inside of brackets perform the operations inside the innermost brackets first and work your way outward.
- **Exponents**—evaluate the terms with exponents.
- **Division/Multiplication**—complete the operations of division and multiplication in the order they appear from left to right.
- **Addition/Subtraction**—complete the operations of addition and subtraction in the order they appear from left to right.

The rules for working with the positive and negative signs still apply.

To solve word problems involving fractions, carefully read the question. Translate the words into a mathematical expression. Look for keywords indicating what operation to use to solve the problem. If necessary, underline or highlight the key words.

KEY WORDS
Add
- sum
- total
- altogether
- more than

Subtract
- difference
- less than
- take away
- taken from
- have left

SOLVING A PROBLEM INVOLVING FRACTIONS

To solve problems involving fractions, follow these steps:
Step 1
Identify the fractions and operational keywords.

Step 2
Write an expression to represent the problem.

Step 3
Solve the expression and reduce the answer to lowest terms if required.

Example

In total, James owns $2\frac{3}{5}$ acres of land, and his brother Art owns $3\frac{1}{5}$ acres.

One day, Sheila offers to buy $1\frac{2}{5}$ acres of the brothers' combined land.

If the brothers decide to sell the land to Sheila, how much land will they still own?

Solution

Step 1

Identify the fractions and the operational keywords.

James owns $2\frac{3}{5}$ acres of land. Art owns $3\frac{1}{5}$ acres of land.

Sheila wants to buy $1\frac{2}{5}$ acres of land.

"In total" means addition.
"How much land will they still own?" means subtraction.

Step 2

Write an expression to represent the problem.

$$\left(2\frac{3}{5}+3\frac{1}{5}\right)-1\frac{2}{5}$$

Step 3

Solve the expression and reduce the answer to lowest terms if required.

Change the mixed numbers into improper fractions.

$$2\frac{3}{5}=\frac{2\times5+3}{5} \qquad 3\frac{1}{5}=\frac{3\times5+1}{5} \qquad 1\frac{2}{5}=\frac{1\times5+2}{5}$$
$$=\frac{13}{5} \qquad\qquad\quad =\frac{16}{5} \qquad\qquad\quad =\frac{7}{5}$$

Follow the order of operations.

$$\left(\frac{13}{5}+\frac{16}{5}\right)-\frac{7}{5}$$

Brackets first.

$$\left(\frac{13}{5}+\frac{16}{5}\right)-\frac{7}{5}=\left(\frac{13+16}{5}\right)-\frac{7}{5}$$
$$=\frac{29}{5}-\frac{7}{5}$$

Complete the subtraction.

$$\frac{29}{5}-\frac{7}{5}=\frac{29-7}{5}$$
$$=\frac{22}{5}$$

Step 4
Change the improper fraction to a mixed number.
$22 \div 5 = 4 \ R2$

$$\frac{22}{5} = 4\frac{2}{5}$$

The brothers will still own $4\frac{2}{5}$ acres of land if they decide to sell some of it to Sheila.

Your Turn 1
Rheanna and Abdu take turns driving to their friend's house, which is $9\frac{1}{4}$ km away. Rheanna drives $2\frac{3}{4}$ km, and Abdu drives $4\frac{2}{4}$ km. How much farther do they have to drive?

Example
Everyone should drink $8\frac{1}{4}$ cups of water and $2\frac{2}{5}$ cups of milk a day. In total, how much fluid should everyone drink on a daily basis?

Solution
Step 1
Identify the fractions and the operational keywords.

$8\frac{1}{4}$ cups of water

$2\frac{2}{5}$ cups of milk

"In total" means addition.

Step 2
Write an expression to represent the problem.
$8\frac{1}{4} + 2\frac{2}{5}$

Step 3

Solve the expression and reduce the answer to lowest terms if required.

Change the mixed numbers into improper fractions.

$$8\frac{1}{4} = \frac{8 \times 4 + 1}{4} \qquad 2\frac{2}{5} = \frac{2 \times 5 + 2}{5}$$

$$= \frac{33}{4} \qquad\qquad = \frac{12}{5}$$

Rewrite the improper fractions with a common denominator.

The lowest common denominator of 4 and 5 is 20.

$$\frac{33 \times 5}{4 \times 5} = \frac{165}{20} \qquad \frac{12 \times 4}{5 \times 4} = \frac{48}{20}$$

Add the numerators while keeping the denominator the same.

$$\frac{165}{20} + \frac{48}{20} = \frac{165 + 48}{20}$$

$$= \frac{213}{20}$$

Step 4

Change the improper fraction to a mixed number.

$$213 \div 20 = 10 \text{ R}13$$

$$\frac{213}{20} = 10\frac{13}{20}$$

Everyone should drink $10\frac{13}{20}$ cups of fluid a day.

Your Turn 2

Rachel bought $3\frac{3}{4}$ m of blue fabric and $4\frac{1}{3}$ m of purple fabric to make a quilt. In total, how much fabric did Rachel buy?

PRACTICE EXERCISES

Use the following information to answer the next question

Holly bought $4\frac{2}{7}$ gallons of paint on Sunday to paint her bedroom. She used $\frac{3}{4}$ of a gallon of paint on Monday and $1\frac{1}{2}$ gallons on Tuesday.

1. How much paint does she still have left?

$$1\frac{5}{4}$$

$$4\frac{14}{28} - 1\frac{35}{28} = 3\frac{42}{28} - 1\frac{35}{28} = 2\frac{7}{28}$$

Use the following information to answer the next question

Mrs. Sommers planted $3\frac{3}{8}$ rows of seeds in her garden. Crows came along and ate $2\frac{5}{6}$ rows of them.

2. How many rows of seeds does she still have left?

$$3\frac{9}{24} - 2\frac{20}{24} = 2\frac{33}{24} - 2\frac{20}{24} = \frac{13}{24}$$

Use the following information to answer the next question

Ginny bought $2\frac{2}{3}$ kg of jellybeans and $3\frac{1}{6}$ kg of gummy bears.

3. How much candy did she buy in total?

$$5\frac{5}{6}$$

Use the following information to answer the next question

Andrew baked 24 cookies. He ate 2 and gave 3 cookies to Missy, 2 cookies to Charlie, and 4 cookies to Bella.

4. Of the original cookies, what fraction is left?

$$\frac{11}{24}$$

Use the following information to answer the next question

Josh spent $2\frac{3}{4}$ hours on his homework. He babysat $4\frac{2}{3}$ hours for his older sister.

5. How many more hours did he spend babysitting than on homework?

$$4\frac{8}{12} - 2\frac{9}{12} = 3\frac{20}{12} - 2\frac{9}{12} = 1\frac{11}{12}$$

Use the following information to answer the next question

Eloise and Ellen walk daily. During the week Eloise walked $15\frac{7}{9}$ km, and Ellen walked $13\frac{2}{3}$ km.

6. How many more kilometres does Ellen need to walk to equal the Eloise?

$$15\frac{7}{9} - 13\frac{6}{9} = 2\frac{1}{9}$$

Use the following information to answer the next question

Ms. Olsen bought $6\frac{9}{10}$ kg of cheese for three foods classes to make pizza. She used $2\frac{1}{6}$ kg with the first class and $3\frac{3}{5}$ with the second class.

7. How much cheese is left for the third class?

$$2\frac{5}{30} + 3\frac{18}{30} = 5\frac{23}{30} \qquad 6\frac{27}{30} - 5\frac{22}{30} = 1\frac{5}{30}$$

Use the following information to answer the next question

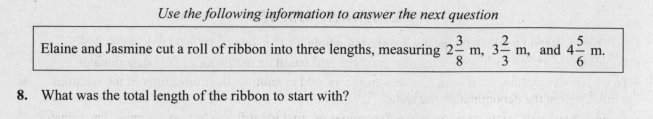

Elaine and Jasmine cut a roll of ribbon into three lengths, measuring $2\frac{3}{8}$ m, $3\frac{2}{3}$ m, and $4\frac{5}{6}$ m.

8. What was the total length of the ribbon to start with?

Use the following information to answer the next question

Ayden, Ben, and Hirsh are all working together on a science report. Ayden has to prepare $3\frac{1}{2}$ pages for the report, Ben has to prepare $4\frac{1}{9}$ pages , and Hirsh has to prepare $4\frac{1}{3}$ pages .

9. In total, how many pages will their science report be?

Use the following information to answer the next question

Jonas's mom was packing boxes to get ready for the move to their new house. She had $6\frac{3}{4}$ boxes of clothing and $11\frac{5}{8}$ of boxes of books.

10. How many more boxes of books than boxes of clothing were there?

REVIEW SUMMARY

- Fractions are used to show the parts of a set or a whole.
- To add and subtract fractions pictorially draw the grid based on the factors of the denominator.
- To add or subtract fractions with like denominators, add or subtract the numerators of the fractions while keeping the denominators the same.
- To add or subtract fractions with unlike denominators, first identify the lowest common denominator (LCD), rewrite the fractions using the LCD, and add or subtract the numerators while keeping the denominators the same.
- Always reduce a fraction to lowest terms by dividing both the numerator and denominator by the greatest common factor (GCF).
- Improper fractions have a larger numerator than the denominator.
- Mixed numbers consist of a whole number and a fraction.
- When adding or subtracting mixed numbers, convert them into improper fractions before performing any operations on them.

PRACTICE TEST

1. Use a diagram to solve $\dfrac{4}{12} + \dfrac{3}{12}$.

2. Solve $\dfrac{2}{6} + \dfrac{3}{6}$

3. Use a diagram to solve $\dfrac{9}{12} - \dfrac{3}{12}$.

4. Solve $\dfrac{12}{21} - \dfrac{5}{21}$.

5. Solve $\dfrac{3}{4} + \dfrac{5}{6}$.

6. Solve $\dfrac{1}{5} + \dfrac{3}{4}$.

7. Solve $3\dfrac{2}{12} + 4\dfrac{8}{12}$.

8. Solve $3\dfrac{8}{10} + 4\dfrac{1}{2}$.

9. Solve $4\dfrac{3}{10} - 1\dfrac{1}{5}$.

10. Solve $3\frac{2}{6} - 1\frac{1}{3}$.

11. Solve $5\frac{3}{4} - 3\frac{2}{3}$.

Use the following information to answer the next question.

Carmen is moving. On Monday, she packed $\frac{1}{8}$ of the dishes in her kitchen. On Tuesday, she packed $\frac{1}{4}$ of the dishes.

12. In total, how much has she packed? How many dishes does she have left to pack?

Use the following information to answer the next question.

Sam shovelled $\frac{2}{3}$ of the driveway yesterday and $\frac{1}{6}$ of it the day before.

13. To finish shovelling the whole driveway, how much does he have left to do today?

Use the following information to answer the next question.

Geoff ran $1\frac{1}{6}$ km on Monday, $1\frac{7}{8}$ km on Wednesday, and $5\frac{2}{3}$ km on Friday.

14. How much further did he run on Friday than on Monday and Wednesday in total?

Use the following information to answer the next question.

Ryan surveyed his class about their favourite school activities.

Favourite activities included sports ($\frac{1}{3}$ of the class), band ($\frac{3}{10}$ of the class), and art ($\frac{1}{6}$ of the class). The remaining students chose drama.

15. What fraction of the class chose drama?

THE CARTESIAN PLANE

When you are finished this unit, you will be able to…
- label the axes of a four quadrant Cartesian plane, and identify the origin
- identify the location of a given point in any quadrant of a Cartesian plane using an integral ordered pair
- identify the coordinates of the vertices of a given two-dimensional (2-D) shape on a Cartesian plane
- plot the point corresponding to a given integral ordered pair on a Cartesian plane with units of 1, 2, 5, or 10 on its axes
- draw shapes and designs on a Cartesian plane using given integral ordered pairs
- create shapes and designs and identify the points used to produce the shapes and designs in any quadrant of a Cartesian plane
- describe the horizontal and vertical movement required to move from a given point to another point on a Cartesian plane
- describe the positional change of the vertices of a given 2-D shape to the corresponding vertices of its image as a result of a transformation or successive transformations
- determine the distance between points along horizontal and vertical lines on a Cartesian plane
- perform a transformation or consecutive transformations on a given 2-D shape, and identify the coordinates of the vertices of the image
- describe the image resulting from the transformation of a given 2-D shape on a Cartesian plane by identifying the coordinates of the vertices of the image

PREREQUISITE SKILLS AND KNOWLEDGE

Prior to starting this unit, you should be able to…
- understand the concept of ordered pairs in the first quadrant of the coordinate plane
- create, analyze, and describe translations and reflections

Lesson 1 THE CARTESIAN PLANE

The Cartesian plane consists of two perpendicular number lines intersecting at point (0, 0). This point is called the origin. The horizontal number line is the *x*-axis, and the vertical number line is the *y*-axis. These number lines divide the plane into four equal quadrants. Each quadrant has a set of ordered pairs that are unique to it. The quadrants are shown in the following diagram.

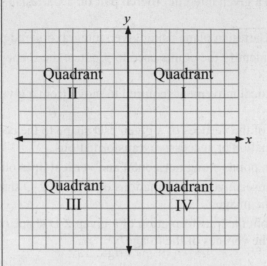

IDENTIFYING POINTS

A point on the Cartesian plane is defined using an ordered pair (*x, y*). The first number in the ordered pair is called the *x*-coordinate. It tells you how far and in which direction to travel from the origin along the *x*-axis.

The second number in the ordered pair is called the *y*-coordinate. It tells you how far and in which direction to travel from the origin along the *y*-axis.

To identify points on the Cartesian Plane, follow these steps:

Step 1
Determine the *x*-coordinate.

Step 2
Determine the *y*-coordinate.

Step 3
Write the ordered pair in the form (*x, y*).

Example

Identify the ordered pairs for points *A, B, C,* and *D*.

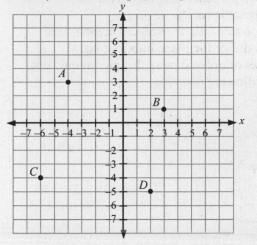

Solution

Step 1

Determine the *x*-coordinate for each point.

Count horizontally from the origin. If the point is to the right of the origin, it is a positive count; if it is to the left of the origin, it is a negative count.

Point *A* is 4 spaces to the left of the origin; its *x*-coordinate is –4.
Point *B* is 3 spaces to the right of the origin; its *x*-coordinate is 3.
Point *C* is 6 spaces to the left of the origin; its *x*-coordinate is –6.
Point *D* is 2 spaces to the right of the origin; its *x*-coordinate is 2.

Step 2

Determine the *y*-coordinate for each point.

Count vertically from the origin. If the point is above the origin, it is a positive count; if it is below the origin, it is a negative count.

Point *A* is 3 spaces above the origin; its *y*-coordinate is 3.
Point *B* is 1 space above the origin; its *y*-coordinate is 1.
Point *C* is 4 spaces below the origin; its *y*-coordinate is –4.
Point *D* is 5 spaces below the origin; its *y*-coordinate is –5.

Step 3

Write the ordered pair for each point.

Record the numbers in brackets, and separate them by a comma.
The *x*-coordinate goes first, and the *y*-coordinate goes second.

Point *A* has the ordered pair (–4, 3).
Point *B* has the ordered pair (3, 1).
Point *C* has the ordered pair (–6, –4).
Point *D* has the ordered pair (2, –5).

NOTES

Your Turn 1

Four points are plotted on the coordinate plane. Identify the coordinates of the given points W, X, Y, and Z.

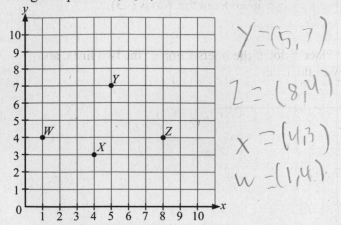

$Y = (5, 7)$

$Z = (8, 4)$

$X = (4, 3)$

$W = (1, 4)$

The following table will help you remember where the points on the Cartesian plane are located.

Quadrant	(Sign of x-coordinate, Sign of y-coordinate)
I	(pos, pos)
II	(neg, pos)
III	(neg, neg)
IV	(pos, neg)

PLOTTING POINTS AND MAKING SHAPES

When you plot points on the Cartesian plane, determine the placement of the x-coordinate first. Then, determine the placement of the y-coordinate. Finally, plot the point, and label it with a letter.

Example

Plot points $A(-2, 1)$, $B(0, 3)$, $C(2, 1)$, and $D(0, -3)$ on the Cartesian plane, and connect the points. Identify the shape created.

Solution

Step 1

Determine the placement of the x-coordinate for each point. If the coordinate is positive, move to the right of the origin. If the coordinate is negative, move to the left of the origin.

For point A, move 2 spaces to the left of the origin (-2).

For point B, do not move from the origin (0).

For point C, move 2 spaces to the right of the origin (2).

For point D, do not move from the origin (0).

Step 2

Determine the placement of the y-coordinate for each point.

Count vertically from the x-axis. If the coordinate is positive, move up from the x-axis. If the coordinate is negative, move down from the x-axis.

For point *A,* move 1 space up from the *x*-axis (1).
For point *B,* move 3 spaces up from the *x*-axis (3).
For point *C,* move 1 space up from the *x*-axis (1).
For point *D,* move 3 spaces down from the *x*-axis (−3).

Step 3

Plot the points. Place a dot at the intersection of the two lines, and
label the point with the letter.

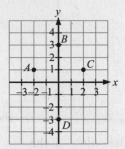

Step 4

Connect the points and identify the shape.

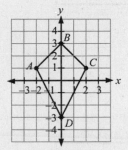

When the points are connected, the resulting shape is called a kite.

Your Turn 2

Plot points *P*(−2, 3), *Q*(−2, −3), *R*(3, 4), and *S*(4, −2) on the
Cartesian plane.

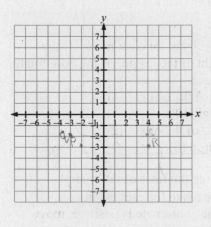

PRACTICE EXERCISES

Use the following information to answer the next question.

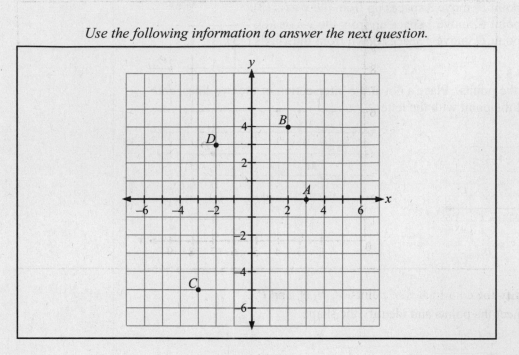

1. Identify the coordinates of points *A*, *B*, *C*, and *D*.

Use the following information to answer the next question.

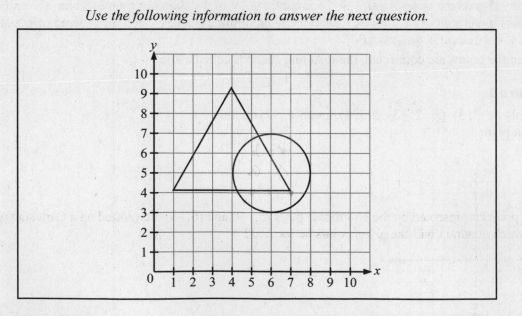

2. What are the coordinates of the three points that could be plotted inside the lines of the triangle and circle?

Use the following information to answer the next question.

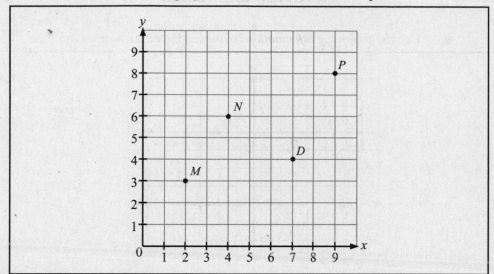

3. Identify the coordinates of points *M*, *N*, *D*, and *P*.

m (2,3) N (4,6) D (7,4) P (9,8)

4. Shirley plotted the ordered pair (–4, 2) in quadrant IV of the Cartesian plane. Later, she realized that she had made a mistake. In which quadrant should Shirley have plotted the ordered pair, and why does it not belong in quadrant IV?

5. The points represented by the coordinate pairs (5, –9) and (6, –3) are plotted on a Cartesian plane. In which quadrant will the given points be located?

IV

6. Plot points $F(4, 8)$, $G(3, -5)$, $H(-4, -6)$, and $J(-5, 4)$ on the given Cartesian plane.

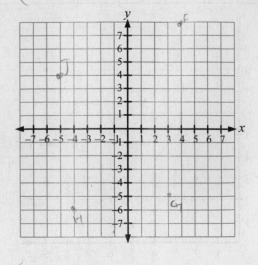

7. The points $A(-4, -1)$, $B(2, -1)$, and $C(-3, 2)$ represent three of the four vertices of a parallelogram. Plot the given points and the missing vertex on the Cartesian plane.

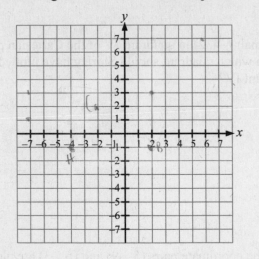

184

8. Nick travels the shortest possible distance between city *A* and city *B*. The coordinates of cities *A* and *B* on a coordinate grid are (2, 3) and (−2, 4), respectively. Which of the following graphs correctly represents the positions of the given cities and the path Nick follows?

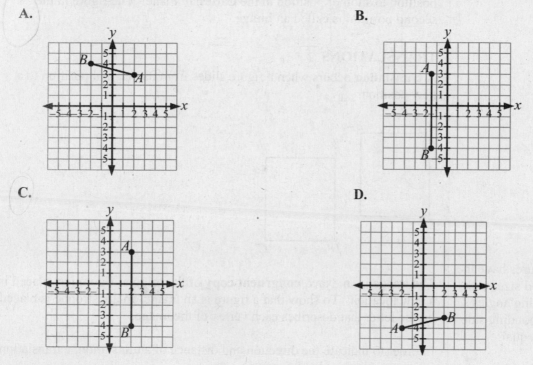

A.

B.

C.

D.

9. Points *A*(1, 7), *B*(2, 3), *C*(7, 3), and *D*(6, 7) are plotted on a Cartesian plane and are connected with line segments. The shape formed by joining the four given points is a

A. parallelogram

B. rectangle

C. trapezoid

D. square

Use the following information to answer the next question.

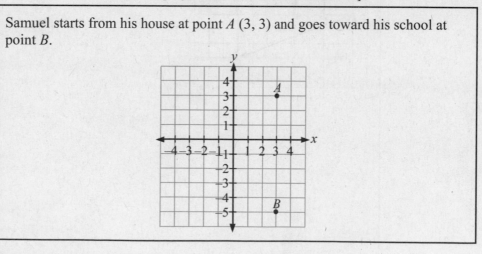

Samuel starts from his house at point *A* (3, 3) and goes toward his school at point *B*.

10. What are the coordinates of Samuel's school at point *B*? (−5, 3)

Lesson 2   TRANSFORMATIONS

Transformations are movements of points or figures from their original position to another position in the Cartesian Plane. The figure in the second position is called an **image**.

TRANSLATIONS

A **translation** occurs when a figure slides from its original position to a new position.

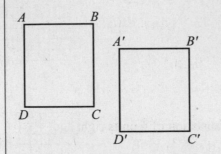

Congruent figures have the same shape and size, with all corresponding angles and all corresponding side lengths being equal.

The image is an exact, **congruent copy** of the original figure just placed in a new location. To show that a figure is an image, an apostrophe is placed on the letter that describes each vertex of the image.

In order to indicate the direction and distance of a translation, a translation arrow or an ordered pair is used.

A **translation arrow** indicates the direction and distance of a slide by indicating the starting (or original) position of the figure and the ending position of the image. A translation arrow is drawn from a vertex on the original figure to the corresponding vertex on the image.

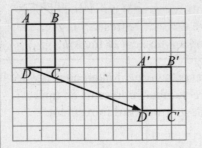

NOTES

Example

Draw a translation arrow to represent a translation of 5 units right and 3 units up.

Solution

Pick a starting point. Draw an arrow that goes from the starting point to a position 5 units right and 3 units up.

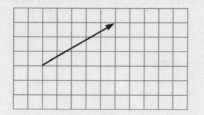

Your Turn 1

Draw a translation arrow to represent a translation of 4 units right and 3 units down.

An **ordered pair** in the form [x, y] indicates the direction and distance of a translation.

The first number in an ordered pair represents horizontal movement along the x-axis on the Cartesian plane. A positive number represents movement to the right, and a negative number represents movement to the left.

The second number in the ordered pair represents vertical movement along the y-axis on the Cartesian plane. A positive number represents an upward movement, and a negative number represents a downward movement.

NOTES

Example

Draw the translation [–3, 8] of figure *QRST*.

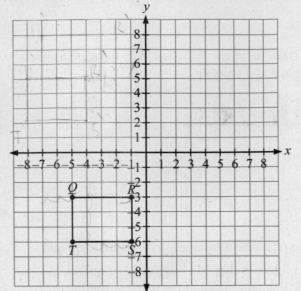

Solution

The translation is [–3, 8].

Since the *x*-coordinate is negative, the figure will move to the left 3 units. Then, since the *y*-coordinate is positive, the figure will move up 8 units to complete the translation [–3, 8].

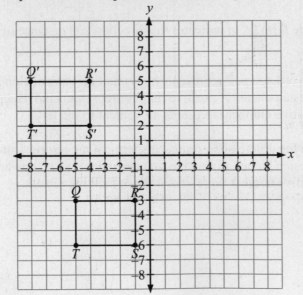

Your Turn 2

Translate the given figure 4 units to the right.

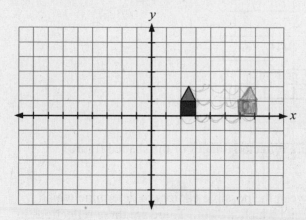

REFLECTIONS

A **reflection** occurs when a figure is flipped along a line of reflection or a mirror line to create a congruent image of the original figure, as illustrated below.

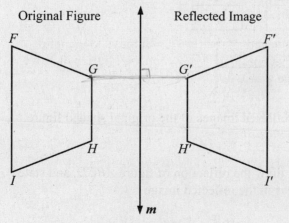

Line of Reflection or Mirror Line

Each vertex of a reflected image is the same distance from the line of reflection as the corresponding vertex of the original figure.

Example

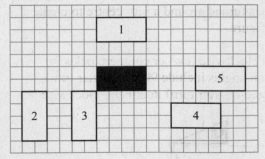

Which numbered figures are reflected images of the shaded figure?

Solution

Place mirror lines between the possible choices to determine which figures are reflections and which are not. There are three reflections in the given diagram, as illustrated.

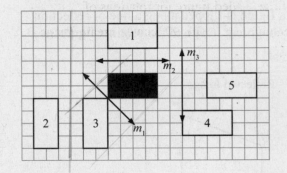

Figures 1, 3, and 5 are reflected images of the original shaded figure.

Your Turn 3

Using the given mirror line, draw the reflection of figure *ABCD*, and state the coordinates of the vertices in the reflected image.

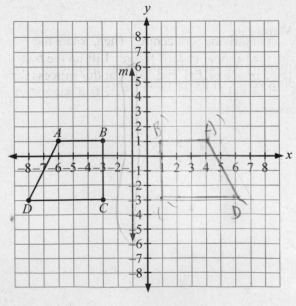

ROTATIONS

A **rotation** occurs when a figure is turned around a turn centre to create a congruent image of the original figure.

Rotations can be done in either a clockwise (cw) or counterclockwise (ccw) direction. Common rotation angles include 90° (a quarter turn), 180° (a half turn), and 270° (a three-quarter turn) in either a clockwise or counterclockwise direction.

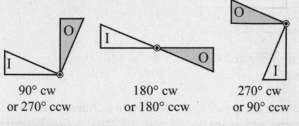

| 90° cw | 180° cw | 270° cw |
| or 270° ccw | or 180° ccw | or 90° ccw |

Example

Draw the rotated images of the shaded figure for rotations of

a) 90° cw to create image A   **b)** 90° ccw to create image B

c) 180° cw to create image C

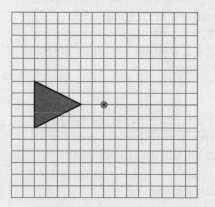

Solution

Trace the shaded figure, and mark the turn centre. Then, rotate the traced image 90° cw from the original shaded figure. Lift up the traced image, and draw the rotated image on the grid. Repeat this process for the other rotations of 90° ccw and 180° cw. Make sure to always start the rotations from the original figure.

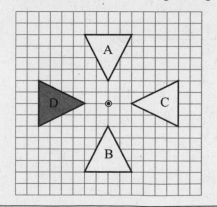

A rotation is a turn.
A **turn centre** is the rotational point that a figure rotates around.

Your Turn 4

Draw the corresponding images of the shaded figure for the given rotations. Label each image

a) Perform a rotation of 270° ccw to create image *a*.

b) Perform a rotation of 180° cw to create image *b*.

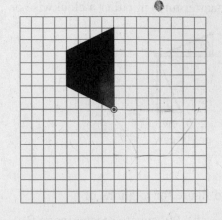

COMBINING TRANSFORMATIONS

When you are asked to make multiple transformations, always complete them in the order they are given in the question. Perform the first transformation using the original shape. Then, perform the second transformation using the transformed image. Continue to use the most recent image for any additional transformations.

Example

Quadrilateral *DEFG* has vertices $D(2, -1)$, $E(1, 2)$, $F(4, 3)$, $G(4, -1)$. Draw quadrilateral *DEFG* and its image after it is reflected about the *y*-axis and then translated 4 units right and 4 units up. Label final image $D''E''F''G''$.

Solution

Step 1

Draw the original shape on the Cartesian plane.
Plot and label each point as given. Then, connect the points with line segments.

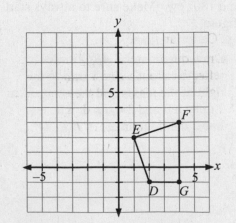

Step 2

Perform the first transformation using the original shape.
The first transformation is a reflection about the *y*-axis.
Plot and label each new point, then connect these points with line
segments to form the reflected quadrilateral *D'E'F'G'*.

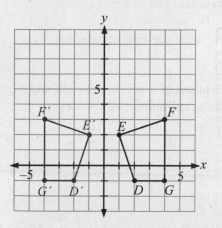

Step 3

Perform the second transformation using the transformed image.
The second transformation is a translation 4 units right and 4 units up.
Plot and label each new point, then connect these points with line
segments to form the translated quadrilateral *D"E"F"G"*.

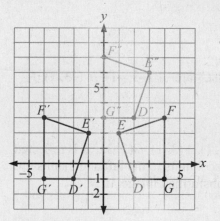

Your Turn 5

Quadrilateral *ABCD* is located on the Cartesian plane.

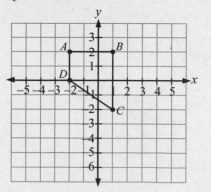

Draw quadrilateral *ABCD* after it is
reflected about a line 1 unit to the
right of the *y*-axis and then translated
2 units left and 3 units down.
Label the final image *A"B"C"D"*.

NOTES

Example

Triangle ABC has the vertices $A(2, 2)$, $B(2, 6)$, $C(6, 2)$. The original triangle is translated 1 unit to the right and 3 units down. Then it is reflected about the y-axis. Determine the coordinates of triangle $A''B''C''$.

Solution

Step 1

Identify the coordinates of $A'B'C'$ after the first transformation is applied.

The first transformation is a translation of 1 unit to the right and 3 units down. Add 1 to every x-coordinate, and subtract 3 from every y-coordinate.

$A'(2+1, \ 2-3) = (3, \ -1)$
$B'(2+1, \ 6-3) = (3, \ 3)$
$C'(6+1, \ 2-3) = (7, \ -1)$

Step 2

Identify the coordinates of $A''B''C''$ after the second transformation is applied.

The second transformation is a reflection about the y-axis. The x-coordinates change to their opposite values while the y-coordinates stay the same.

$A''(3, -1)$ becomes $(-3, -1)$
$B''(3, \ 3)$ becomes $(-3, 3)$
$C''(7, -1)$ becomes $(-7, -1)$

The coordinates of triangle $A''B''C''$ are $A''(-3, -1)$, $B''(-3, 3)$, $C''(-7, 1)$.

Your Turn 6

Triangle MNO has the vertices $M(1, 1)$, $N(3, 1)$, $O(2, 3)$. It is reflected about the x-axis. Then it is translated 4 units to the left and 2 units up. Determine the coordinates of the transformed image $M''N''O''$.

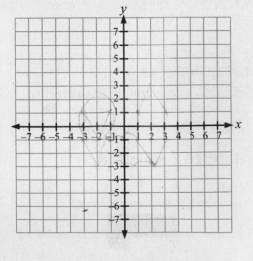

PRACTICE EXERCISES

1. Describe the translation [5, –6] in words.

Use the following diagram to answer the next question.

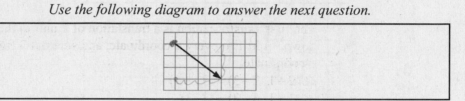

2. Describe the given translation in words.

[4, –3]   4 units right, 3 units up

3. Draw the translation [–2, –5] of figure *ABCD*, and state the coordinates of the vertices in the translated image.

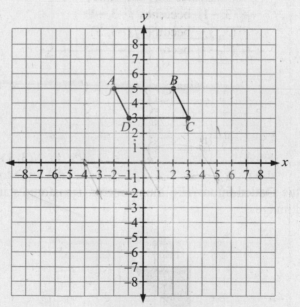

4. Draw the reflection of the shaded figure along mirror line *m*.

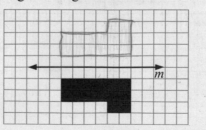

5. Draw the reflection of figure *WXYZ*, and state the coordinates of each vertex in the reflected image.

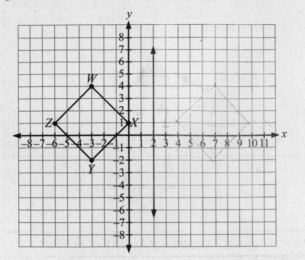

6. Draw the translation [4, –6] of the given figure *VWXY*, and state the coordinates of the vertices in the transformed image.

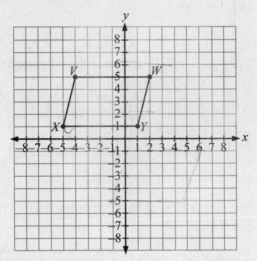

7. Draw the reflection of the shaded figure *ABC* along mirror line *m*, and state the coordinates of the vertices of the reflected image.

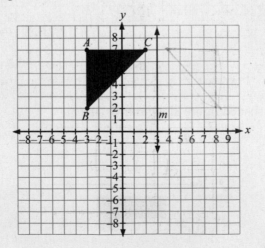

8. Rotate the shaded figure **a)** 90° ccw and **b)** 180° cw. Draw the rotated image in both new positions.

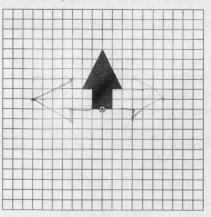

Use the following information to answer the next question.

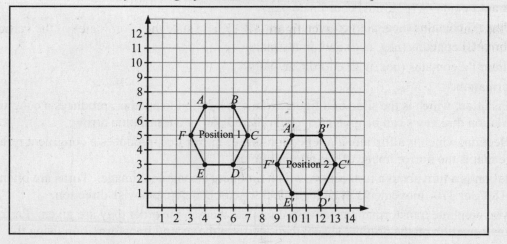

9. Describe the transformation of hexagon *ABCDEF* to hexagon *A′B′C′D′E′F′*.

10. Draw the reflected image of the given figure, *ABCD*.

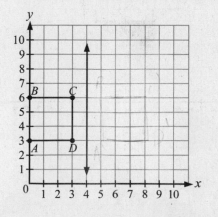

REVIEW SUMMARY

- The Cartesian plane consists of two perpendicular number lines that intersect at point (0, 0) to create four equal quadrants.
- A point on the Cartesian plane is defined using an ordered pair (x, y). The first number in the ordered pair is the x-coordinate. It tells you how far and in which direction to travel from the origin along the x-axis. The second number in the ordered pair is the y-coordinate. It tells you how far and in which direction to travel from the origin along the y-axis.
  - To determine the x-coordinate, count along the x-axis. If the point is to the right of the origin, it is a positive count; if it is to the left of the origin, it is a negative count.
  - To determine the y-coordinate, count along the y-axis. If the point is above the origin, it is a positive count; if it is below the origin, it is a negative count.
- To plot points on the Cartesian plane, determine the placement of the x-coordinate first. Then, determine the placement of the y-coordinate. Finally, plot the point, and label it with a letter.
- The four quadrants contain coordinate pairs that have certain characteristics.
  - Quadrant I contains (pos, pos) coordinate pairs.
  - Quadrant II contains (neg, pos) coordinate pairs.
  - Quadrant III contains (neg, neg) coordinate pairs.
  - Quadrant IV contains (pos, neg) coordinate pairs.
- Transformations
  - A translation, which is the slide of a figure from one location to another, produces a congruent image. Translation directions can be given using an ordered pair or a translation arrow.
  - A reflection, which is a flip along a reflection line or mirror line, produces a congruent reflection image that is the mirror image of the original figure.
  - A rotation is a turn about a turn centre, which produces a congruent image. Turns are often done in 90°, 180°, or 270° movements in either a clockwise or counterclockwise direction.
- When you combine transformations, always complete them in the order they are given. Perform the first transformation on the original shape; then, perform the second transformation using the transformed image, and so on.

PRACTICE TEST

1. Points $P(3, 5)$, $Q(-3, 5)$, and $R(3, -5)$ are plotted on a coordinate plane. Which of the following graphs correctly represents the locations of the three points?

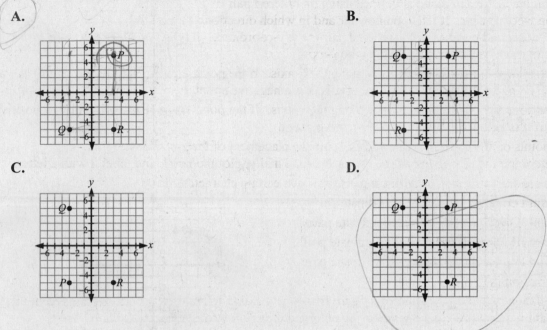

A.

B.

C.

D.

Use the following information to answer the next question.

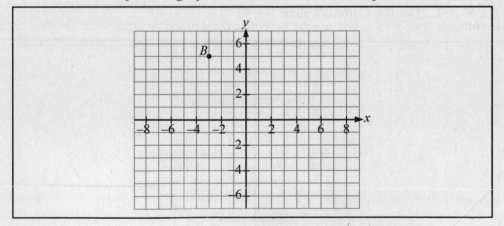

2. What are the coordinates of point B?

3. Points $P(3, -2)$ and $Q(-3, -4)$ are plotted on a coordinate plane. Which of the following graphs correctly represents the locations of the two points?

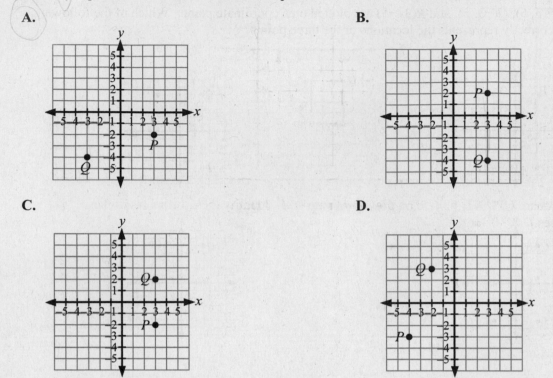

A.

B.

C.

D.

4. Plot the point $A(2, 2)$ on this Cartesian plane.

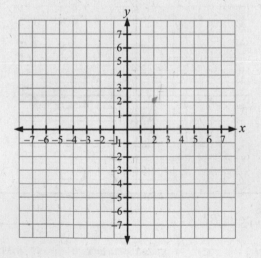

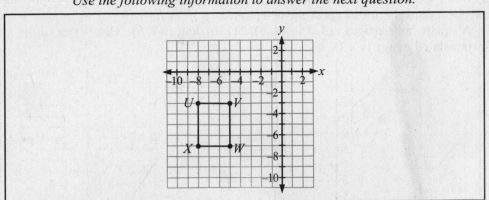

5. The square *UVWX* is plotted on this coordinate grid. Identify the coordinates of the vertices *U, V, W,* and *X*.

U(-8,-3) V(-5,-3) W(-5,-7) X(   )

Use the following information to answer the next question.

A triangle has vertices *A*(2, 1), *B*(3, 4), and *C*(5, 1). One vertex of the slide image is *A′*(7, 6).

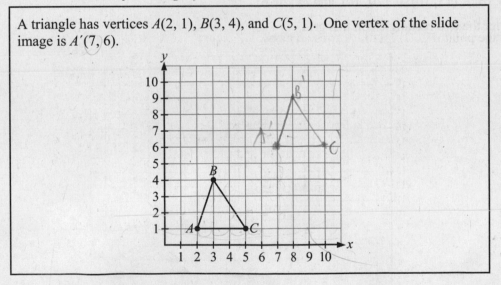

6. What is the translation rule used for the transformation of the given triangle?

the translation [5,5] of tigr ABC

Use the following information to answer the next question.

A square has vertices $A(4, 3)$, $B(4, 6)$, $C(7, 6)$, and $D(7, 3)$. One vertex of the translated image is $A'(8, 6)$.

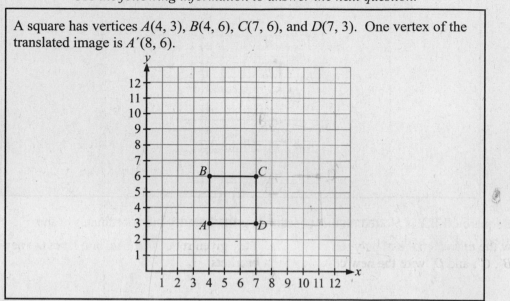

7. Draw the translated image of the given figure, and give the coordinates of the translated image.

8. A rectangle has vertices at $A(2, 2)$, $B(2, 6)$, $C(9, 6)$, and $D(9, 2)$. A second rectangle has vertices at $A'(13, 6)$, $B'(13, 10)$, $C'(20, 10)$, and $D'(20, 6)$.

   a) Plot the two rectangles on this grid.

   b) What is the translation rule for the image above?

Use the following information to answer the next question.

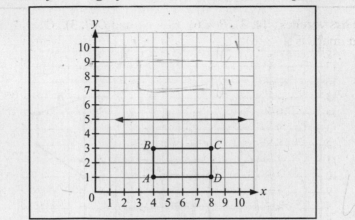

9. Draw the mirror image of polygon *ABCD* about the given reflection line, and label the new vertices *A′*, *B′*, *C′*, and *D′* with the new coordinates in brackets.

Use the following information to answer the next question.

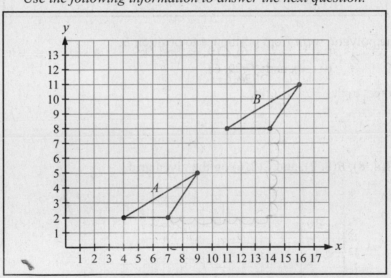

10. Describe the movement of the triangle from position *A* to position *B*.

translation of [7, 6]

Use the following information to answer the next question.

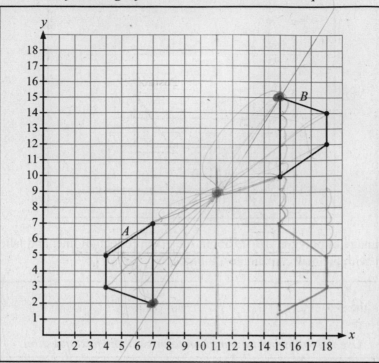

11. Describe how the polygon went from position *A* to position *B*.

12. Plot the points *A*(4, 8), *B*(8, 2), and *C*(2, 6) on the given grid.

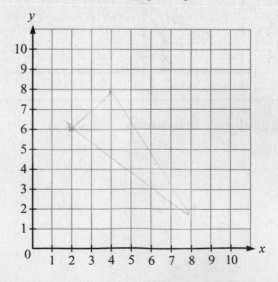

204

Use the following information to answer the next question.

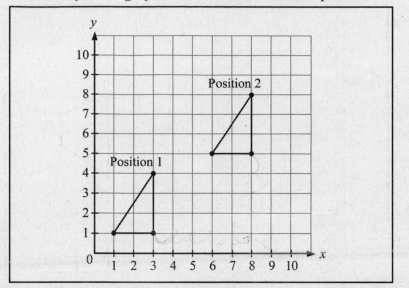

13. Write the rule for the movement of the triangle from position 1 to position 2.

14. On the coordinate grid, draw image *B* as the reflection of figure *A*.

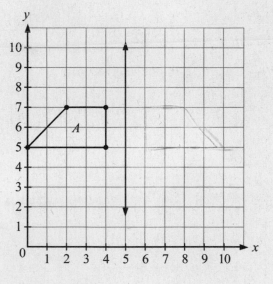

NOTES

PATTERNS

When you are finished this unit, you will be able to…
• formulate a linear relation to represent the relationship in a given pattern
• create a table of values for a given linear relation by substituting values for the variable
• create a table of values using a linear relation, and graph the table of values
• sketch the graph from a table of values created for a given linear relation, and describe the patterns found in the graph to draw conclusions
• describe using everyday language in spoken or written form the relationship shown on a graph to solve problems

PREREQUISITE SKILLS AND KNOWLEDGE

Prior to starting this unit, you should be able to…
• find approximate number values from a given graph
• create and extend patterns
• predict how patterns grow
• plot ordered pairs

Lesson 1   RELATING PATTERNS TO LINEAR RELATIONS

Determining a number pattern in mathematics involves looking closely at the information given in a problem for clues to help identify the pattern. Once a pattern is found, the pattern can be used to continue a sequence of numbers or predict a possible *n*th value.

Patterns can be represented by linear relations. A **relation** is anything that connects one set of information to another. A **linear relation** is a relationship between two variables that is represented as a straight line on a graph.

Example

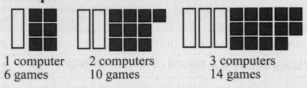

1 computer
6 games

2 computers
10 games

3 computers
14 games

These diagrams illustrate the relationship between the number of computers and computer games sold at an electronics store.

a) Using words, describe the relationship between the number of computers and computer games sold.

Solution

For every computer sold after the first computer, four more computer games are also sold.

b) Use the pattern to predict how many games would be sold if 12 computers were sold.

Solution

Make a table to help continue the pattern.

Number of Computers Sold	Number of Computer Games Sold
1	6
2	10
3	14
4	18
5	22
6	26
7	30
8	34
9	38
10	42
11	46
12	50

If 12 computers were sold then 50 computer games would also be sold.

You can also determine the number of computer games sold by using a linear relation. The relationship between the number of computer games sold (g) and the number of computers sold (c) is represented by $g = 4c + 2$.

To calculate the number of computer games sold when 12 computers are sold, 12 is substituted for c and solve for g.

$$g = 4c + 2$$
$$= 4(12) + 2$$
$$= 48 + 2$$
$$= 50$$

There would be 50 computer games sold if 12 computers were sold.

A linear relation can be used to get the same results as when using a table of values.

Your Turn 1

The distance that a vehicle travels over a period of time is illustrated in the following table.

Time (h)	1	2	3	4	5	6
Distance (km)	80	160	240			

a) Complete the table.

b) Describe the pattern in words.

c) Write a linear relation that can be used to represent the distance travelled (d) for any time (t).

d) Using the linear relation, predict how far the vehicle will travel in 12 h.

It is possible to represent an everyday situation as a linear relation.

To write a context for a given linear relation, follow these steps:

Step 1
Determine what the first term could represent.

Step 2
Determine what the constant could mean.

Step 3
Create a context that fits within those terms.

Example
Give a possible context for the linear relation $20p + 50$.

Solution

Step 1
Determine what the first term could represent.
Assuming the variable is meaningful, p could represent person and 20 multiplies p.

Step 2
Determine what the constant could mean.
A constant 50 is added to $20p$. It could represent a booking fee.

Step 3
Create a context that fits within those terms.
The school is having a party. The caterer charges $20 a person plus a $50 booking fee.

The solution will vary depending on what the first term represents.

Your Turn 2

Give a possible context for the linear relation $17.50h - 10$.

PRACTICE EXERCISES

Use the following diagrams to answer the next four questions.

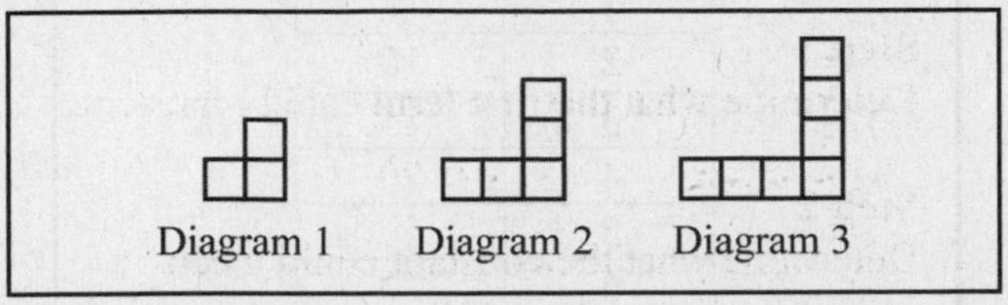

Diagram 1   Diagram 2   Diagram 3

1. Draw the next two diagrams in the pattern.

2. Describe the pattern in words.

   Add one each time to either side

3. Identify a linear relation that represents the relationship between the number of squares (*n*) for any diagram (*d*) in the pattern.

   $n = d + (d + 1)$

4. Determine how many squares will be in diagram 54.

   109

Use the following table to answer the next five questions.

x	y
1	5
2	10
3	15
4	20
5	25
6	30
7	35

5. Fill in the missing information to complete the table of values.

6. Describe the pattern in words.

    y equals x times five.

7. Write a linear relation that can be used to represent the relationship between the value of *y* and the value of *x*.

    y = x 5

8. Using the linear relation, predict the value of *y* when *x* is 45.

    45
    × 5
    ‾‾‾‾
    225

9. Give a possible context for the linear relation $1 + 0.25l$.

Lesson 2   TABLE OF VALUES AND GRAPHING

A **table of values** is a chart that shows the relationship between two variables, one is the input number and the other is the output number.

The numbers that are inputted into the relation first are called the input numbers. The values that result after the relation has been evaluated are called the output numbers.

A table of values is organized in such a way that the input number is listed in the first column and the output number is listed in the second column.

Input Number (x)	Output Number (y)

When given a linear relation, substitute in the given number and evaluate for the unknown variable.

Example

Create a table of values for the linear relation $y = 4x + 2$.

Solution

Step 1

Set up a table of values and use any numbers you like to represent x.

x	y
1	
2	
3	
4	

Step 2

Substitute in the values for x and evaluate the linear relation for y.

x	y
1	$4(1) + 2 = 6$
2	$4(2) + 2 = 10$
3	$4(3) + 2 = 14$
4	$4(4) + 2 = 18$

Your Turn 1

Create a table of values for the linear relation $y = 5x - 7$.

When graphing a linear relation, follow these steps:

Step 1

Create a table of values to determine the set of ordered pairs.

Step 2

Identify the ordered pairs.

Step 3

Plot the ordered pairs on a graph.

Example

Graph the relation represented in the given table of values.

Time (h)	Distance (km)
0	0
1	10
2	20
3	30

Solution

Step 1

Identify the ordered pairs.

The input and corresponding output number create the ordered pair in the form (x, y).

Time (h)	Distance (km)	Ordered Pair
0	0	(0, 0)
1	10	(1, 10)
2	20	(2, 20)
3	30	(3, 30)

There are no units of measurement placed in the ordered pairs.

214

Step 2
Label the *x*- and *y*- axis.
Plot the ordered pairs on the graph.

For each ordered pair, start at the origin and move horizontally to the value of the *x*-coordinate. Then, move vertically to the value of the *y*-coordinate.

Give the graph a title.

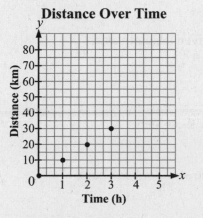

Distance Over Time

In a linear relation, the points will form a straight line.

The *x*-axis is the horizontal axis, and the *y*-axis is the vertical axis.

The arrowheads at the end of each axis mean that the relation continues along each axis.

The origin is where the *x*-axis and *y*-axis meet at coordinates (0, 0).

Your Turn 2

A periodic reading of the temperature during a four-hour visit in the evening in Jasper is illustrated in the following table of values.

Time	Temperature (°C)
5 P.M.	30
6 P.M.	25
7 P.M.	20
8 P.M.	15

Graph the relation represented in the given table of values.

To interpret a graph that represents a linear relation, observe the pattern formed by the points.

- If the points rise to the right, that means that as one value increases, so does the other value.
- If the points fall to the right, that means that as one value increases, the other value decreases.
- If the points have no distinct pattern, then there is no relationship between them.

Example

One day, Sandy decided to make a graph of the distance she walked in relation to the time it took to walk that distance. Then she plotted three points.

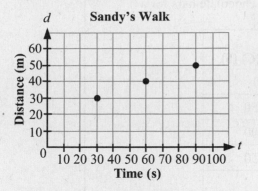

Determine the relationship between time and distance during Sally's walk.

Solution

Since the points are rising to the right, the pattern indicates that the more time Sally spends walking, the more distance she covers.

Your Turn 3

Tim works at his dad's bakery during the summer months. The following graph shows his wages over an eight-hour shift.

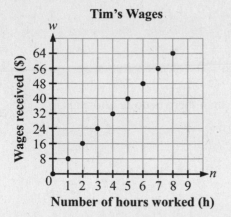

What pattern is illustrated in the given graph?

PRACTICE EXERCISES

Use the following information to complete the next four questions.

The given table of values shows the cost of buying chocolate bars for a school fundraiser.

Number of chocolate bars (n)	Cost (C) ($)
0	0
1	1.50
2	3.00
3	4.50
4	6.00
5	7.5
6	9

1. Complete the table of values.

2. Graph the linear relation on the following grid. Then represent the relationship between the number of chocolate bars sold (n) and cost (C) of purchasing them using a linear relation.

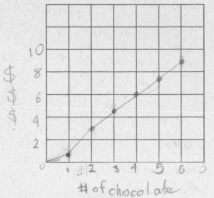

3. How much will it cost to purchase 10 chocolate bars?

$15

4. How much will it cost to purchase 45 chocolate bars?

75
× 9

67.5

Use the following information to complete the next four questions.

The cost of going to yoga classes is illustrated in the following table.

Number of classes (n)	Cost (C) ($)
0	0.00
1	14.00
2	28.00
3	42
4	56
5	70
6	84

5. Complete the table of values.

6. Graph the linear relation on the following grid. Then represent the relationship between the number of classes (n) and cost (C) using a linear relation.

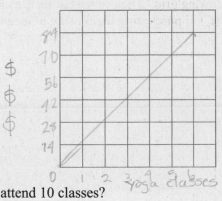

7. How much will it cost to attend 10 classes?

$140

8. How much will it cost to attend 25 classes?

280
+ 70
$350

Use the following information to answer the next question.

The following graph shows the relationship between the total mass of a crate and the number of watermelons in the crate.

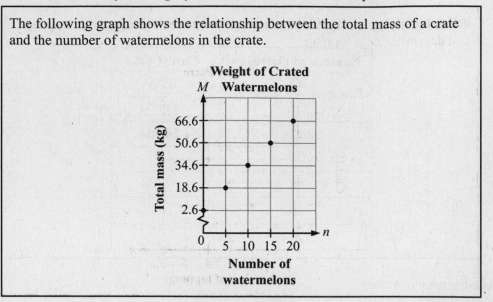

9. What is the pattern that is illustrated in the given graph?

+16

Use the following information to answer the next question.

The following graph shows the relationship between the number of toppings and the cost of each topping.

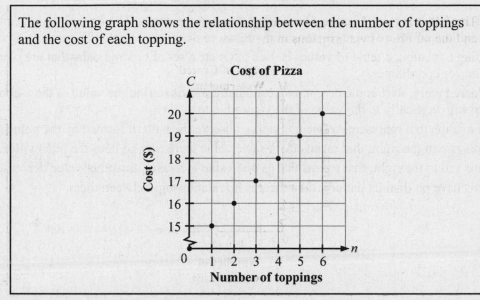

10. What is the pattern that is illustrated in the given graph?

REVIEW SUMMARY

- A linear relation can be created from a relationship found in a pattern. The linear relation can be used to make predictions of future events without drawing more diagrams or extending a table of values.
- When graphing a relation, a table of values is used to create a set of ordered pairs that are plotted on a graph as points or coordinates.
- To graph ordered pairs, start at the origin, move along the *x*-axis to find the value of the *x*-coordinate, and then move up vertically to the value of the *y*-coordinate.
- To interpret a graph that represents a linear relation, observe the pattern formed by the points.
  - If the points rise to the right, that means that as one value increases, so does the other value.
  - If the points fall to the right, that means that as one value increases, the other value decreases.
  - If the points have no distinct pattern, then there is no relationship between them.

Looking for extra practice?

- Extra practice questions

- Detailed curriculum-aligned lessons

- Available online and on mobile devices

solaro

www.solaro.com

PRACTICE TEST

Use the following information to answer the next four questions.

The rental fees for DVD movies at a video store are given in this table.

Number of DVDs rented	0	1	2	3	4
Rental fee ($)	0	3.50	7.00	10.5	14

1. Complete the table of values.

2. Explain the relationship between the number of DVDs rented and the rental fee.

$1r = 3.5$

3. Identify a linear relation that can be used to represent the relationship between the rental fee (r) and the number of DVDs rented (n).

$3.5h = r$

4. What is the rental fee for 13 movies?

$$3.5$$
$$\times 13$$
$$105$$
$$35$$
$$\$455$$

Use the following information to answer the next five questions.

The cost of hiring a company to remove snow from parking lots is illustrated in this table of values. The time is always rounded up to the nearest hour.

Time (t) (h)	Cost (C) ($)
0	0
1	60
2	120
3	180
4	240

5. Complete the table of values.

6. Identify the order pairs from the completed table of values.

(1,60) 2,120 (3,180) 4,240

7. Graph the linear relation. Identify the linear relation that represents the relationship between the time (t) it takes to clear the snow and the cost (C) of clearing the snow.

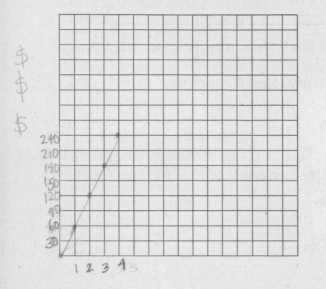

8. What is the cost if it takes 7 h to complete the snow removal?

$420

9. How much will it cost if it takes 10 hours to clear a parking lot?

$600

10. Using the values 1, 2, 3, 4, and 5 for x, graph the linear relation $2x + 7$.

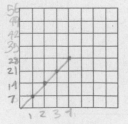

11. Using the values 1, 2, 3, 4, and 5 for *b,* graph the linear relation 4*b*.

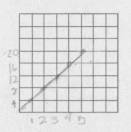

12. The relationship between purchasing *n* DVDs and the cost is 20*n*. Using the values 1, 2, 3, 4, and 5 for *n*, graph this relation.

13. The cost of a hall rental is a $50 booking fee and $75 for each hour used. Using the values 1, 2, 3, 4, and 5 as the number of hours, graph this relation.

$$\begin{array}{r} 275 \\ +\ 75 \\ \hline 340 \end{array}$$

NOTES

EXPRESSIONS AND EQUATIONS

When you are finished this unit, you will be able to…
- evaluate algebraic expressions given the value of the variable
- explain the difference between an expression and an equation
- apply preservation of equality to solve equations
- demonstrate how to solve a one-step, single-variable, first-degree equation by using concrete materials or diagrams
- solve and verify one-step linear equations
- solve and verify two-step linear equations

PREREQUISITE SKILLS AND KNOWLEDGE

Prior to starting this unit, you should be able to…
- create expressions to describe patterns and relationships
- represent a given problem with an equation
- model the preservation of equality for addition, subtraction, multiplication, and division

Lesson 1   EVALUATING EXPRESSIONS

NOTES

Mathematical **expressions** consist of numbers, variables (x, y, xy), and operational symbols ($+$, $-$). Expressions can be as short as a single term, or they can consist of two or more terms joined by an operation.

Variables are letters used to represent numbers when the values are not known in an expression. If the value of a variable is given, it is possible to solve the expression by substituting in the given number.

Brackets
Exponents
Division
Multiplication
Addition
Subtraction
Multiply or divide in order from left to right.
Add or subtract in order from left to right

When evaluating expressions, the order of operations still applies. BEDMAS tells you in what order to perform the required operations.

For more complicated expressions, place the value of the variable in brackets. This makes it easier to recognize the order in which to perform the operations.

Example

What is the value of $5v - 5$ if $v = 3$?

Solution
Step 1
Substitute the value of the variable into the expression using brackets.
$5v - 5$
$= 5(3) - 5$

If brackets are not used, a common mistake is to write 53 instead of 5(3) in the second line of the calculation.   This will result in an incorrect answer.

Step 2
Evaluate the expression using BEDMAS.
$5(3) - 5$
$= 15 - 5$
$= 10$

Your Turn 1

What is the value of $4(x - 7) + 2$ if $x = 9$?

Equations and expressions are similar in that they both can contain constant terms, numerical coefficients, and variables.

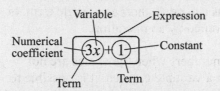

But they have one main difference: equations have an equal sign and can be solved, whereas expressions do not have an equal sign and can have an infinite number of answers depending on the values used for the variable.

Example

Given the following mathematical statements, identify which one is an expression and which one is an equation: $v - 4$ and $v - 4 = 8$.

Solution

The expression is $v - 4$ because it is not set equal to any particular value.

The equation is $v - 4 = 8$ because it is equal to 8.

Your Turn 2

Given $5x + 2 = 17$, identify whether it is an expression or an equation.

PRACTICE EXERCISES

Evaluate the following expressions when $x = 6$, $y = 10$, and $z = 5$.

1. $3x - 4$

2. $4y + 9$

3. $14z + 11$

4. $5x + 7y$

5. $3y - 9z + 13$

6. $10x - 6z + x$

7. $4z - 9y - 12x + 21$

Identify the constant term, numerical coefficient, and variable in the following expressions and equations.

8. $18n + 3 = 39$

9. $17 - 12b$

10. Given the following mathematical statements, identify which one is an expression and which one is an equation: $10p - 7 = 13$ and $-7 + 10p$.

Lesson 2   PRESERVING EQUALITY

Preserving equality means to retain the same value on both sides of the equation while performing any mathematical operation.

Let's use algebra tiles to model the preservation of equality.

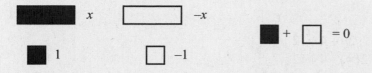

NOTES

Algebra tiles can be used to model the preservation of equality. Different shape tiles are used to represent the variable and constant. The colour represents positive and negative values.

For example, $x + 4 = 10$ is modelled using the following arrangement of algebra tiles:

When 2 unit tiles are added to both sides of the equal sign, the arrangement of algebra tiles becomes:

The equation becomes:
$$x + 4 + 2 = 10 + 2$$
$$x + 6 = 12$$

In the equations $x + 4 = 10$ and $x + 6 = 12$, x represents the same value. Therefore, equality has been preserved.

To preserve equality, the most important thing to remember is that an operation performed on the left side of the equal sign must also be made to the right side.

Example

Using each of the following operations addition, subtraction, multiplication, division, and the number 4, manipulate $2n = 8$ while preserving equality.

Solution

Addition: $2n = 8$
$$2n + 4 = 8 + 4$$
$$2n + 4 = 12$$

Subtraction: $2n = 8$
$$2n - 4 = 8 - 4$$
$$2n - 4 = 4$$

Multiplication: $2n = 8$
$$2n \times 4 = 8 \times 4$$
$$8n = 32$$

Division:
$$2n = 8$$
$$2n \div 4 = 8 \div 4$$
$$\frac{n}{2} = 2$$

Substitute 4 for n to verify that equality was preserved in each of the equations.

Addition:
$$2n + 4 = 12$$
$$2(4) + 4 = 12$$
$$8 + 4 = 12$$
$$12 = 12$$

Subtraction:
$$2n - 4 = 4$$
$$2(4) - 4 = 4$$
$$8 - 4 = 4$$
$$4 = 4$$

Multiplication:
$$2n \times 4 = 32$$
$$2(4) \times 4 = 32$$
$$8 \times 4 = 32$$
$$32 = 32$$

Division:
$$2n \div 4 = 2$$
$$2(4) \div 4 = 2$$
$$8 \div 4 = 2$$
$$2 = 2$$

Your Turn 1

Using each of the following operations—addition, subtraction, multiplication, division—and the number 3, manipulate $3r = 6$ while preserving equality.

SOLVING EQUATIONS USING PRESERVATION OF EQUALITY

In order to preserve equality of an equation, it is important to perform the *same operation* to both sides of the equation.

Preserving equality is a fundamental principle that is used to identify the value of an unknown variable in an equation.

Algebra tiles can be used to determine the value of an unknown variable in an equation.

Example

Solve the equation $x + 5 = 10$ using algebra tiles and a balance scale.

Solution

Step 1

Draw a diagram using algebra tiles to represent the equation.

The equation $x + 5 = 10$ can be represented pictorially using the following arrangement of algebra tiles on a balance scale.

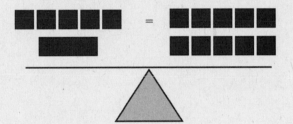

On the left side of the balance, there is 1 shaded x-tile and 5 shaded unit tiles. This represents $x + 5$.

On the right side of the balance, there are 10 shaded unit tiles. This represents 10.

Step 2

Perform the opposite operation to both sides of the equation.

The opposite of adding 5 is to subtract 5, so remove 5 squares from each side of the balance scale.

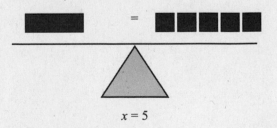

$x = 5$

When there is one x-tile left on either side of the balance, you have solved for the value of x.

In this case, $x = 5$.

The main goal in one-step equation solving is to isolate the variable.

Removing five squares from each side does not unbalance the scale, so both sides of the balance scale are still equal to each other.

Checking an answer by substitution will verify if the calculated answer is correct or not. If the sides of the equation do not match, then the calculated answer is incorrect.

It is good practice to check your answer by substituting the value of x back into the original equation.

$$x + 5 = 10$$
$$(5) + 5 = 10$$
$$10 = 10$$

Since both sides of the equation are equal, equality was preserved.

Your Turn 2

Solve the equation $n + 6 = 8$ using algebra tiles and a balance scale.

PRACTICE EXERCISES

Use algebra tiles to represent and solve each equation.

1. $x - 4 = 5$

   $x = 4 + 5$
   $x = 9$

2. $3x = 9$

   $3 = x$

3. $4n - 3 = 9$

   $4n = 3 + 9$
   $4n = 12$
   $n = 3$

4. $10 + 5r = -10$

   $5r = -10 + 10$
   $5r = -20$
   $r = -4$

5. $6g - 2 = 10$

   $6g = 2 + 10$
   $6g = 12$
   $g = 2$

$$3565x - 2545 = 3$$

$$3000n - 5000 = 2000$$

$$3n - 5 = 2$$

Lesson 3 SOLVING ONE-STEP AND TWO-STEP EQUATIONS

One step linear equations require the use of one operation in order to solve for the variable.

Two step linear equations require the use of two operations in order to solve for the variable.

SOLVING ONE-STEP LINEAR EQUATIONS

One-step equations can be solved using the principles of preservation of equality.

Remember the operation that is performed on the left side of the equation must also be performed on the right side of the equation.

To verify your answer, substitute the value of the variable back into the original equation.

Example

Find the value of n in the equation $n + 6 = 10$.

Solution

Step 1
Perform the opposite operation to both sides of the equation.
The opposite of adding 6 is subtracting 6. Subtract 6 from both sides of the equation.

$$n + 6 = 10$$
$$n + 6 - 6 = 10 - 6$$
$$n = 4$$

Step 2
Check by substitution.
$$n + 6 = 10$$
$$(4) + 6 = 10$$
$$10 = 10$$

Your Turn 1

Find the value of p in the equation $p - 13 = 54$.

Example

Solve for n in the equation $3n = 45$.

Solution

Step 1

Perform the opposite operation to both sides of the equation.

The opposite of multiplying n by 3 is dividing n by 3.

$$3n = 45$$

$$\frac{\cancel{3}n}{\cancel{3}} = \frac{\cancel{45}^{15}}{\cancel{3}}$$

$$n = 15$$

Step 2

Check by substitution.

$$3n = 45$$

$$3(15) = 45$$

$$45 = 45$$

Your Turn 2

Solve for m in the equation $4m = 16$.

Example

Solve for t in the equation $\frac{t}{4} = 8$.

Solution

Step 1

Perform the opposite operation to both sides of the equation.
The opposite of dividing t by 4 is multiplying t by 4.

$$\frac{t}{4} = 8$$

$$\frac{(4)t}{4} = 8(4)$$

$$t = 32$$

Step 2

Check by substitution.

$$\frac{t}{4} = 8$$

$$\frac{(32)}{4} = 8$$

$$8 = 8$$

NOTES

Your Turn 3

Solve for h in the equation $\dfrac{h}{8} = 11$.

SOLVING TWO-STEP LINEAR EQUATIONS

When solving two-step equations, you use the same techniques used in solving one-step equations except you will perform two operations rather than just one.

Example

Solve for x in the equation $4x - 1 = 11$.

Solution

Step 1

Perform the opposite operation of the constant on both sides of the equation.

The opposite operation of subtracting 1 is adding 1. Add 1 to both sides.

$$4x - 1 = 11$$
$$4x - 1 + 1 = 11 + 1$$
$$4x = 12$$

Step 2

Perform the opposite operation of the variable on both sides of the equation.

The opposite of multiplying x by 4 is to divide by 4. Divide both sides by 4.

$$\frac{4x}{4} = \frac{12}{4}$$
$$x = 3$$

Step 3

Check by substitution.

$$4x - 1 = 11$$
$$4(3) - 1 = 11$$
$$12 - 1 = 11$$
$$11 = 11$$

Your Turn 4

Solve for n in the equation $5n - 9 = 21$.

PROBLEM SOLVING WITH LINEAR EQUATIONS

Problem solving in mathematics can often be done algebraically using an equation to find an answer instead of guessing and checking to find the answer.

To solve problems using a linear equation, follow these steps:

Step 1
Define the variable.

Step 2
Write the equation to represent the situation.

Step 3
Isolate the variable by preserving equality on both sides of the equation.

Step 4
Check your answer by substituting the calculated value of the variable back into the original equation.

Example

Pearl has some photographs and divides them into sets of 4 per page to put into her photo album. Pearl makes exactly 25 sets of photographs. How many photographs does Pearl have in total?

Solution

Step 1
Define the variable.
Let p equal the total number of photographs in the album.

Step 2
Write the equation.
Since Pearl divides all the photographs into sets of four and makes exactly 25 sets of photographs, the equation that represents this situation is $\dfrac{p}{4} = 25$.

Step 3
Isolate the variable to find the value of p.

$$\frac{p}{4} = 25$$

$$4\left(\frac{p}{4}\right) = 4(25)$$

$$p = 100$$

Step 4

Check by substitution.

$$\frac{p}{4} = 25$$

$$\frac{(100)}{4} = 25$$

$$25 = 25$$

Pearl has 100 photographs in her photo album.

Your Turn 5

Raquel wants to make necklaces for each of her friends. She divides her beads into groups of exactly 20 beads per necklace. If Raquel makes 6 necklaces, how many beads does Raquel have in total?

PRACTICE EXERCISES

Solve for the variable in each of the following equations. Check by substitution.

1. $3r = 15$

$r = 15/3$
$r = 5$

2. $\dfrac{h}{5} = 6$

$h = 5 \times 6$
$h = 30$

3. $w + 8 = 2$

$w = 8 + 2$
$w = 10$

4. $y - 12 = 5$

$y = 12 + 5$
$y = 17$

5. $3t + 5 = 23$

$3t = 23 - 5$
$3t = 18$
$t = 6$

6. $2c + 6 = 22$

$2c = 28$
$c = 14$

7. $7n - 4 = 31$

$7n = 35$
$n = 5$

8. $9t - 8 = 28$

$9t = 36$
$t = 4$

9. Tina had some balloons. If Tina gave away 6 balloons and still had 13 left, how many balloons did she have to start with?

10. Walter rented a garden tractor for the weekend to do his landscaping. The cost included a rental fee of $150 and an hourly rate of $10 for use. How many hours did he use the garden tractor if it cost him $250?

REVIEW SUMMARY

- A variable is a letter used to represent a number when its value is unknown. Different variables represent different numbers.
- An expression is a combination of at least one variable, number, and mathematical operation.
- Expressions, unlike equations, have an infinite number of answers because the variable can have any value.
- Expressions can be evaluated by substituting a given number for a variable into the expression and then using order of operations to find the answer.
- Equations differ from expressions because they include the equal sign, so there is only one number that the variable can represent.
- Equations can be solved using algebra tiles or algebraically by performing the opposite mathematical operation on both sides of the equation.
- It is good practice to check the answer by substituting the calculated value into the original equation to see if both sides of the equation are equal to each other.

PRACTICE TEST

Evaluate the following expressions, when $p = 2$, $q = 4$, and $r = 7$.

1. $7p + 8r$

$14 + 56$

$= 70$

2. $3p - q + 5r$

$6 - 4 + 35$

$= 6 - 39$

$= 33$

Identify the <u>constant term</u>, numerical coefficient and variable in:

3. $\underset{c}{\underline{36}} - \underset{h}{\underline{9g}}$

4. Given the following mathematical statements, identify which one is an expression and which one is an equation: $\underset{\sim\sim\sim\sim\sim\sim}{7h - 13 = 48}$ and $\underline{-11 + 6z}$.

$\sim\sim$ = equation —— expression

Use algebra tiles to represent and solve these equations.

5. Solve the equation $m + 4 = -5$ using algebra tiles.

$m = -5 - 4$
$m = -9$

6. Solve the equation $2x + 6 = 10$ using algebra tiles.

$2x = 10 - 6$
$2x = 4$
$x = 2$

Solve each of the following equations.

7. $45 = n - 8$

$n = 45 + 8$
$n = 53$

8. $t + 13 = 49$

$t = 49 + 13$
$t = 64$

9. $9h = 72$

$72/9 = h$

10. $7 = \dfrac{t}{6}$

$6 \times 7 = t$
$42 = t$

11. $5n - 2 = 13$

$5n = 2 + 13$

$n = 3$

12 $3p + 2 = 23$

$3p = 23 - 2$

$3p = 21$

$p = 7$

13 $t - 11 = 70$

$t = 70 + 11$

$t = 81$

14 $54 = 6 + n$

$n = 54 - 6$

$n = 48$

15. $12h - 6 = 30$

$12h = 30 + 6$

$h = 3$

16. $\dfrac{r}{4} = 20$

$r = 20 \times 4$

$r = 80$

17. $4k + 6 = 34$

$4k = 40$

$k = 10$

18. Each player on the provincial Under-15 tennis team had to bring 6 tennis balls for the first practice. There were a total of 54 tennis balls brought to the first practice. How many players are on the team?

19. The temperature at 7 o'clock in the evening was −16°C and had risen by 10 degrees since noon. What was the temperature at noon?

20. Miss Adams bought 6 packs of coloured markers and 8 black markers for her students to use on a particular assignment. Each pack had the same number and colour of markers. There are a total of 56 markers. How many markers were in each pack?

GEOMETRIC CONSTRUCTIONS

When you are finished this unit, you will be able to...

- describe examples of parallel line segments, perpendicular line segments, perpendicular bisectors, and angle bisectors in the environment
- identify line segments on a given diagram that are parallel or perpendicular
- draw a line segment perpendicular to another line segment, and explain why they are perpendicular
- draw a line segment parallel to another line segment, and explain why they are parallel
- draw the bisector of a given angle using more than one method, and verify that the resulting angles are equal
- draw the perpendicular bisector of a line segment using more than one method, and verify the construction

PREREQUISITE SKILLS AND KNOWLEDGE

Prior to starting this unit, you should be able to...

- measure angles using a protractor
- draw angles
- know the definition of parallel and perpendicular lines
- use a compass

Lesson 1   LINE SEGMENTS

A **line** is actually an infinite number of points all arranged in a row. The arrows on either end of the line indicate that it continues on in either direction indefinitely.

A **line segment** consists of all the points between two given points on a line.

A ●————————————————● B

Perpendicular lines (⊥) are lines that intersect at exactly 90° to each other. For example, lampposts are perpendicular to the ground because they intersect the ground at 90°. Table legs are perpendicular to a table top because they intersect the table at 90°.

When drawing perpendicular lines, a square is placed in the corner of one of the angles to indicate that the lines are perpendicular.

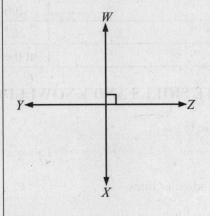

Line segment *WX* is perpendicular to line segment *YZ* because they intersect at 90° to each other.

Use the following example to learn how to draw perpendicular lines using a compass and a straight edge.

Example

Draw a perpendicular line segment from point *K*.

Solution

Step 1
Draw line segment.

————————————————
        ● K

Label point K.

248

Step 2

Place the point of the compass on point K, and draw two small arcs (with the same spread) that cut the line segment.

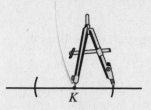

Step 3

Place the compass point on one arc with a spread of about three-quarters of the distance between the two arcs, and draw a semicircle.

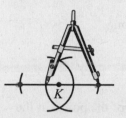

Repeat this procedure on the other side of the line.

Step 4

Connect the two points of intersection.

Your Turn 1

Line segment *JK* is 40 mm long. Draw a perpendicular line segment at point *L*.

Parallel lines are line segments that remain the same distance apart from one another, which means they never cross or intersect each other.
For example, railroad tracks are parallel lines because they remain an equal distance apart and they never intersect.

When drawing parallel lines, arrows are drawn along each of the lines to indicate the lines are parallel.

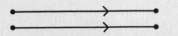

Use the following example to learn how to draw parallel lines using a compass and a straight edge.

Example

Draw two parallel line segments 2 cm apart and 9 cm long.

Solution

Step 1
Draw a line segment.
Draw the first line segment 9 cm long. Label each of the points at the ends of the line with a letter.

A 9 cm *B*

Step 2
Draw a circle with a radius equal to the distance the two lines need to be apart.
Spread the two ends of the compass 2 cm apart. Place the point of the compass on one end of the line segment, and draw a circle. Repeat on the other end, keeping the same spread.

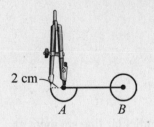

2 cm

A   *B*

Step 3
Use a straight edge to draw a line segment connecting the top of the two circles.

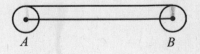

A   *B*

Your Turn 2

Draw two parallel line segments 1.5 cm apart and 5 cm long.

PRACTICE EXERCISES

Use the following information to answer the next question.

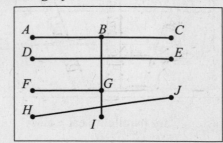

1. List the perpendicular line segments in the given diagram.

2. Draw two parallel line segments 2 cm apart and 4 cm long.

3. Line segment *CD* is 12 cm long. Draw a parallel line segment 3 cm above it.

Use the following diagram to answer the next question.

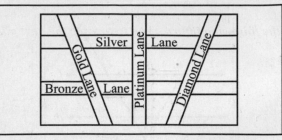

4. Which two lanes in the diagram shown are parallel to each other?

   A. Platinum Lane and Diamond Lane

   B. Gold Lane and Diamond Lane

   C. Gold Lane and Platinum Lane

   D. Silver Lane and Bronze Lane

5. Line segment *EF* is 10 cm long. Draw a parallel line segment 0.1 cm below it.

Use the following information to answer the next question.

Samuel observed the following:
1. A lamppost in front of the school
2. A school bus parked in a parking lot
3. A fallen fence post on the ground
4. His dog napping on the grass
5. A pine tree on his front lawn
6. His parents standing on the sidewalk

6. Which three observations are examples of perpendicular segments in relation to the ground?

Use the following information to answer the next question.

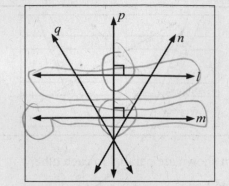

7. Identify two perpendicular lines from the given diagram.

8. Line segment *CD* is 3 cm long. Point *K* is on the line segment. Draw a perpendicular line segment at point *K*.

9. Line segment *FG* is 0.75 dm long. Draw a perpendicular line segment at point *H*.

Use the following information to answer the next question.

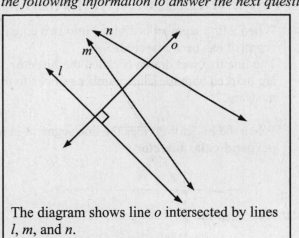

The diagram shows line *o* intersected by lines *l*, *m*, and *n*.

10. Which lines are perpendicular to line *o*?

Lesson 2 PERPENDICULAR AND ANGLE BISECTORS

Bi means "two" and *sect* means "cut."

When a line segment is divided into two equal halves by another line, the segment has been **bisected**.

The line that was drawn is called the **bisector**. The bisected line segments are marked with the same number of ticks to indicate that they are equal in measure.

When the bisector divides the line segment in half at 90°, it is called a **perpendicular bisector**.

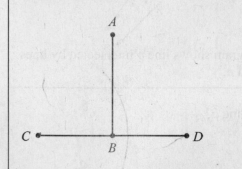

To draw a perpendicular bisector for a line segment using a compass and a straight edge, follow these steps:

Step 1
Draw the line segment.

Step 2
Draw the first arc.

Place the compass on one end or point of the line segment. Draw an arc or circle that crosses the line segment close to the other end.

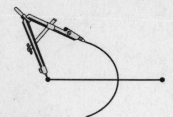

Step 3
Draw the second arc.

Repeat the process from the other end of the line. Keep the same spread.

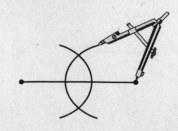

Step 4
Draw the perpendicular bisector.

Use a straight edge to draw a line segment connecting the two points where the arcs meet.

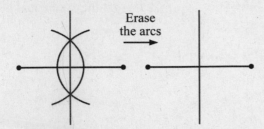

The new line is a perpendicular bisector to the original line segment.

Your Turn 1
Line segment *JK* is 40 mm long. Draw the perpendicular bisector for line segment *JK*.

Use the steps in the following example to draw a perpendicular bisector using a right triangle.

Example

Line segment *EF* is 10 cm long. Draw the line segment and its perpendicular bisector using a right triangle.

Solution
Step 1
Draw line segment *EF* 10 cm long.

E ────────── 10 cm ────────── F

Step 2
Divide the length by 2.
10 cm ÷ 2 = 5 cm

Step 3
Plot a point *D*, 5 cm from either side. Place the corner of the right triangle at point *D*. Draw a line segment, making sure to extend the line above and below line segment *EF*.

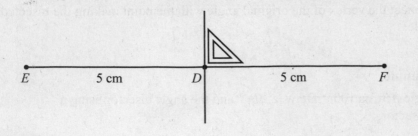

Your Turn 2

Line segment *GH* is 14 cm long. Draw the line segment and its perpendicular bisector using a right triangle.

Just as a line segment can be bisected, an angle can also be bisected. When an angle is divided into two equal halves by a line, the angle has been **bisected**. The line that cuts an angle into two equal halves is called the **angle bisector**. The angles are marked with the same symbol to indicate that they are equal in measure.

To draw an angle bisector using a protractor, follow these steps:

Step 1
Draw and label angle if it is not provided.

Step 2
Calculate the size of the bisected angle.

Step 3
Use the protractor to make this angle.

Step 4
Draw the angle bisector.

Connect the vertex of the original angle with the point making the bisected angle.

Example
Angle *ABC* is 100°. Draw ∠*ABC* and the angle bisector using a protractor.

Solution
Step 1
Draw and label the angle.

Draw line segment *AB*. Use a protractor to add line segment *BC* at 100°.

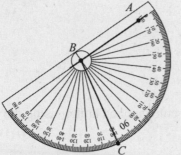

Step 2
Calculate the size of the bisected angle.

Divide the measure of the angle by 2. $100 \div 2 = 50$

Step 3
Use a protractor to mark this angle.

Place the zero line on one of the line segments. Follow the outside numbers to 50. Plot point *U* at 50°.

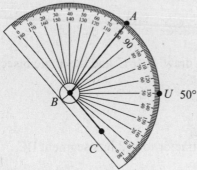

Step 4
Draw the angle bisector using the straight edge of the protractor. Use a straight edge to connect point *B* to point *U*.

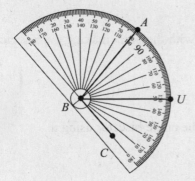

Your Turn 3

Angle *MKL* is 66°. Draw ∠*MKL* and the angle bisector using a protractor.

Another way to bisect the angle is with a compass and aruler, using the following steps:

Step 1

Draw and label the angle if it is not already provided.

Step 2

Draw an arc to intersect the two line segments of the angle.

Step 3

From both points of intersection between the arc and the arms of the angle, draw two more intersecting arcs.

Step 4

Using a ruler, draw a line from the angle to this intersection point.

Example

Angle *ABC* is 100°. Using a compass, draw ∠*ABC* and the angle bisector.

Solution

Step 1

Draw and label the angle.

Draw line segment AB. Use a protractor to add line segment BC at 100°.

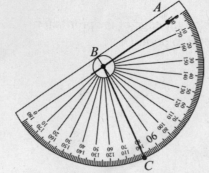

Step 2

Draw an arc to intersect the two line segments of the angle.
Place the point of the compass on point B. Draw an arc intersecting
line segment AB and line segment BC. Label the points of intersection
as F and G.

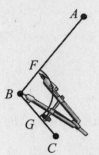

Step 3

Draw two more intersecting arcs from points F and G. Place the point
of the compass on point F. Draw an arc toward the middle of the
angle. Repeat the process at point G, keeping the size of the compass
opening the same. Label the point of intersection as U.

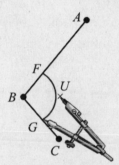

Step 4

Draw a line from the angle to the intersection point.
Use a straight edge to connect point B to point U.

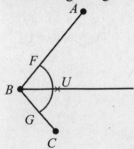

Step 5
Verify that the angles are equal. Use a protractor to measure the two new angles.

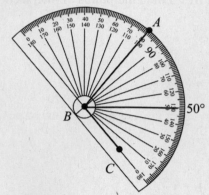

Your Turn 4
Angle *NOP* is 128°. Using a compass, draw ∠*NOP* and the angle bisector.

PRACTICE EXERCISES

1. A bisector is perpendicular if it intersects the line segment at

   A. a 90° angle

   B. a 45° angle

   C. an angle less than 90°

   D. an angle less than 45°

2. Line segment *AB* is 9 cm long. Draw the line segment and its perpendicular bisector using a compass.

3. Line segment *CD* is 12 cm long. Draw the line segment and its perpendicular bisector using a compass.

4. Angle *DEF* is 80°. Draw ∠*DEF* and the angle bisector using a compass and a straight edge.

5. Line segment *AB* is 36 mm long. Draw the line segment and its perpendicular bisector using a right triangle.

Use the following diagram to answer the next question.

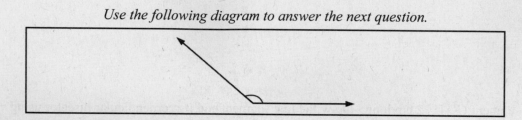

6. Divide the given angle into four equal angles.

7. Angle *MNO* is 140°. Draw ∠*MNO* and the angle bisector, using a protractor.

8. Which of the following statements about an angle bisector is **false**?

   A. It divides an angle into two equal parts.

   B. It can be drawn using a compass and a straight edge.

   C. Each of the resulting angles is half the size of the original angle.

   D. Each of the resulting angles is twice the size of the original angle.

9. One example of a **perpendicular bisector** is

   A. a post on a platform for tether ball

   B. the poles of a set-up tent to the ground

   C. a caterpillar crawling along the ground

   D. a piece of lumber laid flat on the ground

10. Line segment *CD* is 3 cm long. Draw a perpendicular line segment at point *K*.

REVIEW SUMMARY

- Perpendicular lines are two lines that intersect at exactly 90°.
- Parallel lines are lines that are always the same distance apart from each other; that is, they do not intersect.
- An angle bisector divides an angle into two equal or congruent parts. A compass can be used to create arcs (or circles) to determine the exact location to divide an angle into congruent parts.
- An angle bisector can also be created using a protractor and a straight edge.
- A perpendicular bisector divides a line segment at the exact centre at a 90° angle. A compass can be used to create arcs (or circles) used to determine the exact location to divide a line segment in half.
- A perpendicular bisector can also be created using a right triangle and a straight edge.

PRACTICE TEST

Use the following information to answer the next question.

In her study of graphic design, Terry is learning how to draw and lay out different shapes. Terry uses a ruler, compass, and protractor for some tasks, and uses her computer for many others. On the diagram shown, Terry has used a straight edge and compass in place of a protractor.

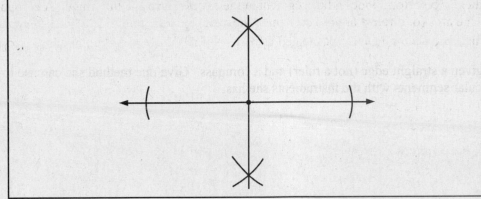

1. What did Terry construct?

   perpendicular lines

2. Which of the following observations is **not** true of a perpendicular bisector?

   A. It can be drawn using a compass and a straight edge.

   B. Each of the resulting segments is half the size of the original segment.

   C. Each of the resulting segments is double the size of the original segment.

   D. It divides a segment into two equal parts.

3. Which of the following observations is a property of an angle bisector?

   A. It divides an angle into two equal parts.

   B. It crosses the line segment at a right angle.

   C. It divides a line segment into two equal parts.

   D. It is perpendicular to the angle it crosses.

4. Draw two parallel line segments 1.5 cm apart and 5 cm long.

5. Kelly is given a straight edge (not a ruler) and a compass. Give one method she can use to construct perpendicular segments with the instruments she has.

6. Create the perpendicular bisector for the given line segment.

A ———————————— B

7. Create the angle bisector of the angle drawn below.

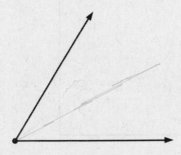

Use the following information to answer the next question.

Line *AB* has a length of 12.6 m. Line *CD* perpendicularly bisects line *AB* at *O*.

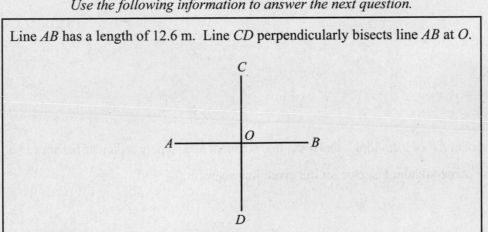

8. What is the length of line *OB?*

6.3

Use the following information to answer the next question.

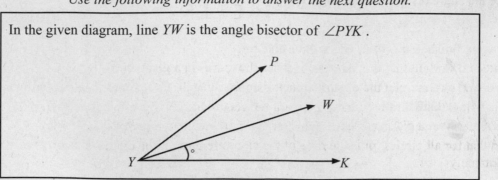

In the given diagram, line *YW* is the angle bisector of ∠*PYK* .

9. If the measure of ∠*PYK* is 38°, what is the measure of ∠*WYK* ?

19°

10. Angle *GHI* is 120°. Draw ∠*GHI* using a protractor and the angle bisector using a compass and a straight edge.

11. Line segment *EF* is 1 dm long. Draw the line segment and its perpendicular bisector using a right angle triangle.

12. Explain the difference between a perpendicular segment and a perpendicular bisector.

13. Line segment *GH* is 14 cm long. Draw the line segment and its perpendicular bisector using a right triangle.

CIRCLES

When you are finished this unit, you will be able to...

- illustrate and explain that the diameter is twice the radius in a given circle
- illustrate and explain that the circumference is approximately three times the diameter in a given circle
- explain, using an illustration, that the sum of the central angles of a circle is 360°
- draw a circle with a given radius or diameter, with and without a compass
- explain that for all circles, pi is the ratio of the circumference to the diameter and its value is approximately 3.14
- solve a given problem involving circles
- identify common attributes of circle graphs
- create and label a circle graph
- translate percentages displayed in a circle graph into quantities to solve a given problem.
- interpret a given circle graph to answer questions

Lesson	Page	Completed on
1. Introduction to Circles	272	
2. Constructing Circle Graphs	282	
Review Summary	290	
Practice Test	291	
Answers and Solutions	at the back of the book	

PREREQUISITE SKILLS AND KNOWLEDGE

Prior to starting this unit, you should be able to...

- calculate and solve problems involving measurement
- demonstrate an understanding of circles
- estimate and measure angles using a protractor
- sketch and draw an angle when the size is given
- read and interpret graphs

Lesson 1 INTRODUCTION TO CIRCLES

Bicycle tires, inline skate wheels, and compact discs are just a few examples of circles. The distance around a circle is called its **circumference** (C).

The distance between a point along the edge of the circle to a point on the exact opposite side of the circle is called the **diameter** (d). The diameter goes through the centre of the circle, and it cuts the circle into two halves.

The **radius** (r) of a circle is the distance from the centre of a circle to a point along the edge of the circle; it is equal to half the value of the diameter.

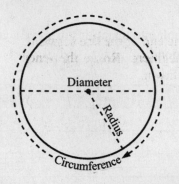

Using a given point for the centre of the circle and a radius or diameter, it is possible to construct a diagram of any circle. You will need a ruler and a compass. The ruler is used to measure out the radius, while the compass will draw the actual circle. The radius is used to determine the distance between the pencil tip and the pivot point of the compass.

To draw a circle, follow these steps:
Step 1
Determine the value of r.

Step 2
Draw the line segment using a ruler.

Step 3
Draw the circle using a compass.

Example

Draw a circle with a radius of 4 cm using a compass.

Solution

Step 1

Determine the value of r.
The radius is 4 cm.

Step 2

Draw a line segment 4 cm long using a ruler.

Step 3

Draw the circle using a compass.

Place the pointed end of the compass at one end of the line segment. Place a pencil at the other end of the line segment. Rotate the pencil tip around the pivot point until a circle is drawn.

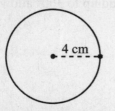

Your Turn 1

Draw a circle with a diameter of 10 cm using a compass.

NOTES

If a circle is cut into sectors, the sum of all the central angles always equals 360°. This is proven using two diameters.

When two diameters intersect at 90°, four equal right angles are formed. A right angle is equal to 90°.
$4 \times 90 = 360°$

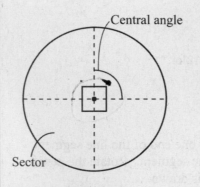

Central angle

Sector

Knowing that all the central angles in a circle must add up to 360° allows you to calculate missing angle measures.

Example

The two unknown angles are equal.

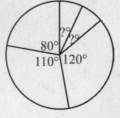

What is the angle measure of each sector?

Solution
Step 1
Calculate the total of the known angles.
$80 + 110 + 120 = 310$

Step 2
Calculate the unknown angle measure.

Subtract the total of the known angles from 360°.
$360° - 310° = 50°$

Because there are two equal angles, divide 50° in half.
$50° \div 2 = 25°$

The missing angles are 25° each.

Your Turn 2

The three unknown angles are equal.

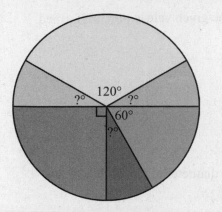

What is the angle measure of each sector?

CIRCUMFERENCE

The circumference of any circle divided by its diameter gives the mathematical constant pi (π). **Pi** is a non-repeating, non-terminating decimal number.

$$\pi = \frac{C}{d}$$
$$= 3.141\,592\,653\,589\ldots$$

In mathematics, the value of π is often shortened to 3.14.

The following formulas show the relationship between the circumference, diameter, and radius of a circle. They are also useful when solving for the missing dimension of a circle. If the diameter or radius of a circle is known, the circumference of a circle can be calculated using one of the formulas.

Dimensions of a Circle	Formula
Circumference (if diameter is known)	$C = \pi d$
Circumference (if radius is known)	$C = 2\pi r$
Diameter	$d = \dfrac{C}{\pi}$
Radius	$r = \dfrac{C}{2\pi}$

NOTES

To calculate any of the dimensions, follow these steps:

Step 1
Choose the appropriate formula using the given values.

Step 2
Substitute in the known values.

Step 3
Solve for the unknown.

Example

Find the circumference of a circle if the diameter of the circle is 5 cm.

Solution
Step 1
Choose the appropriate formula.

Use the formula $C = \pi d$ to find the circumference (C).

Step 2
Substitute in the known values.

The diameter is 5 cm, and π is 3.14.

Step 3
Solve for the unknown.
$$C = \pi d$$
$$= 3.14 \times 5$$
$$= 15.7 \text{ cm}$$

Therefore, the circumference of the circle is 15.7 cm.

Your Turn 3

Find the circumference of a circle if the diameter of the circle is 3 cm.

Example

The circumference of a car tire is 120 cm. Find the diameter of the tire to the nearest tenth of a centimetre.

Solution
Step 1
Choose the appropriate formula using the given values.

Use the formula $d = \dfrac{C}{\pi}$ to find the diameter.

Step 2

Substitute in the known values.

The circumference is 120 cm and π is 3.14.

Step 3

Solve for the unknown.

$$d = \frac{C}{\pi}$$
$$= \frac{120}{3.14}$$
$$= 38.216\,560\,51\ldots \text{ cm}$$

Rounded to the nearest tenth, the diameter is 38.2 cm.

Your Turn 4

The circumference of a bicycle wheel is 188.4 cm. Find the radius of the wheel.

PRACTICE EXERCISES

1. Draw a circle with a radius of 2.5 cm using a compass.

2. Draw a circle with a diameter of 12 cm using a compass.

Use the following information to answer the next question.

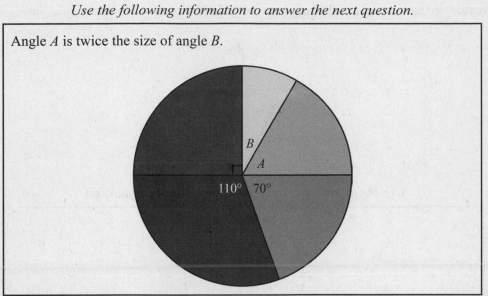

Angle *A* is twice the size of angle *B*.

3. What are the angle measures of each sector?

A=60
B=30

4. The circumference of a Ferris wheel is 37.68 m. Find the diameter.

6

5. The circumference of a circle is 28.26 cm. Find the radius.

2.25

6. A motorcycle tire has a radius of 25 cm. How far will the tire travel in one revolution?

Use the following diagram to answer the next question.

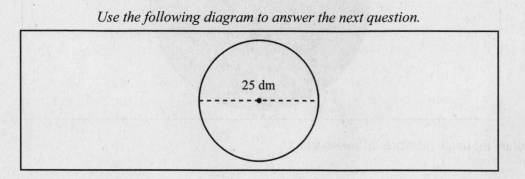

25 dm

7. Calculate the circumference.

157

8. A mountain bike wheel has a diameter of 59 cm. What is the circumference of this wheel to the nearest whole number?

371

9. The circumference of a circle divided by π is

   A. the radius

   B. the diameter

   C. half the radius

   D. twice the diameter

Use the following diagram to answer the next question.

The diameter of this ring is 1.5 cm.

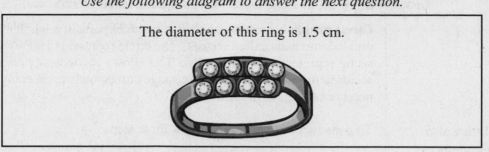

10. What is the circumference of the ring?

$$
\begin{array}{r}
6.28 \\
\times\ 1.5 \\
\hline
3110 \\
628 \\
\hline
9.320
\end{array}
$$

Lesson 2   CONSTRUCTING CIRCLE GRAPHS

Circle graphs represent data that constitutes parts of a whole. The data is divided into parts called sectors. The circle represents 100% while each sector represents a part of 100%. This allows you to easily compare each sector to one another. Each percentage corresponds to an equivalent number of degrees in the circle.

Circle graphs are also known as pie charts.

To construct a circle graph, follow these steps:

Step 1
If necessary, convert the data into decimal numbers.

Step 2
Calculate each percentage as an angle in degrees.

Step 3
Draw a circle. Then draw each of the angles using a protractor and straight edge.

Step 4
Label the sectors with a title and the corresponding percentage.

Example
The table shows Jolanda's movie rentals by category for the past three months.

Category	Number of Rentals
Drama	10
Comedy	7
Action	2
Horror	1

Construct a circle graph to represent this information.

Solution
Step 1
Convert the data into decimal numbers.

Divide each part of the data by the total data.
The total number of movie rentals is $10 + 7 + 2 + 1 = 20$.
$$\text{Drama} = 10 \div 20$$
$$= 0.5$$

$$\text{Comedy} = 7 \div 20$$
$$= 0.35$$

Action $= 2 \div 20$
$\quad\quad = 0.1$

Horror $= 1 \div 20$
$\quad\quad = 0.05$

The total decimal numbers should add up to 1.
$0.5 + 0.35 + 0.1 + 0.05 = 1$

Step 2
Calculate each decimal number as an angle in degrees.
Multiply each decimal number by 360°.

$\quad$ Drama $= 0.5 \times 360°$
$\quad\quad\quad = 180°$

$\quad$ Comedy $= 0.35 \times 360°$
$\quad\quad\quad = 126°$

$\quad$ Action $= 0.1 \times 360°$
$\quad\quad\quad = 36°$

$\quad$ Horror $= 0.05 \times 360°$
$\quad\quad\quad = 18°$

Step 3
Draw a circle.
Use a compass to make a circle large enough to label the sectors.

Use a protractor to draw each of the angles or sectors. Start at the top of the circle graph, using the largest angle. Move in a clockwise direction until the smallest angle is drawn:

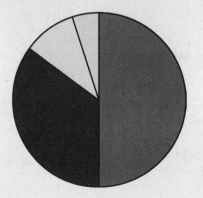

NOTE

Step 4

Label the circle graph.

Include the category and percentage for each sector. Give the graph a title.

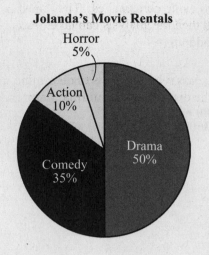

Jolanda's Movie Rentals

Your Turn 1

The table shows how Andre used his $1000 pay cheque for the month.

Item	Amount of Money ($)
Food	150
Clothes	400
Entertainment	100
Savings	350

Construct a circle graph to represent this information.

INTERPRETING CIRCLE GRAPHS

When you read and interpret a circle graph, you are analyzing the information presented to answer questions about the data. Often, the questions ask you to compare one category to another. However, you cannot perform mathematical operations using percentages. They must be converted into whole numbers first, and then the analysis can take place.

Example

Mariah surveyed the 20 students in her class who own pets to determine the type of pet that each student has. She displayed her information in this circle graph.

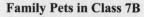

Family Pets in Class 7B

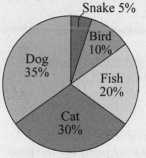

Use the circle graph to calculate how many students had each of the pets.

Solution

Step 1
Calculate each percentage as a decimal number.
Divide the percentage by 100.

$$\text{Dog} = 35 \div 100$$
$$= 0.35$$

$$\text{Cat} = 30 \div 100$$
$$= 0.30$$

$$\text{Fish} = 20 \div 100$$
$$= 0.20$$

$$\text{Bird} = 10 \div 100$$
$$= 0.10$$

$$\text{Snake} = 5 \div 100$$
$$= 0.05$$

NOTES

Step 2
Multiply the decimal number by the total quantity.
$$Dog = 0.35 \times 20$$
$$= 7$$

$$Cat = 0.30 \times 20$$
$$= 6$$
$$Fish = 0.20 \times 20$$
$$= 4$$

$$Bird = 0.10 \times 20$$
$$= 2$$

$$Snake = 0.05 \times 20$$
$$= 1$$

To verify the calculations were done correctly, add up the number of students. It should equal a total quantity of 20.
$$7 + 6 + 4 + 2 + 1 = 20$$

Your Turn 2

Erik made a circle graph to illustrate the Cougars' team record for the past 50 games.

Cougars' Record

a) How many games did the Cougars win?

b) How many games did the Cougars lose?

c) How many games were tied?

d) How many games did the Cougars either win or tie?

PRACTICE EXERCISES

Use the following information to answer the next question.

The circle graph shows how Linda spent her $40 allowance at the shopping mall.

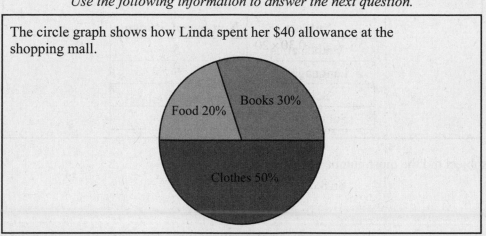

1. How much money did she spend on clothes and food altogether?

Use the following information to answer the next question.

The circle graph shows how Marcus spent his $400 pay cheque.

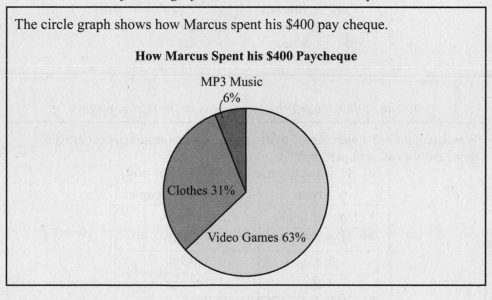

2. How much money did Marcus spend on video games?

Use the following information to answer the next two questions.

Maxine surveyed her class to determine their favourite subject in school.

Subject	Number of Students
Mathematics	5
Language arts	7
Science	10
Social studies	8

3. Which subject did the most number of students like the best?

4. Construct a circle graph to represent Maxine's data?

Use the following information to answer the next question.

Wanda conducted a web survey to determine the favourite musical artist of those individuals that participated.

Artist	Number of People
Jennifer Lopez	5 000
Snoop Dog	7 500
50 Cent	6 000
Usher	11 500
Eminem	4 500

5. Construct a circle graph to represent this information.

Use the following information to answer the next four questions.

Alice surveyed the students in her grade who own pets to determine the type of pet that each student has. There are 20 students in her class.

Pet	Percentage of Students
Snake	5
Dog	35
Cat	30
Fish	20
Bird	10

6. How many students have fish as pets?

7. How many students have either a dog or a cat as a pet?

8. What two pets make up 50% of the pets that students have?

9. How many more people have cats than snakes?

REVIEW SUMMARY

- The perimeter of a circle is known as the circumference of a circle.
- Circumference is calculated by using the formula $C = \pi d$ or $C = 2\pi r$, where d represents the diameter of the circle and r represents the radius of the circle. The formula can be rearranged to solve for diameter $\left(d = \dfrac{C}{\pi} \right)$ or radius $\left(r = \dfrac{C}{2\pi} \right)$.
- Pi (π) is a mathematical constant found by dividing the circumference of any circle by its diameter. Pi is often shortened to 3.14 for ease of calculations, but is actually a non-repeating, non-terminating decimal number.
- Circle graphs display data in sections called sectors.

    290

PRACTICE TEST

Calculate the circumference of each circle below. (*Use* $\pi = 3.14$)

1.

2.

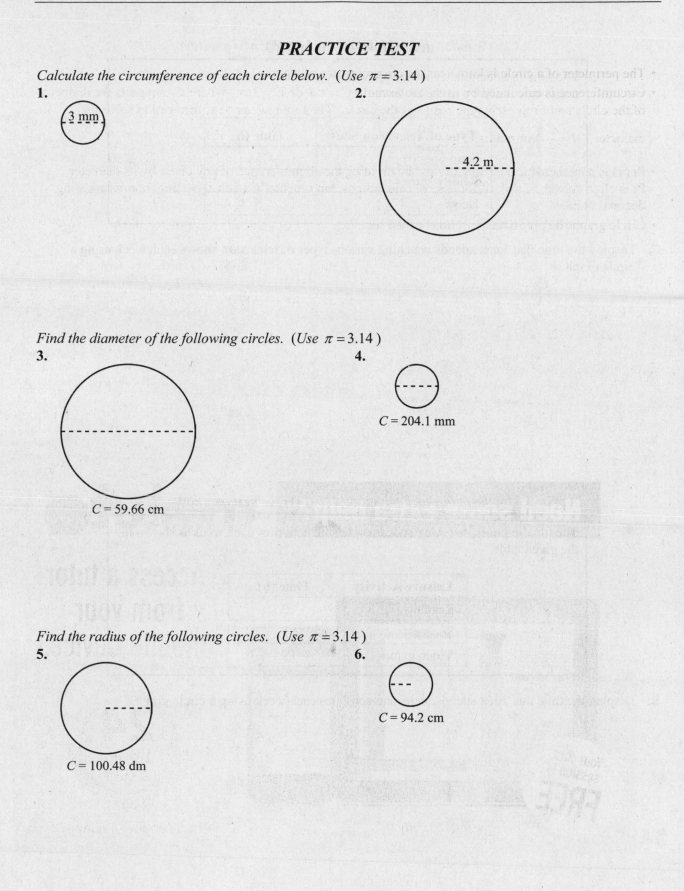

3 mm

4.2 m

Find the diameter of the following circles. (*Use* $\pi = 3.14$)

3.

4.

$C = 204.1$ mm

$C = 59.66$ cm

Find the radius of the following circles. (*Use* $\pi = 3.14$)

5.

6.

$C = 94.2$ cm

$C = 100.48$ dm

Use the following information to answer the next question.

The time in hours that Janet spends watching various types of television shows each week is shown in the table.

Type of Television Show	Time (h)
Soap opera	5
Reality shows	15
News	5

7. Display the time that Janet spends watching various types of television shows each week using a circle graph.

Use the following information to answer the next question.

The time in hours that Alex spends on leisure activities each week is shown in the given table.

Leisure Activity	Time (h)
Reading	3
Soccer	5
Video games	2

8. Display the time that Alex spends on leisure activities each week using a circle graph.

Use the following information to answer the next three questions.

The given table shows the different types of footwear sold by a shoe store in an average week. Overall, 184 sales were made.

Footwear	Sales
Sandals	36
Boots	28
Loafers	24
Sneakers	48
Slippers	20
Pumps	28

9. What percentage of the shoe sales were sandals?

10. What percentage of the shoe sales were sneakers?

11. Construct a circle graph using the data in the given table.

Use the following information to answer the next two questions.

Gwen recorded the weather in Lethbridge for a 30-day period and used a circle graph to display the information.

Weather in June

☀	Sunny	12 days
	Windy	3 days
	Cloudy	9 days
	Rainy	6 days

12. What percentage of the circle graph is used for sunny days?

13. When drawing the circle graph, how many degrees will Gwen use to represent the sunny days?

14. Of 200 students surveyed, 25 indicated they spend too much time instant messaging when they are doing homework on the computer. If this data were displayed in a circle graph, what angle size would instant messaging represent?

AREA

When you are finished this unit, you will be able to...

- use measurement to determine relationships between diameter, radius, and circumference of circles, and between base and height of parallelograms and triangles
- calculate the area of parallelograms, triangles, and circles
- solve problems involving the area of parallelograms, triangles, and circles

PREREQUISITE SKILLS AND KNOWLEDGE

Prior to starting this unit, you should be able to...

- convert between different metric units of measurement
- calculate the perimeter and area of rectangles

Lesson 1   AREA OF A PARALLELOGRAM

The area of a parallelogram can be found by transforming the parallelogram into a rectangle. To transform it, slide a triangular section of the parallelogram as shown in the following diagram.

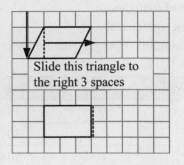

Slide this triangle to the right 3 spaces

A rectangle is a special parallelogram. Opposite sides are equal and opposite angles are equal.

The rectangle is 2 units high and 3 units long, so its area is 6 square units.

The base of the parallelogram is 3 units and the height is 2 units.

The area of the parallelogram is equal to the area of the rectangle.

Therefore, the area of the parallelogram is also 6 square units.

To find the area of a parallelogram, multiply the base by the height. $A = b \times h,$ where b represents the base and h represents the height.

To find the area of a parallelogram use the following steps:
Step 1
Determine the given measurements

Step 2
Apply the area formula, substitute the values in, solve.

Example

A parallelogram has a base that is 6.75 cm long and a height that is 5 cm. Calculate the area of the parallelogram.

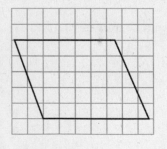

Solution

Step 1
Determine the given values. The base is 6.75 cm and the height is 5 cm.

Step 2
Apply the area formula, substitute in the given values and solve.
$$A = b \times h$$
$$= 6.75 \times 5$$
$$= 33.75 \text{ cm}^2$$

The area of the parallelogram is 33.75 cm².

Your Turn 1

Calculate the area of the following parallelogram.

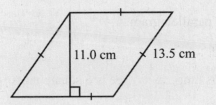

When given the area of a parallelogram, you can find the value of a missing measurement by substituting the values you do know into the area formula.

Example

A parallelogram has a base that is 17.3 m long and an area of 95.15 m². Find the height of the given parallelogram.

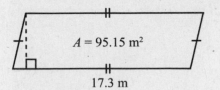

Solution
Step 1
Determine the given values. The base is 17.3 m and the area is 95.15 m²

Step 2

Apply the area formula, substitute in the given values and solve.

$$A = b \times h$$
$$(95.15) = (17.3) \times h$$
$$\frac{95.15}{17.3} = \frac{17.3h}{17.3}$$
$$5.5 = h$$

The height of the parallelogram is 5.5 m.

Your Turn 2

Find the length of the base for the given parallelogram.

27 mm $A = 2\ 538$ mm^2

b

PRACTICE EXERCISES

1. The height of a parallelogram is 2 cm more than its base. If the base of the rectangle is 5 cm, what is its area? B= 5 H=7

    A=35cm²

Use the following information to answer the next question.

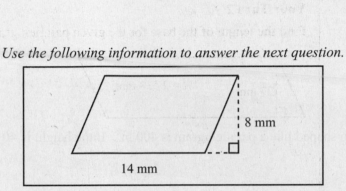

14 mm

8 mm

2. Calculate the area of the given parallelogram.

    14
    x 8
    ——
    11 2 mm²

3. How much carpet is needed to cover a floor shaped like a parallelogram that is 1.8 m by 1.4 m?

    1.8
    x 1.4
    ——
    72
    18
    ——
    25 2 m²

4. A particular rectangle measures 8 cm by 10 cm, and a particular parallelogram has a base of 16 cm and a height of 5 cm. Which of these shapes has the greater area and by how much?

    R=80 Parrellogram = 16
                        x 5
                        ——
                        80

5. The side lengths of a parallelogram, with a base of 3 m and a height of the 7m are doubled. How many times greater is the area of the new parallelogram than the original parallelogram.

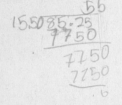

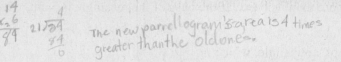

The new parrellogram's area is 4 times greater than the old one.

6. Calculate the base of a parallelogram that has a height of 15.5 cm and an area of 85.25 cm^2.

$$15.50\overline{)85.25}$$

55
7750
7750
7750
. 6

7. The area of a garden shaped like a parallelogram is 400 m^2. If the height is 40 m, what is the length of the base? 400/40 = 10 m

8. The height of a parallelogram is equal to five times the base and the base is 6 cm. What is the area of the parallelogram?

30
× 6
18.0 cm^2

9. The area of a parallelogram is 72 cm^2. If the base is one-half the height, what are the dimensions of the parallelogram?

B= 6
H=12

10. The area of a parallelogram is 90 cm^2. If the base is 15 cm, what is the height of the parallelogram?

B=6

Lesson 2   *AREA OF A TRIANGLE*

The area of a triangle uses the same principles applied to finding the area of a rectangle.

Start with the formula used to find the area of a rectangle, which is $A = b \times h$.

Then cut the rectangle in half by drawing a line between opposite vertices. This cut produces two identical triangles.

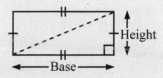

Since the area of a triangle is equal to half the area of a rectangle, the formula to calculate the area of a triangle is $A = \frac{1}{2}bh$.

Example

Calculate the area of one of the triangles in the given diagram.

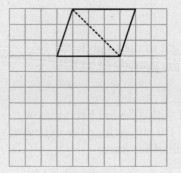

Solution

Step 1
Determine the given values.
The base is 4 square units and the height is 3 square units.

Step 2
Apply the area formula, substitute in the given values, and solve.

$$A = \frac{1}{2}bh$$
$$= \frac{4 \times 3}{2}$$
$$= \frac{12}{2}$$
$$= 6 \text{ units}^2$$

The area of each of the triangles is 6 square units.

NOTES

Your Turn 1

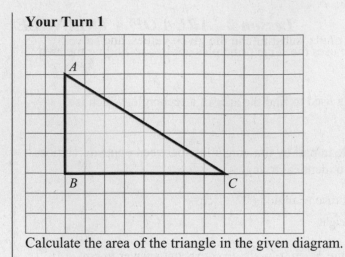

Calculate the area of the triangle in the given diagram.

When looking at diagrams of triangles, the height of the triangle is indicated with a line that goes from the top of the triangle to its base. It will form a right angle with the base.

In the following example, the base is extended with a dotted line to show where it would meet and form the right angle. Do not include the extended part in the area calculation, just the given length of the base.

The height of a triangle is the distance between the base and the vertex opposite.

The base and height of a triangle must be perpendicular to each other.

Example

Calculate the area of the given triangle.

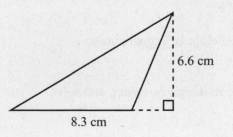

6.6 cm

8.3 cm

Solution

Step 1
Determine the given values.
The base is 8.3 cm and the height is 6.6 cm.

Step 2

Apply the area formula, substitute in the given values, and solve for the area.

$$A = \frac{1}{2}bh$$
$$= \frac{(8.3) \times (6.6)}{2}$$
$$= \frac{54.78}{2}$$
$$= 27.39 \text{ cm}^2$$

The area of the obtuse triangle is 27.39 cm^2.

Your Turn 2

Calculate the area of the given triangle. Express the answer in cm^2.

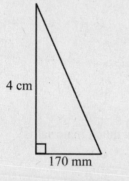

4 cm

170 mm

PRACTICE EXERCISES

Use the following information to answer the next question.

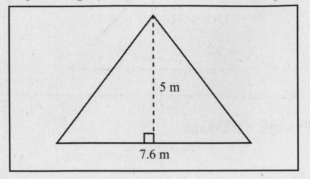

5 m

7.6 m

1. Calculate the area of the triangle.

$$\begin{array}{r} 7.6 \\ \times\ 5 \\ \hline 38.0 \end{array}$$ $\!/_2 = 19\,m^2$

2. A triangular sail has a height of 10 m and a base that is one-half the height. How much material is needed to make the sail?

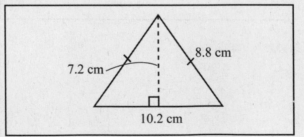

$25m^2$

Use the following information to answer the next question.

8.8 cm

7.2 cm

10.2 cm

3. Calculate the area of the triangle.

$$\begin{array}{r} 7.2 \\ \times\ 5.1 \\ \hline 7\ 2 \\ 360 \\ \hline 36.7\ 2\,m^2 \end{array}$$

Use the following information to answer the next question.

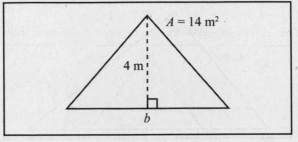

4. Calculate the base of the given triangle.

14×2=28
28/4=7
Ans b=7 m

Use the following information to answer the next question.

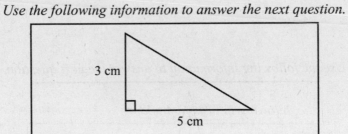

5. Calculate the area of the given triangle.

7.5m²

Use the following information to answer the next question.

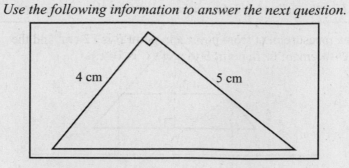

6. Calculate the area of the given triangle.

10cm²

Use the following information to answer the next question.

In a triangle, the base is three times greater than the height.

7. If the base is 27 cm, what is the area of the triangle?

27
×9
243cm²

Use the following information to answer the next question.

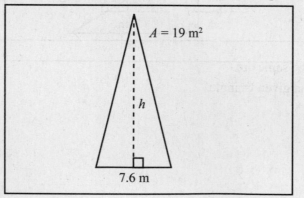

8. Calculate the height of the given triangle.

25
76⟌190
152
380
380
6

H=125

Use the following information to answer the next question.

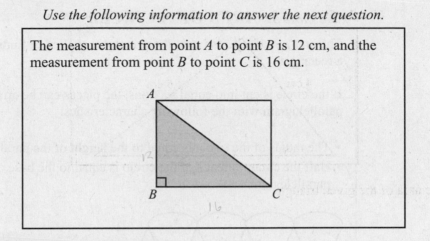

The measurement from point *A* to point *B* is 12 cm, and the measurement from point *B* to point *C* is 16 cm.

9. Calculate the area of the shaded triangle.

96 cm^2

Use the following information to answer the next question.

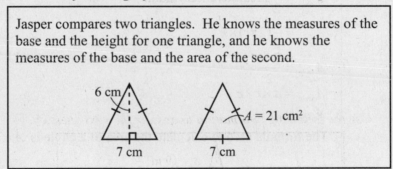

Jasper compares two triangles. He knows the measures of the base and the height for one triangle, and he knows the measures of the base and the area of the second.

10. Do the triangles have the same area?

Yes

Lesson 3   AREA OF A CIRCLE

The area of a circle also uses the principles applied to finding the area of a rectangle.

If the circle is cut into equal sections, the pieces can be arranged to form a parallelogram with the following characteristics:

- The radius of the circle is equal to the height of the parallelogram.
- Half the circumference of the circle is equal to the base of the parallelogram.

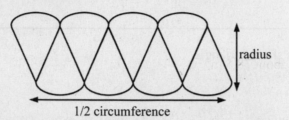

1/2 circumference

Therefore,

$A_{circle} = A_{parallelogram}$

$A_{circle} = base \times height$

$A_{circle} = \dfrac{1}{2} circumference \times radius$

$A_{circle} = \dfrac{1}{2}(2\pi r) \times r$

$A_{circle} = \dfrac{2\pi r}{2} \times r$

$A_{circle} = \pi \times r \times r$

$A_{circle} = \pi r^2$

The formula used to calculate the area of a circle is $A = \pi r^2$.

$base = \dfrac{1}{2} Circumference$

$= \dfrac{1}{2}(2\pi r)$

$height = radius$

$= r$

Use 3.14 in place of π when calculating the area of a circle. Using 3.14 approximates the answers.

Example

Calculate the area of the given circle.

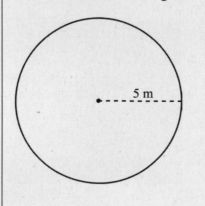

5 m

Solution

Step 1

Determine the given values.
The radius is 5 m.

Step 2

Apply the area formula, substitute in the given values, and solve.

$$A = \pi r^2$$
$$= (3.14)(5)^2$$
$$= (3.14)(25)$$
$$= 78.5 \text{ m}^2$$

The area of the circle is about 78.5 m².

Your Turn 1

Calculate the area of the given circle.

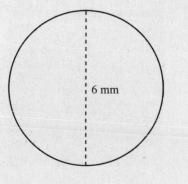

6 mm

If you are given the area of a circle and asked to find the missing radius, substitute in the values you are given and solve for the radius.

Example

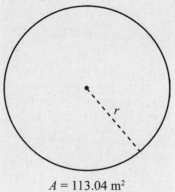

r

$A = 113.04$ m²

Calculate the radius of the given circle.

Solution

Step 1
Determine the given values.
The area is 113.04 m^2.

Step 2
Apply the area formula, substitute in the given values, and solve for the radius.

$$A = \pi r^2$$
$$113.04 = (3.14)r^2$$
$$\frac{113.04}{3.14} = \frac{3.14r^2}{3.14}$$
$$36 = r^2$$

The opposite of something squared is the square root. So take the square root of both sides to solve for *r*.

$$\sqrt{36} = \sqrt{r^2}$$
$$6 = r$$

The radius of the circle is 6 m.

Your Turn 2

Calculate the diameter of the given circle.

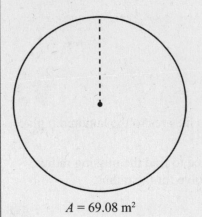

$A = 69.08$ m^2

PRACTICE EXERCISES

Use the following information to answer the next question.

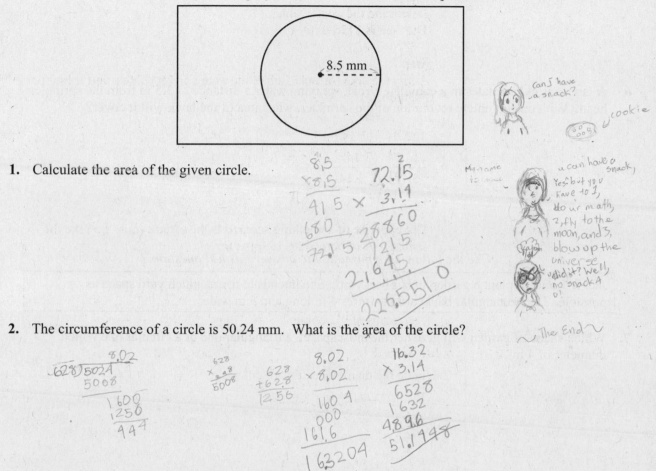

8.5 mm

1. Calculate the area of the given circle.

2. The circumference of a circle is 50.24 mm. What is the area of the circle?

3. The radius of a circle is 4.2 cm. What is the area to the hundredth place?

4. The diameter of a circle is 9 cm. What is the area?

5. If the radius of a circular garden doubles, how many times larger will the new area be?

×4

6. A lawn sprinkler rotates in a complete circle, spraying water a distance of 3.5 m from the sprinkler head. With one complete revolution of the sprinkler, what area of the lawn will it cover?

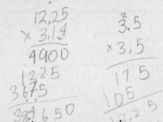

Use the following information to answer the next question.

Jackie wants to plant a garden in her backyard. She intends to use as much yard space as possible. Her rectangular backyard measures 4 m long and 5 m wide.

7. Which shape of garden will give her the most space: a triangular one or a circular one with a diameter of 4 m?

a circular one

Use the following information to answer the next question.

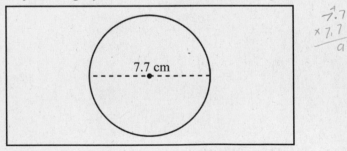

8. Rounded to the nearest tenth of a centimetre, calculate the area of the circle.

9. A circular base with a diameter of 2.5 m is built for a fountain in a park. What is the area of the base, rounded to the nearest tenth of a metre?

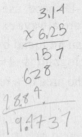

$$\begin{array}{r} 3.14 \\ \times\, 6.25 \\ \hline 157 \\ 628 \\ \underline{1884} \\ 19.4737 \end{array}$$

Use the following information to answer the next question.

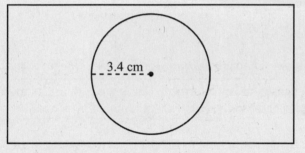

3.4 cm

10. Calculate the area of the given circle, rounded to the nearest tenth of a centimetre.

$$\begin{array}{r} 11.56 \\ \times\, 3.1 \\ \hline 105 \\ 335 \\ \hline 3465 \end{array}$$

$$\begin{array}{r} 3.14 \\ \times\, 4 \\ \hline 12.56 \end{array}$$

REVIEW SUMMARY

- To calculate the area of any 2-D shape, use the given formulas for area, substitute in the known values, and solve. The units for area are always expressed in squared units.

- The area of a parallelogram can be found by transforming the parallelogram into a rectangle. The area formula for a parallelogram is $A = b \times h$.

- The area of a triangle is half the area of a rectangle. Therefore, the area formula for a triangle is $A = \dfrac{1}{2}bh$.

- The area of a circle uses the principles applied to finding the area of a parallelogram and can be found by using the formula $A = \pi r^2$.

- Other missing measurements can be found by substituting the given values into the appropriate area formulas, and solving for the unknown measurement.

314

PRACTICE TEST

Use the following information to answer the next question.

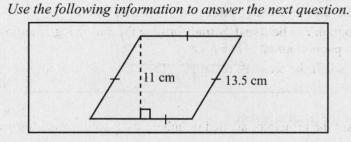

1. Calculate the area of the parallelogram if the given measurements are cut in half.

$$6.75$$
$$\times\ 5.5$$
$$\overline{3375}$$
$$3375$$
$$\overline{37)25}\ cm^2$$

Use the following information to answer the next question.

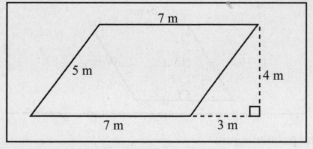

2. Calculate the area of the parallelogram in the given diagram.

$$28m^2$$

Use the following information to answer the next question.

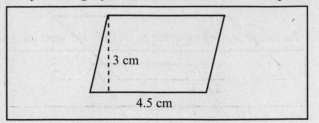

3. Calculate the area of the parallelogram.

Use the following information to answer the next question.

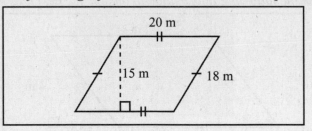

4. Calculate the area of the parallelogram.

Use the following information to answer the next question.

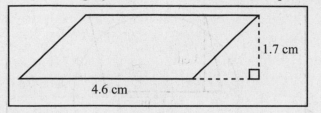

4.6 cm

1.7 cm

5. Calculate the area of the given parallelogram.

4.6
× 1.7
──────
32 2
46
──────
7.82

6. The radius of a circle is 37 cm. What is the area of the circle?

37
× 37
──────
259
111
──────
1369

1369
× 3.14
──────
5476
1369
4107.
──────
4298.66

7. If a circle has a radius of 2.8 cm, what is its area? (to a hundredth of a cm²)

2.8
× 2.8
──────
224
56
──────
7.84

3.1
× 7.8
──────
248.
211.
──────
24.18

Use the following information to answer the next question.

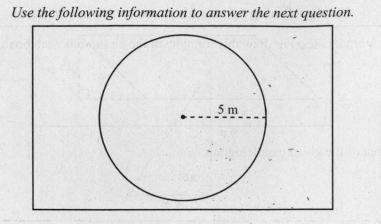

8. Calculate the area of the circle if the radius is doubled.

314

Use the following information to answer the next question.

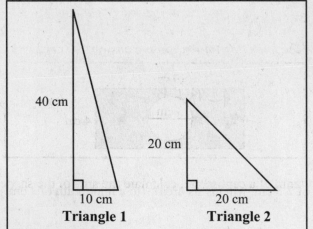

9. Do the two given triangles have the same area?

yes

Use the following information to answer the next question.

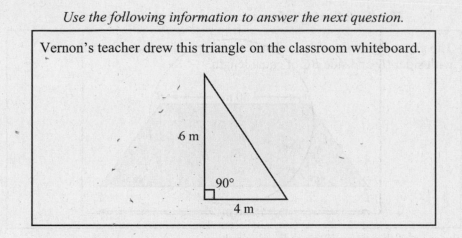

Vernon's teacher drew this triangle on the classroom whiteboard.

6 m

90°

4 m

10. If Vernon correctly calculated the area of the given triangle, what answer did he get?

12 m²

Use the following information to answer the next question.

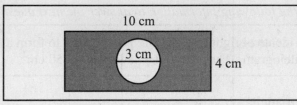

10 cm

3 cm

4 cm

11. Rounded to the nearest tenth of a centimetre, calculate the area of the shaded region in the given figure.

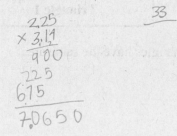

2.25
× 3.14
─────
900
225
675
─────
7.0650

33

Use the following information to answer the next question.

The given figure shows a garden in the shape of an isosceles trapezoid with side *AD* and side *BC* of equal length.

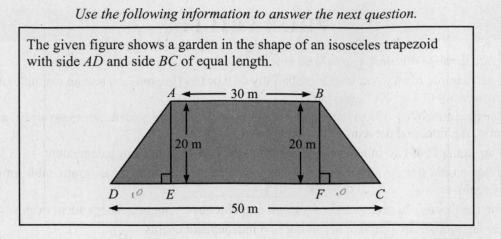

12. What is the area of each of the two triangular sections of the garden in the given figure?

100m, or, 200m total

Use the following information to answer the next question.

Two identical right triangles are put together to form a parallelogram. The area of the new shape is 50 cm^2.

13. What is the area of each triangle?

25 cm^2

PROBABILITY

When you are finished this unit, you will be able to…

- provide an example of an event with a probability of 0 or 0% (impossible) and an example of an event with a probability of 1 or 100% (certain)
- determine the probability of a given outcome occurring for a given probability experiment, and express it as a ratio, fraction, and percentage
- provide an example of two independent events and explain why they are independent
- identify the sample space for each of two independent events, using a tree diagram, table, or other graphic organizer
- determine the theoretical probability of a given outcome involving two independent events
- solve a given probability problem involving two independent events
- conduct a probability experiment for an outcome involving two independent events and compare the experimental probability with the theoretical probability

PREREQUISITE SKILLS AND KNOWLEDGE

Prior to beginning this unit, you should be able to…

- list possible outcomes for a single event.
- find the probability for single events.
- compare outcomes as equally likely, more likely, or less likely to occur.
- demonstrate that different outcomes may occur when repeating the same experiment.

Lesson 1   *INTRODUCTION TO PROBABILITY*

Probability is a measure of how likely it is for an event to occur.

An event with a probability of 0 means that event is impossible and will never happen. For instance, humans will never walk to the moon. The probability of that event is 0.

An event with a probability of 1 means that event is certain and will always happen. For instance, the sun will always rise in the east. The probability of that event occurring is 1.

The probability of everything else falls in between 0 and 1.

Example

Sophie goes to the candy store and purchases 5 red sour candies, 10 red liquorice candies, 5 red dolphin candies, and 10 red cola candies. The cashier puts all of her candies in a bag for her.

a) What is the probability of Sophie picking a red candy out of the bag?

Solution

All of the candies that Sophie purchased are red. Therefore, the probability of Sophie picking a red candy out of the bag is 1.

b) What is the probability of Sophie picking a blue dolphin candy out of the bag?

Solution

None of the candies that Sophie purchased are blue dolphin candies. Therefore, the probability of Sophie picking a blue dolphin candy out of the bag is 0.

Your Turn 1

Hank goes into a sports store and purchases 3 pairs of sweat socks, 2 pairs of soccer socks, and 5 pairs of ankle shoes. The cashier puts all of Hank's socks in a bag for him.

a) What is the probability of Hank pulling out a pair of shoelaces from the bag?

b) What is the probability of Hank pulling out a pair of socks from the bag?

NOTES

Probability is the ratio of favourable outcomes to the total possible outcomes. The following formula can be used to calculate the probability of any given event:

$$P = \frac{\text{favourable outcome}}{\text{total possible outcomes}}$$

When determining the probability of a given experiment, substitute the known values into the probability formula and evaluate for the probability, P.

Probability can be expressed as a fraction, ratio, or a percentage.

Example

In a jar of jellybeans, there are 6 red jellybeans, 8 green jellybeans, and 10 yellow jellybeans.

What is the probability of picking a red jellybean out of the jar without looking?

Solution

Determine the number of favourable outcomes and total possible outcomes, substitute them into the probability formula, and evaluate for P.

$$P = \frac{\text{favourable outcome}}{\text{total possible outcomes}}$$

$$P(\text{red jellybean}) = \frac{6}{24}$$

$$= \frac{1}{4}$$

The probability of picking a red jellybean from the jar, expressed in fraction form is $\frac{1}{4}$.

The ratio can be expressed as $a{:}b$, where a represents the numerator and b represents the denominator. In this case, the ratio that compares the probability of picking a red jellybean from all the jellybeans in the jar is 1:4.

To express the fraction as a percentage, divide the numerator by the denominator and multiply the result by 100.

$$\frac{1}{4}$$
$$= 0.25 \times 100$$
$$= 25\%$$

There is a 25% chance of picking a red jellybean from the jar.

Probability calculations are always reduced to lowest terms whenever possible.

Favourable outcomes are the outcomes that meet the criteria of a given event.

Express percentages to the nearest whole number.

NOTES

Your Turn 2

A bag contains 3 red marbles, 2 green marbles, and 1 black marble.

If a person reaches into a bag and selects 1 marble without looking, what is the probability that the person will pull out a green marble? Express the probability as a fraction, ratio, and percentage.

$$\frac{2}{6} = \frac{1}{3}$$

$$1 : 3$$

PRACTICE EXERCISES

Use the following information to answer the next 5 questions.

Eight cards are randomly laid facedown on a table. Each card is numbered from 1 to 8. A person who does not know the placement of any of the cards draws one at a time.

Find the probability of each of the events.

1. Drawing a 4

2. Drawing an even number

10%

3. Drawing a multiple of 2

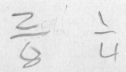

4. Drawing a 9

0

5. Drawing a 1 or a 3

$\frac{2}{8}$ $\frac{1}{4}$

6. Express the probability of rolling a number equal to or greater than 5 on a regular number cube as a fraction, ratio, and percentage.

A box contains 2 red pens, 5 black pens, and 3 blue pens. A pen is drawn at random from the box.

7. What is the probability that a red pen is drawn? Express the probability as a fraction, ratio, and percentage.

20%

Use the following information to answer the next question.

Ten cards with the letters shown are shuffled and then placed facedown on a table.

S	T	A	T	I	S	T	I	C	S

A person who does not know the placement of any of the cards draws one at a time.

8. Express the probability of selecting an S as a fraction, ratio, and percentage.

9. At Jasmine's school, 132 out of 660 students have a pet cat. Express the probability of randomly choosing a student that has a cat as a fraction, ratio, and percentage.

10. A card store gets 52 cards in a shipment. 13 cards are birthday cards, 13 are get-well cards, 13 are anniversary cards, and 13 are mother's day cards. Expressed as a ratio, what is the probability that a card selected at random from the inventory is **not** an anniversary card?

Lesson 2   INDEPENDENT EVENTS AND SAMPLE SPACE

Independent events are events in which the occurrence of one event has no effect on the occurrence of another event.

An example of independent events would be the tossing of two coins. The first coin could have the outcome of heads or tails, and the second coin could have the same outcome of heads or tails. The outcome of the first event has no effect on the second event.

To identify all the possible outcomes of two or more independent events, follow these steps:

1. Identify all possible outcomes of the first event.
2. Identify all possible outcomes of the second event as they pertain to each outcome in the first event.
3. Organize the outcomes in a table or a tree diagram.

When all the possible combinations are listed, you have identified the **sample space.**

Sample space is a data set that contains all possible outcomes of a probability experiment that involves two or more independent events.

Each outcome in the sample space is expressed as an ordered pair, and the entire sample space is enclosed in a set of curly brackets, such as { }.

Example

Glynn has a four-sided die and a spinner with the colours red, blue, green, and yellow distributed in equal sections.

Draw a table and tree diagram to identify all the possible outcomes. Then determine the sample space.

Solution

Step 1
Identify the outcomes of the first event.
Outcomes of rolling the die are: 1, 2, 3, 4.

Step 2
Identify the outcomes of the second event.
Outcomes of spinning the spinner are: Red, Blue, Green, Yellow.

Step 3
Organize the outcomes in a table or a tree diagram.

Use a table:
The table headers are the events in the experiment. Combine the outcome on the side of the table with the outcome at the top of the table.

	Spinner			
	Red (R)	**Blue (B)**	**Green (G)**	**Yellow (Y)**
1	1R	1B	1G	1Y
2	2R	2B	2G	2Y
3	3R	3B	3G	3Y
4	4R	4B	4G	4Y

(The leftmost column is labelled **Die** vertically.)

Use a Tree Diagram:
Start with the first event (die), and list the outcomes (1, 2, 3, 4).
Draw a branch from each of these outcomes to each of the outcomes
(red, blue, green, yellow) of the second event.

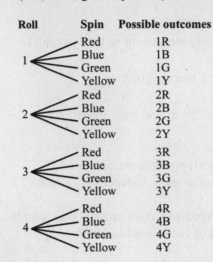

Roll	Spin	Possible outcomes
1	Red	1R
	Blue	1B
	Green	1G
	Yellow	1Y
2	Red	2R
	Blue	2B
	Green	2G
	Yellow	2Y
3	Red	3R
	Blue	3B
	Green	3G
	Yellow	3Y
4	Red	4R
	Blue	4B
	Green	4G
	Yellow	4Y

The sample space according to the table and the tree diagram is
{1R, 1B, 1G, 1Y, 2R, 2B, 2G, 2Y, 3R, 3B, 3G, 3Y, 4R, 4B, 4G, 4Y}.

Your Turn 1

Tarik is rolling a regular number cube and tossing a coin.
Draw a table to identify all the possible outcomes. Then determine the
sample space.

Your Turn 2

Albert is spinning a spinner coloured yellow, blue, purple, and orange distributed in equal sections and tossing a coin.
Determine the sample space for the outcomes of the two independent events using a tree diagram.

PRACTICE EXERCISES

1. Warwick has two regular number cubes, Cube A and Cube B. Draw a table to identify all the different possible outcomes. Then determine the sample space.

2. John has a coin and a spinner coloured red, orange, blue, green, and yellow distributed in equal segments. Draw a tree diagram to identify all the possible outcomes. Then determine the sample space.

3. Kurt has a coin and a bag with 1 red, 1 orange, 1 blue, and 1 green marble. Draw a table to identify all the possible outcomes. Then determine the sample space.

4. A man is selected randomly and asked on which day of the week he was born. Determine the sample space and use it to identify the total number of possible outcomes.

5. When a coin is tossed two times, what is the sample space for the probability of getting consecutive tails? Draw a tree diagram to indentify the total number of possible outcomes.

6. Jesse rolls a 6-sided die numbered 4-9 and tosses a coin. Draw a table to identify all the possible outcomes. Then determine the sample space.

7. A spinner is divided into six equally coloured parts: red, blue, green, black, yellow, and pink. The spinner is spun and then a coin is tossed. Draw a tree diagram to identify all the possible outcomes. Then determine the number of outcomes in the sample space.

rTYt
rHYh
BtPt
BhPh
Gt
Gh
lBh
lBt

8. A bag contains 1 red, 1 blue, 1 green, 1 yellow, and 1 white ball. A coin is tossed and then a ball is drawn at random from the bag. Draw a tree diagram to identify all the possible outcomes. Then determine the number of outcomes in the sample space.

rt Wt
rh wh
bt
bh
Gt
Gh
Yh
A

9. Two regular number cubes are rolled simultaneously. Which of the following statements about the outcome of the roll is **true**?

A. The appearance of a certain number on the first number cube depends upon the occurrence of a similar event on the second number cube.

B. The appearance of a certain number on the second number cube depends on the occurrence of a similar event on the first number cube.

C. The appearance of a certain number on the two number cubes is an independent event.

D. The appearance of a certain number on the two number cubes is a dependent event.

10. In a game, a coin is tossed and then a regular number cube is rolled. The player who gets tails on the coin and a four on the regular number cube is pronounced the winner. Draw a table to identify all the possible outcomes. Then determine the sample space.

1t 5t
1h 5h
2t 6t
2h 6h
3t 7t
3h
4t
4h

Lesson 3 *THEORETICAL PROBABILITY VS. EXPERIMENTAL PROBABILITY*

There are two types of probability: theoretical probability and experimental probability.

Theoretical probability is the probability of an event occurring, and it is calculated mathematically. It is the number of favourable outcomes compared to the total number of possible outcomes.

Experimental probability is determined by actually conducting an experiment and using those results to calculate the probability.

Both theoretical probability and experimental probability are calculated using the probability formula:

$$P = \frac{\text{favourable outcome}}{\text{total possible outcomes}}$$

For example, when a coin is tossed, it is equally likely to obtain either heads or tails; therefore, the theoretical probability of the coin landing on heads is $\frac{1}{2}$. When the experiment is actually performed, heads might be obtained 3 times out of 4; thus, the experimental probability of the coin landing on a head is $\frac{3}{4}$.

When calculating experimental probability use the results of the experiment to identify the favourable outcomes and the total possible outcomes.

Calculate the probability of two independent events, follow these steps:

Step 1
Use a table or a tree diagram to determine the sample space.

Step 2
Calculate the probability by applying the probability formula.

Example

What is the probability of tossing heads on a coin and rolling a 4 on a regular number cube? Express the probability as a fraction.

Solution

Step 1

Determine the sample space using a table or tree diagram.

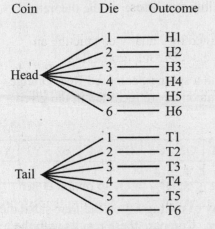

Coin   Die   Outcome

Head
1 —— H1
2 —— H2
3 —— H3
4 —— H4
5 —— H5
6 —— H6

Tail
1 —— T1
2 —— T2
3 —— T3
4 —— T4
5 —— T5
6 —— T6

Step 2

Calculate the probability.

There are 12 possible outcomes and 1 favourable outcome.

$$P = \frac{\text{favourable outcome}}{\text{total possible outcomes}}$$

$$P(\text{H4}) = \frac{1}{12}$$

The probability of tossing heads and rolling a 4 is $\frac{1}{12}$.

Your Turn 1

If a regular number cube is rolled and a fair coin is tossed, what is the probability of rolling a prime number and tossing heads? Express the probability as a fraction.

Experimental probability is the likelihood of an event occurring when a trial is conducted. With experimental probability, a different outcome is possible each time the experiment is conducted.

The theoretical probability of two independent events and the experimental probability of two independent events need not always be the same.

However, as the number of trials in the experiment increases, the experimental probability will come closer and closer to the theoretical probability.

Example

A four-sided die is rolled 24 times and a spinner, coloured Red, Orange, and Yellow, is spun 24 times. The outcomes are recorded in the given table.

Outcomes	R1	R2	R3	R4	O1	O2	O3	O4	Y1	Y2	Y3	Y4
Frequency	1	2	0	2	3	4	4	2	1	3	1	1

Calculate the experimental probability of rolling a 3 on the four-sided die and spinning an orange on the spinner. Compare these results with the theoretical probability of rolling a 3 on the four-sided die and spinning orange on the spinner. Express the probabilities as percentages.

Solution
Step 1
Calculate the theoretical probability.
There are 24 possible outcomes and 4 favourable outcomes.

$$P = \frac{\text{favourable outcome}}{\text{total possible outcomes}}$$
$$P(O3) = \frac{4}{24}$$
$$= \frac{1}{6}$$
$$\doteq 17\%$$

The total possible outcomes in experimental probability is the number of times the experiment is carried out.

Step 2
Calculate the experimental probability, using the outcomes in the given table. There are 12 possible outcomes and 1 favourable outcome.

$$P = \frac{\text{favourable outcome}}{\text{total possible outcomes}}$$
$$P(O4) = \frac{1}{12}$$
$$\doteq 8\%$$

The theoretical probability of rolling a 3 and spinning orange is much higher than its experimental probability.

Your Turn 2

A four-sided die is rolled 24 times and a spinner, coloured Red, Orange, and Yellow, is spun 24 times. The outcomes are recorded in the given table.

Outcomes	R1	R2	R3	R4	O1	O2	O3	O4	Y1	Y2	Y3	Y4
Frequency	1	2	0	2	3	4	4	2	1	3	1	1

Calculate the experimental probability of rolling an odd number on the four-sided die and spinning yellow on the spinner. Compare these results with the theoretical probability of rolling an odd number on the four-sided die and spinning yellow on the spinner. Express the probabilities as percentages.

PRACTICE EXERCISES

1. As a probability experiment is repeated numerous times, the experimental probability will

   A. increase

   B. decrease

   C. get closer to the theoretical probability

   D. move farther away from the theoretical probability

Use the following information to answer the next question.

> Two regular number cubes are rolled once, and their sum is recorded.
> After conducting this experiment 10 times, a sum of less than 7 is obtained five times.

2. Find the difference between the experimental and theoretical probability of recording a sum less then 7 when two regular number cubes are rolled.

   $E = {}^5\!/\!_{10} \quad T = {}^6\!/\!_{10}$

3. Determining the probability of two coins landing heads up by tossing them both several times is an example of what type of probability?

   $\overline{E}P$

Use the following information to answer the next question.

> Both a coin is flipped and a regular number cube is rolled 16 separate times.
> The combination of heads and a number on the number cube greater than 4 was obtained in 4 of the 16 trials.

4. Determine the theoretical probability of obtaining heads and a number greater than 4 using a percentage, and compare this to the experimental probability of obtaining the same combination.

   $4/12$

5. If the probability of winning a game is $\dfrac{6}{10}$, then what is the probability of losing a game?

   $\dfrac{4}{10}$

6. If a regular number cube is rolled, what is the theoretical probability of rolling a number that is **not** a 3? Express the probability as a fraction.

$\frac{5}{6}$

Use the following information to answer the next question.

A bag contains 2 black, 1 pink, 1 red, and 1 green ball. Ken randomly picks one ball from the bag, returns it, and then picks another one.

7. Expressed as a percentage, hat is the probability that Ken will pick a green ball and then a pink one?

50%

Use the following information to answer the next question.

In a large flower pot, there are 2 red flowers, 3 pink flowers, and 1 white flower.
A bee lands on one of the flowers.

8. Expressed as a ratio, what is the probability of the bee landing on a pink flower first and then buzzing away to a red flower?

3:6

Use the following information to answer the next question.

> An experiment is performed where both a coin is flipped and a four-sided die is rolled five different times. On three of the five trials, heads is flipped and the number 4 is obtained.

9. What is the difference between the experimental and theoretical probability of the coin landing on heads and obtaining a 4 on the die? Express the probability as a ratio.

11.5:5

Use the following information to answer the next question.

> In a bag of 5 jellybeans, there are 2 red ones, 1 black one, and 2 green ones.

10. Expressed as a percentage, what is the theoretical probability of pulling and black jellybean out of the bag, putting it back, and then pulling out a green one?

2/5

REVIEW SUMMARY

- Probability is a measure of how likely it is for an event to occur. It is expressed as a number between 0 and 1.
- Outcomes are the possible results of conducting a probability experiment. Outcomes can be impossible, certain, or somewhere in between.
- Theoretical probability is the probability of an event occurring, and it is calculated mathematically using a formula.
- Experimental probability is determined by actually conducting a probability experiment and using the results of the experiment to calculate the probability.
- Both theoretical probability and experimental probability are calculated using the probability formula:

$$P = \frac{\text{favourable outcome}}{\text{total possible outcomes}}$$

- Independent events are events in which the outcomes of one event do not affect the outcomes of another event.
- Sample space is a data set that contains all possible outcomes of an experiment. Sample space can be identified by using tables or tree diagrams.
- To calculate the probability of two independent events, following these steps:
  1. Use a table or a tree diagram to determine the sample space.
  2. Calculate the probability by applying the probability formula.

PRACTICE TEST

Use the following information to answer the next question.

> A spinner is divided into 10 equal parts, and each part is numbered 1 to 10.
> The spinner is spun once.

1. Expressed as a fraction, what is the probability that the spinner will land on a prime number and then an even number?

    $$\frac{4}{10}, \frac{5}{10}, = \frac{1}{10}$$

2. What is the probability of rolling a 6 followed by an odd number when a regular number cube is rolled twice? Express the probability as a fraction.

    $$\frac{1}{6}, \frac{3}{6}, = \frac{2}{6}$$

3. If the probability that it will rain on Monday is 1, then which of the following statements is **correct**?

    A. It will definitely rain on Monday.

    B. It will definitely rain on Tuesday.

    C. It may or may not rain on Monday.

    D. It will definitely not rain on Monday.

4. Find the probability of rolling a 2 and then a 5 on a regular number cube. Express the probability as a ratio.

    $$1:6$$

5. Which of the following scenarios represents a sequence of independent events?

    A. Morgan has 3 toonies, 4 loonies, and 5 quarters in a bag. She reaches in and draws out a toonie, which she keeps. What is the probability of her drawing out a second toonie?

    B. Slips of paper numbered 1 through 9 are placed in a box. If two slips are drawn without replacement, what is the probability that the sum of the numbers is 9?

    C. A bag has 4 white balls and 6 green balls. A white ball is chosen and not replaced. What is the probability of drawing a second white ball?

    D. A coin is tossed, and a single regular number cube is rolled. What is the probability of getting a tail and a 6?

6. There are three standard coins that are each tossed once. Expressed as a ratio, what is the probability of getting a heads on the first coin?

    1:2

Use the following information to answer the next question.

> Jack and Selma play a game in which a coin is tossed and a regular number cube is rolled. The player who gets a tail on the coin and a four on the number cube is pronounced the winner.

7. What is the probability that Jack will win on his turn? Express the probability as a fraction.

    1:12

8. When two regular coins are tossed, what is the probability of obtaining fewer than three heads? Express the probability as a percentage.

    100%

Use the following information to answer the next question.

> A spinner has four equal parts coloured red, blue, yellow, and green. A coin is tossed, and then the spinner is spun.

9. What is the probability of tossing heads and spinning green? Express the probability as a percentage.

1:8

Use the following information to answer the next question.

> A bag contains five identical red, blue, green, yellow, and white balls. A coin is tossed, and then a ball is drawn at random from the bag.

10. What is the probability of tossing heads and drawing either a blue or red ball from the bag? Express the probability as a fraction.

2:10

Use the following information to answer the next question.

> Brad counts 3 angelfish, 2 wrasses, and 3 clown fish at the pet store. He decides to buy two new fish for his tank.

11. If Brad chooses a fish at random, what is the probability that he chooses an angelfish and then a clown fish? Express the probability as a ratio.

1:8

Use the following information to answer the next question.

In Martha's study group, there are 2 boys (Joe and Ted) and 3 girls (Mary, Maxine, and Joanne).

12. If Martha has to choose 2 people to read out loud, what is the probability that she will choose Ted and Maxine? Express the probability as a fraction.

$\frac{1}{6}$

Use the following information to answer the next question.

A bag contains 3 purple marbles, 2 yellow, and 1 black. Jake reaches into the bag and selects one marble without looking.

13. Expressed as a fraction, ratio, and percentage, what is the probability that Jake will pull out a yellow marble?

$\frac{1}{3}$

Use the following information to answer the next question.

A six-sided number cube numbered 4-9 is rolled, and a spinner is spun. The spinner contains four equal sectors coloured red, green, blue, and yellow.

14. Calculate the probability of rolling an even number and spinning yellow or green. Express the probability as a fraction, ratio, and percentage.

$\frac{5}{29}$

Use the following information to answer the next question.

A man has 2 pairs of shoes: 1 black and 1 brown. He also has 5 pairs of socks: 1 red, 1 white, 1 blue, 1 yellow and 1 grey.

15. If he randomly selects a pair of shoes and socks to wear, what is the probability that the man wears brown shoes with either grey, white, or red socks? Express the probability as a fraction.

3/10

DATA ANALYSIS

When you are finished this unit, you will be able to...

- determine mean, median, and mode for a given set of data, and explain why these values may be the same or different
- determine the range for a given set of data
- provide a context in which the mean, median, or mode is the most appropriate measure of central tendency to use when reporting findings
- solve a given problem involving the measures of central tendency
- explain the effect of outliers on the measures of central tendency for a given data set
- identify outliers in a given set of data, and justify whether or not they are to be included in reporting the measures of central tendency

PREREQUISITE SKILLS AND KNOWLEDGE

Prior to starting this unit, you should be able to...

- draw conclusions from a set of data
- describe the distribution of a set of data using the smallest and largest values, value in the middle, and frequency
- make comparisons between sets of data
- read and understand graphs

Lesson 1 MEASURES OF CENTRAL TENDENCY

When given a set of data, analysis can be performed to determine important information from the data. **Central tendency** is the tendency of data to merge around certain points near the middle of a set of data. The mean, median, and mode are three ways to measure central tendency for a set of data.

A **set of data** is an unordered collection of values. The set is usually within curly brackets { }.

MEAN

The **mean** is the average of all the values that make up a set of data.

To calculate the mean of a set of numbers, follow these steps:

Step 1
Find the sum of the values.

Step 2
Divide the total sum by the number of values.

Example
Calculate the mean of the data set {12, 10, 14, 8, 16}.

Solution
Step 1
Find the sum of the values.

$$12 + 10 + 14 + 8 + 16 = 60$$

Step 2
Divide the total sum by the number of values.

There are five values, so divide the sum by 5.
$$60 \div 5 = 12$$

The mean of the data set is 12.

Your Turn 1
Calculate the mean of the data set {6, 3, 8, 12, 6, 2, 5}.

7R3

MEDIAN

When the data is arranged in ascending order, the **median** is the middle value in a set of data. It divides the data so that 50% of the data is above the median and 50% is below the median.

There are two possibilities when calculating the median:
- An odd number of values in the data set—the number used is located exactly in the middle.
- An even number of values in the data set—the average of the two middle numbers is used.

To determine the median of a set of numbers, follow these steps:

Step 1
Place the values in ascending order.

Step 2
Determine the middle number or numbers.

Example

Determine the median of the data set {14, 18, 16, 12, 13, 17, 15}.

Solution
Step 1
Place the values in ascending order (least to greatest).
12, 13, 14, 15, 16, 17, 18

Step 2
Determine the middle number.

There are an odd number of values. Only one number is in the middle.
12, 13, 14, 15, 16, 17, 18

The median is 15.

Your Turn 2

Determine the median of the data set {20, 12, 16, 26, 15, 24}.

Ascending order means ordering from smallest to largest

NOTES

To remember the definition of mode, notice mode and most both start with the letters *mo*.

MODE

The mode of a set of data is the value that occurs most often.

There are three possibilities when calculating the mode:
- One mode—one number occurs more frequently than the other numbers.
- More than one mode—two or more numbers occur more than the other numbers and occur the same number of times.
- No mode—all the numbers occur the same number of times.

To determine the mode of a set of numbers, follow these steps:

Step 1

Place the values in ascending (least to greatest) order.

Step 2

Determine which numbers occur the most frequently, if any.

Example

Determine the mode of the data set {4, 9, 12, 7, 9, 2, 12, 8, 9, 4, 11, 3}.

Solution

Step 1

Place the values in ascending order.
2, 3, 4, 4, 7, 8, 9, 9, 9, 11, 12, 12

Step 2

Determine which number or numbers occur most frequently.
The numbers 4 and 12 occur twice, and 9 occurs three times. The rest of the numbers occur once.

The mode is 9 because it occurs more than any other number.

Your Turn 3

Find the mode of the numbers 7, 3, 4, 8, 5, 4, 6, and 3.

RANGE

Data is organized in increasing order to investigate the upper and lower extremes. From the extremes, the range can be calculated. **Range** is the difference between the highest and lowest values that make up a data set.

To find the range of a set of numbers, follow these steps:

Step 1

Place the numbers in ascending (least to greatest) order.

Step 2

Subtract the lowest value from the greatest value.

Example

18, 32, 12, 45, 23, 54, 33, 31, 35, 45, 30, 21
Find the upper and lower extremes and the range of the given data.

Solution

Step 1

Place the numbers in ascending order.

12, 18, 21, 23, 30, 31, 32, 33, 35, 45, 45, 54
↑   ↑
Lower extreme   Upper extreme

The smallest value is the lower extreme, and the largest value is the upper extreme. The range is the difference between the upper and lower extremes.

The lower extreme is 12, and the upper extreme is 54.

Step 2

Subtract the lowest value from the greatest value.

range = upper extreme − lower extreme
    $= 54 - 12 = 42$

Therefore, the upper extreme is 54, the lower extreme is 12, and the range is 42.

Your Turn 4

21, 25, 18, 45, 31, 35, 43, 31, 24, 23, 44, 33
Find the upper and lower extremes and the range of the given data.

PRACTICE EXERCISES

Find the mean of the following sets of numbers.

1. 6, 3, 8, 12, 7, 5, 2, 5

2. 23, 21, 54, 26, 16

3. 6, 13, 40, 23, 35, 27, 31

Find the median of the following sets of numbers.

4. 14, 2, 16, 8, 3, 11, 14

5. 135, 114, 249, 187, 196

6. 56, 43, 46, 64, 52, 59

Find the mode and range of the following sets of numbers.

7. 65, 24, 25, 25, 32, 31, 54, 31

8. 25, 64, 21, 52, 26, 21, 16, 36

9. 345, 323, 256, 252, 237, 342

10. Find the upper and lower extremes and the range of the given data.
19, 31, 13, 44, 24, 53, 34, 30, 36, 44, 29, 22

Lesson 2   USING MEASURES OF CENTRAL TENDENCY AND THE EFFECTS OF OUTLIERS

NOTES

A value that is vastly different than the rest of the data is referred to as an **outlier**. This means that there is a great difference between an outlier and the closest value to it. Outliers can affect all measures of central tendency (mean, median, and mode), depending on the numbers in the data set.

A set of data has gaps if there are significant differences between data values. Clusters occur when there is a lot of data centered around one or more values.

The appropriate use of measures of central tendency to describe the data depends on the kind of data that is presented.

The mean is a good representation of central tendency for sets of data that have no major outliers. Because the mean is greatly affected by outliers, it is not a good representation for skewed data.

The median is a good representation of central tendency for data that contain outliers. Because the median is not greatly affected by outliers, it is a good representation for skewed data.

The mode is a good representation for central tendency for sets of categorical data. **Categorical data** is data that can be divided into groups. Examples of categorical data are size (small, medium, large), music style (pop, jazz, rock, hip hop), or age group (infant, toddler, adolescent, adult, senior).

To determine which measure of central tendency is affected by an outlier, follow these steps:

Step 1
Place the values in ascending (least to greatest) order.

Step 2
Determine the outlier.

Step 3
Calculate the mean, median, and mode with the outlier.

Step 4
Calculate the mean, median, and mode without the outlier.

Step 5
Compare the results of the calculations.

352

Example

{10, 8, 21, 13, 8, 9, 10, 11, 12, 11, 8}
Identify which measure of central tendency is **most affected** when the outlier is removed.

Solution

Step 1
Place the values in ascending order.
8, 8, 8, 9, 10, 10, 11, 11, 12, 13, 21

Step 2
Determine the outlier.
The outlier in this set of data is 21 since the difference between it and 13 is the greatest.

Step 3
Calculate the mean, median, and mode with the outlier.

$$8 + 8 + 8 + 9 + 10 + 10 + 11 + 11 + 12 + 13 + 21 = 121$$
$$121 \div 11 = 11$$

The mean is 11.

The value 8 occurs three times, so the mode is 8.

8, 8, 8, 9, 10, $\boxed{10}$, 11, 11, 12, 13, 21
The median is 10.

Step 4
Calculate the mean, median, and mode without the outlier.

$$8 + 8 + 8 + 9 + 10 + 10 + 11 + 11 + 12 + 13 = 120$$
$$100 \div 10 = 10$$
The mean changes from 11 to 10.

There is an even number of values.
8, 8, 8, 9, $\boxed{10, 10}$, 11, 11, 12, 13
The average of the two middle values is 10, so the median is still 10.

8, 8, 8, 9, 10, 10, 11, 11, 12, 13
The value 8 occurs three times, so the mode is still 8.

Step 5
Compare the results of the calculations.
After removing the outlier, the mode is still 8, the median is still 10, and the mean changes from 11 to 10.

Removing the outlier affected the mean most.

NOTES

Your Turn 1

{10, 9, 12, 10, 10, 8, 7, 23, 12, 9}

Identify which measure of central tendency is **most affected** when the outlier is removed.

Example

A golfer wants to know the best representation of his golf score.

The scores for 10 rounds of 18 holes of golf were collected and arranged in ascending order.

63, 63, 71, 73, 75, 79, 79, 83, 86, 88

Which measure of central tendency is **best** used in this situation?

Solution

Step 1

Assess the data.

Look for outliers and type of data.

There are no major outliers, so the data is not categorical.

Step 2

Choose the best measure of tendency.

The mean is a good option to use to describe the golf score since there are no outliers.

$$\frac{63 + 63 + 71 + 73 + 75 + 79 + 79 + 83 + 86 + 88}{10} = \frac{760}{10}$$
$$= 76$$

The golfer's average score is 76.

Mean is the best representation of his golf score using all the scores because there is no outlier.

Your Turn 2

Mr. Mellot wants to know the average test score of his class, so he records these percentages:
75%, 83%, 75%, 82%, 84%, 5%, 77%, 76%, 81%, 79%

Determine the average test score by using the **best** measure of central tendency in this situation.

Example

Evelyn works in a shoe store. She recorded the size of girls' shoes that were sold during the day.
6, 7, 6, 7, 7, 8, 7, 7, 9, 7, 7, 6, 6, 7

Which measure of central tendency is **best** used in this situation?

Solution
Step 1
Assess the data.

Look for outliers and type of data.
The data has no outliers. Shoes can be grouped into sizes, so the data is categorical.

Step 2
Choose the best measure of tendency.

Mode is the best measure of central tendency for categorical data.

Place the values in ascending order.
6, 6, 6, 6, 7, 7, 7, 7, 7, 7, 7, 7, 8, 9
Size 7 shoes were the most popular size of shoe sold.

Mode is the best representation of the shoe sizes sold because the data can be categorized.

Your Turn 3

Betty needs to know which milkshake flavour runs out most often in her store so she can order extra. The data set shows the flavours that she ran out of.

{cherry, banana, melon, cherry, grape, banana, cherry, orange, grape, cherry, root beer, banana, peach, cherry, banana}

Determine which flavours Betty runs out of the most by using the **best** measure of central tendency in this situation.

mode

PRACTICE EXERCISES

Use the following information to answer the next question.

> Shane wants to know his bowling average for the last seven games he played.
> His scores have been {158, 149, 175, 169, 187, 225, and 196}.

1. Determine Shane's bowling average by using the **best** measure of central tendency in this situation?

Use the following information to answer the next question.

> Mr. Smith needs to split his class in half by height on picture day. He records the
> height of each student in centimetres. {128, 158, 137, 149, 164, 133, 146, 137,
> 148, 155, 149, 154, 151, 134, 129, 132, 137, 142, 148, 137}

2. Which measure of central tendency is **best** used in this situation?

3. Micah's test scores are {65%, 62%, 55%, 64%, 78%, 57%, 60%}. Determine Micah's average test score using the **best** measure of central tendency in this situation?

4. Given the set {119, 118, 156, 122, 109, 139, 178, 118, 170, 177, 123, 217, 153}, identify which measure of central tendency is **most affected** when the outlier is removed.

5. Given the set {22, 8, 18, 2, 24, 26, 26, 24, 30}, identify which measure of central tendency is **most affected** when the outlier is removed.

Use the following information to answer the next question.

During his high school basketball season, the number of baskets George scored in each game of 15 games was 12, 10, 18, 12, 13, 20, 28, 19, 12, 9, 3, 18, 17, 9, and 13.

6. Which measure of central tendency would be **most affected** by the outliers in the given set of data?

A. Mean

B. Mode

C. Range

D. Median

7. Given the data set {19, 25, 4, 16, 30, 14, 20, 25, 35, 14, 24}, identify the outlier in the data set.

Use the following information to answer the next question.

Lisa conducted a survey of people in her candy store in order to determine the average age of her customers. The results of her survey are 12, 16, 13, 14, 10, 12, 83, 14, 14, and 12.

8. When Lisa realized that her data had one outlier and decided to delete it, this changed the average age of her customers by

A. 7.5 years

B. 7.0 years

C. 6.5 years

D. 16.0 years

9. A set of data is given as {24, 20, 14, 16, 35, 30, 4, 14, 25, 19, 25}. Which measures of central tendency are influenced by the outlier in the given data set?

A. Mean and mode

B. Range and mode

C. Median and mean

D. Mode and median

10. Given the set {2, 9, 8, 7, 8, 8}, identify which measure of central tendency is **most affected** when the outlier is removed.

REVIEW SUMMARY

- Measures of central tendency are measures of the centre of the data.
- The mean is the average of the data, and it is found by finding the sum of the data and dividing by the number of pieces of data.
- The mode is the most common number or numbers.
- The median is the middle number in a set of data organized in order from lowest in value to highest in value.
- The lower and upper extremes are the smallest and largest numbers, respectively.
- The range is the value that represents the difference between them.
- The lower and upper extremes of the data and the median are also used to separate the data into sections, each with 25% of the data.
- The outliers are values that are a great distance from the next closest value and can influence the measures of central tendency.

20

PRACTICE TEST

1. Calculate the mean of the data set {23, 21, 54, 26, 16}.

2. Find the median of the numbers 135, 114, 249, 187, and 196.

3. Find the median of the numbers 76, 45, 63, 91, 87, 73, 78, and 81.

4. Determine the mode of the data set {25, 64, 21, 52, 26, 21, 16, 26, 21, 36}.

5. Determine the mode of the data set {345, 323, 256, 252, 237, 342}.

Find the mean, median, and mode for each of the following sets of data.

6. 54, 58, 24, 60, 42, 31, 78, 45, 58

7. 15, 12, 8, 12, 8, 19, 21, 7

8. 83, 87, 85, 86, 84, 85, 87, 86, 85

9. Find the lower and upper extremes and the range for the set of data 63, 52, 62, 66, 24, 45, 34, and 23.

Use the following information to answer the next two questions.

> Mary conducted a survey of people in her clothing store one afternoon in order to determine the average age of her customers. The results of her survey are given.
> 34, 27, 45, 43, 36, 24, 34, 55, 46, 45, 29, 33, 44, 51, 34, 38

10. Calculate the mean, median, and mode of the data.

11. Determine the range and upper and lower extremes of the data.

24,5

Use the following information to answer the next question.

> The temperatures Mario recorded for the first nine days of June were
> 22°C, 8°C, 18°C, 2°C, 24°C, 26°C, 26°C, 24°C, 30°C.

12. How do the outliers influence the measures of central tendency and range?

Use the following information to answer the next question.

> 3.3, 6.7, 4.2, 3.7, 3.3, 3.6, 3.5, 4.1

13. Identify which measure of central tendency is most affected when the outlier is removed.

Use the following information to answer the next question.

Emilio used a table to show the number of pizzas sold last week.

Day	Number of Pizzas Sold
Monday	150
Tuesday	155
Wednesday	162
Thursday	27
Friday	170
Saturday	158
Sunday	165

Sales were down on Thursday because of a winter storm, but Emilio wants to know the effect it has on the mean number of pizzas sold that week.

14. What is the difference in the mean number of pizzas sold when Thursday's numbers are included compared to when they are not?

A. 20

B. 19

C. 18

D. 17

NOTES

S
N
A
P

Student Notes and Problems

ANSWERS AND SOLUTIONS

CASTLE ROCK
RESEARCH CORP

OPERATIONS WITH DECIMAL NUMBERS

Lesson 1—Using Front-End Estimation

YOUR TURN
ANSWERS AND SOLUTIONS

1. a) Step 1

Keep the first digit. Make all the other digits zero, and add the numbers.

$$372 \rightarrow 300$$
$$+315 \rightarrow +300$$

Step 2

Perform the operation indicated in the question. In this case, it is addition.

$$300$$
$$+\ 300$$
$$\overline{600}$$

The sum of $372+315$ is about 600.

b) In the estimation, the value of the numbers is decreased. As a result, the value of the estimate is slightly lower than the actual calculation. This can be verified by comparing the two sums.
$$372+315=687$$

2. a) Step 1

Keep the first digit. Make all the other digits zero.

$$5389.12 \rightarrow 5000$$
$$459.28 \rightarrow 400$$
$$9112.94 \rightarrow 9000$$
$$+\ 783.80 \rightarrow +\ 700$$

Step 2

Perform the operation indicated in the question.
In this case, it is addition.

$$5000$$
$$400$$
$$9000$$
$$+\ 700$$
$$\overline{15\ 100}$$

The sum of
$5\ 389.12+459.28+9\ 112.94+783.8$ is approximately 15 100.

b) In the estimation, the value of the numbers is decreased. As a result, the value of the estimate is slightly lower than the actual calculation. This can be verified by comparing the two sums.
$$5\ 389.12+459.28+9\ 112.94+783.8$$
$$=15\ 745.14$$

3. a) Step 1

Keep the first digit. Make all the other digits zero.

$$8\ 962.45 \rightarrow 8\ 000$$
$$-\ \ \ 545.17 \rightarrow -\ \ 500$$

Step 2

Perform the operation indicated in the question. In this case, it is subtraction.

$$8\ 000$$
$$-\ \ 500$$
$$\overline{7\ 500}$$

The difference of $8\ 962.45-545.17$ is approximately 7 500.

b) In the estimation, the value of the numbers is decreased. As a result, the value of the estimate is slightly lower than the actual calculation. This can be verified by comparing the two differences.
$$8\ 962.45-545.17=8\ 417.28$$

4. Step 1

Keep the first digit. Make all the other digits zero.

$$2\ 745.82 \rightarrow 2\ 000$$
$$\times\ 45.72 \qquad \times\ \ 40$$

Step 2

Perform the operation indicated in the question.
In this case, it is multiplication.

$$2\ 000$$
$$\times\ \ \ 40$$
$$\overline{80\ 000}$$

The product of $2\ 745.82\times45.72$ is approximately 80 000.

5. Step 1
Keep the first digit. Make all the other digits zero.
Drop the digits after the decimal.

$$32.43 \rightarrow 30\overline{)900}$$
$$\uparrow$$
$$972.981$$

Step 2
Perform the operation indicated in the question.
In this case, it is division.

$$\frac{30}{30\overline{)900}}$$

The quotient of $972.981 \div 32.43$ is about 30.

6. Step 1
Use front-end estimation.

$$
\begin{array}{rcl}
32 & \rightarrow & 30 \\
43 & \rightarrow & 40 \\
+22 & \rightarrow & +20
\end{array}
$$

Step 2
Perform the operation indicated in the problem.
In this case, it is addition.

$$
\begin{array}{r}
30 \\
40 \\
+\ 20 \\
\hline
90
\end{array}
$$

Since Janet committed to making more than 100 cookies, she should bake a few more to guarantee that there will be at least 100 cookies at the bake sale.

PRACTICE EXERCISES
ANSWERS AND SOLUTIONS

1. Step 1
Keep the first digit. Make all the other digits zero.

$$
\begin{array}{rcl}
43.781 & \rightarrow & 40 \\
+\ 28.3 & \rightarrow & +\ 20
\end{array}
$$

Step 2
Perform the operation indicated in the question.
In this case, it is addition.

$$
\begin{array}{r}
40 \\
+\ 20 \\
\hline
60
\end{array}
$$

The sum of $43.781 + 28.3$ is about 60.

3. Step 1
Keep the first digit. Make all the other digits zero.

$$
\begin{array}{rcl}
85.96 & \rightarrow & 80 \\
-\ 34.50 & \rightarrow & -\ 30
\end{array}
$$

Step 2
Perform the operation indicated in the question.
In this case, it is subtraction.

$$
\begin{array}{r}
80 \\
-\ 30 \\
\hline
50
\end{array}
$$

The difference of $85.96 - 34.5$ is about 50.

5. Step 1
Keep the first digit. Make all the other digits zero.

$$
\begin{array}{rcl}
64.8 & \rightarrow & 60 \\
\times\ 36.2 & \rightarrow & \times\ 30
\end{array}
$$

Step 2
Perform the operation indicated in the question.
In this case, it is multiplication.

$$
\begin{array}{r}
60 \\
\times\ 30 \\
\hline
1\ 800
\end{array}
$$

The product of 64.8×36.2 is about 1 800.
The actual answer will be greater than 1 800.

7. Step 1
Keep the first digit. Make all the other digits zero.

$$9.4 \rightarrow 9\overline{)90}$$
$$\uparrow$$
$$92.7$$

Step 2
Perform the operation indicated in the question.
In this case, it is division.

$$\frac{10}{9\overline{)90}}$$

The quotient of $92.7 \div 9.4$ about 10.

9. Step 1
Use front-end estimation.

$$
\begin{array}{rcl}
32 \text{ vases} & \rightarrow & 30 \\
317 \text{ roses} & \rightarrow & 300 \\
91 \text{ baby's breath} & \rightarrow & 90
\end{array}
$$

Step 2
Perform the operation indicated in the problem.
In this case, it is division.

Roses:

$$30\overline{)300} = 10$$

Baby's breath:

$$30\overline{)90} = 3$$

The party planner can place approximately 10 rose stems and 3 baby's-breath in each vase.

Lesson 2—Adding Decimals

YOUR TURN
ANSWERS AND SOLUTIONS

1. **Step 1**
   Identify the base ten blocks required.
   There is 1 one; you will need one cube.
   There are 3 tenths; you will need three flats.
   There are 2 hundredths; you will need two rods.

   Step 2
   Model the decimal number.

   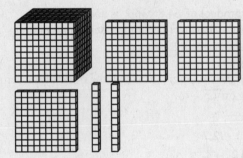

2. **Step 1**
   Model each addend.
   Model 1.285.

   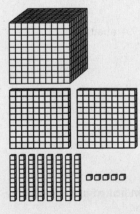

Model 2.834.

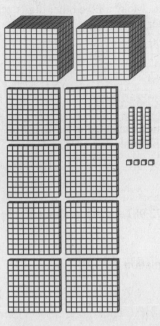

Step 2
Combine like blocks together, and regroup for the most efficient set in each place value.

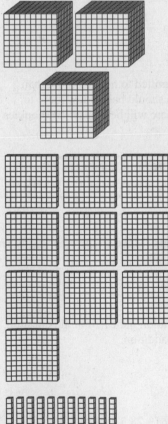

The final set becomes

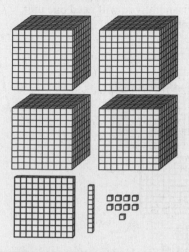

The sum of $1.285 + 2.834 = 4.119$.

3. **Step 1**

Determine the number of columns necessary, and construct the table.

The largest place value is tens, and the smallest place value is hundredths. Make a place value table that includes all these place values.

Tens	Ones	.	Tenths	Hundredths
		.		
		.		
		.		
		.		
		.		
		.		

Step 2

Enter the numbers into the table, making sure the decimals are lined up.

Tens	Ones	.	Tenths	Hundredths
	0	.	4	3
7	6	.	0	0
1	9	.	4	2
6	3	.	2	0
	9	.	5	2
		.		

Step 3

Beginning at the right, add the digits in each column.

Hundreds	Tens	Ones	.	Tenths	Hundredths
1	2 0	1 0	.	4	3
	7	6	.	0	0
	1	9	.	4	2
	6	3	.	2	0
	0	9	.	5	2
1	6	8	.	5	7

4. **Step 1**

Write the numbers one on top of the other, lining up the decimal points.

```
   41.47
    9.04
  385.82
+ 111.71
```

Step 2

Start at the far right, and add all the numbers in the column. Bring down the decimal point, and align it directly below the other decimal points.

```
 1 12 1
   41.47
    9.04

  385.82
+ 111.71
  548.04
```

5. a) **Step 1**

Use front-end estimation.

$$
\begin{array}{rcr}
14.99 & \rightarrow & 10 \\
+7.49 & \rightarrow & +7 \\
\hline
      &   & 17
\end{array}
$$

Penny will spend over $17.00 on the scarf and mittens.

Step 2
Calculate the exact cost.

$$\begin{array}{r} \overset{1\ 1\ \ 1}{14.99} \\ +\ 7.49 \\ \hline 22.48 \end{array}$$

The exact cost of the scarf and mittens is $22.48.

b) **Step 1**
Use front-end estimation.

$$\begin{array}{rcr} 14.99 & \rightarrow & 10 \\ +12.49 & \rightarrow & +10 \\ \hline & & 20 \end{array}$$

Penny will spend over $20.00 on the mittens and toque.

Step 2
Calculate the exact cost.

$$\begin{array}{r} \overset{1\ \ 1}{14.99} \\ +\ 12.49 \\ \hline 27.48 \end{array}$$

The exact cost of the mittens and toque is $27.48.

PRACTICE EXERCISES
ANSWERS AND SOLUTIONS

1. **Step 1**
Identify the base ten blocks required.
There are 2 tenths; you will need two flats.
There are 4 hundredths; you will need four rods.
There are 3 thousandths; you will need three units.

Step 2
Model the decimal number.

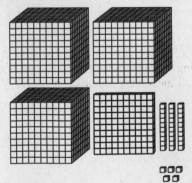

3. **Step 1**
Identify the base ten blocks required.
There are 2 ones; you will need two cubes.
There are 3 tenths; you will need three flats.

There are 2 hundredths; you will need two rods.
There is 1 thousandth; you will need one unit.

Step 2
Model the decimal number.

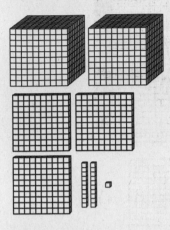

5. **Step 1**
Model each addend.

Model 1.362.

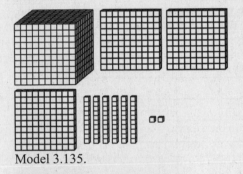

Model 3.135.

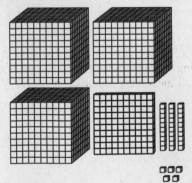

Step 2
Combine like blocks together, and regroup for the most efficient set in each place value.

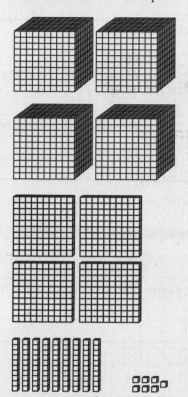

The sum of 1.362 + 3.135 is 4.497 .

7. **Step 1**
Write the numbers one on top of the other, lining up the decimal points.

```
  1.278
+ 2.510
```

Step 2
Start at the far right, and add all the numbers in the column. Bring down the decimal point, and align it directly below the other decimal points.

```
  1.278
+ 2.510
  3.788
```

9. **Step 1**
Determine the number of columns necessary, and construct the table.

The largest place value is hundreds, and the smallest place value is hundredths. Make a place value table that include all these place values.

Hundreds	Tens	Ones	.	Tenths	Hundredths
			.		
			.		
			.		
			.		
			.		

Step 2
Enter the numbers into the table, making sure the decimals are lined up.

Hundreds	Tens	Ones	.	Tenths	Hundredths
	4	2	.	3	6
		8	.	1	4
2	6	7	.	2	2
3	3	1	.	6	3
			.		

Step 3
Beginning at the right, add the digits in each column.

Hundreds	Tens	Ones	.	Tenths	Hundredths
¹0	¹4	¹2	.	¹3	6
0	0	8	.	1	4
2	6	7	.	2	2
3	3	1	.	6	3
6	4	9	.	3	5

11. Similarities:
When adding decimal numbers, you must line up the digits according to their place values.
You use the same procedures for adding decimal numbers as you do when adding whole numbers.

Differences:
When adding decimal numbers, instead of lining up the digits on the right, you line up the decimal points.

Lesson 3—Subtracting Decimals

YOUR TURN
ANSWERS AND SOLUTIONS

1. **Step 1**
   Model the minuend, and cross out the blocks representing the subtrahend.
   Model 2.34 and cross out 1.12.

   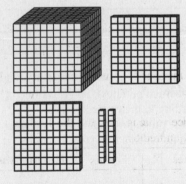

   Step 2
   Identify the quantity of the remaining base ten blocks.

   The value of the expression 2.34 –1.12 is 1.22.

2. **Step 1**
   Determine the number of columns necessary, and construct the table.

   The largest place value is tens, and the smallest place value is thousandths. Make a place value table that includes all five place values and a column for the decimal (six columns in all).

Tens	Ones	.	Tenths	Hundredths	Thousandths
		.			
		.			
		.			

   Step 2
   Enter the numbers into the table, making sure the decimals are lined up.

Tens	Ones	.	Tenths	Hundredths	Thousandths
1	9	.	6	2	3
1	5	.	4	2	
		.			

   Step 3
   Beginning at the right, subtract the digits in each column.

Tens	Ones	.	Tenths	Hundredths	Thousandths
1	9	.	6	2	3
1	5	.	4	2	0
0	4	.	2	0	3

3. **Step 1**
   Write the numbers one on top of the other, lining up the decimal points in a column.

   $$\begin{array}{r} 3\,185.82 \\ -\ 116.73 \\ \hline \end{array}$$

   Step 2
   Start at the far right, and subtract all the numbers in the column. Bring down the decimal point, and align it directly below the other decimal points.

   $$\begin{array}{r} 3\,185.\overset{7}{\cancel{8}}\overset{12}{\cancel{2}} \\ -116.7\,3 \\ \hline 3\,069.0\,9 \end{array}$$

   The difference for 3 185.82 – 116.73 is 3 069.09.

4. **Step 1**
   Estimate the differences in mass using front-end estimation.

   $$\begin{array}{rcr} 62.8 & \to & 60 \\ -\,46.5 & \to & -\,40 \\ \hline & & 20 \end{array}$$

   The difference is about 20 kg.

Step 2
Calculate the difference.

$$\overset{5}{\cancel{6}}\,\overset{12}{\cancel{2}}.8$$
$$-46.5$$
$$\overline{16.3}$$

The exact difference of the two masses is 16.3 kg.

PRACTICE EXERCISES
ANSWERS AND SOLUTIONS

1. **Step 1**
Model the minuend, and cross out the blocks representing the subtrahend.
Model 3.443 and cross out 1.21.

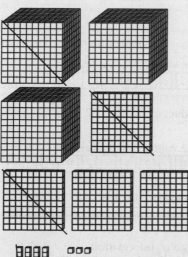

Step 2
Identify the quantity of the remaining base ten blocks.

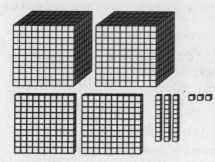

The value of the expression 3.443 – 1.21 is 2.233.

3. **Step 1**
Model the minuend, and cross out the blocks representing the subtrahend.
Model 1.748 and cross out 0.542.

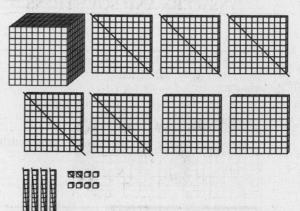

Step 2
Identify the quantity of the remaining base ten blocks.

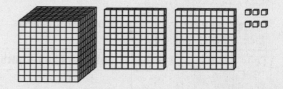

The value of the expression 1.748 – 0.542 is 1.206.

5.
$$34.\overset{9}{\cancel{0}}\,\overset{15}{\cancel{5}}$$
$$-12.39$$
$$\overline{21.66}$$

7. **Step 1**
Determine the number of columns necessary, and construct the table.

The largest place value is tens, and the smallest place value is hundredths.

Tens	Ones	.	Tenths	Hundredths
		.		
		.		
		.		

Step 2

Enter the numbers into the table, making sure the decimals are lined up.

Tens	Ones	.	Tenths	Hundredths
9	5	.	8	7
	6	.	2	5
		.		

Step 3

Beginning at the right, subtract the digits in each column.

Tens	Ones	.	Tenths	Hundredths
8 9̸	15 5̸	.	8	7
	6	.	2	5
8	9	.	6	2

9. Step 1

Determine the number of columns necessary, and construct the table.

The largest place value is tens, and the smallest place value is thousandths.

Tens	Ones	.	Tenths	Hundreds	Thousandths
		.			
		.			
		.			

Step 2

Enter the numbers into the table, making sure the decimals are lined up.

Tens	Ones	.	Tenths	Hundreds	Thousandths
8	5	.	2	6	1
5	2	.	1	4	
		.			

Step 3

Beginning at the right, subtract the digits in each column.

Tens	Ones	.	Tenths	Hundreds	Thousandths
8	5	.	2	6	1
5	2	.	1	4	0
3	3	.	1	2	1

YOUR TURN
ANSWERS AND SOLUTIONS

1.

$$4.23 \text{ (2 digits behind the decimal)}$$
$$\times\ 1.62 \text{ (2 digits behind the decimal)}$$

$$846$$
$$25\ 380$$
$$+\ 42\ 300$$
$$68\ 526 \xrightarrow[\text{to the left}]{\text{move decimal four places}} 6.8526$$

Check the reasonableness of the solution by estimation.

$$4.23 \rightarrow 4$$
$$\times 1.62 \quad \times 2$$
$$\overline{8}$$

2. a) Enter the values into a calculator.

$$\boxed{3}\boxed{2}\boxed{5}\boxed{.}\boxed{1}\boxed{8}\boxed{\times}\boxed{3}\boxed{2}\boxed{.}\boxed{1}\boxed{1}\boxed{=}$$

The product of 325.18×32.11 is $10\ 441.5298$

b) Enter the values into the calculator.

$$\boxed{7}\boxed{6}\boxed{0}\boxed{.}\boxed{3}\boxed{8}\boxed{\times}\boxed{2}\boxed{9}\boxed{.}\boxed{8}\boxed{=}$$

The product of 760.38×29.8 is $22\ 659.324$.

3. Step 1

Identify the given information.
The apples cost \$2.20/kg, and 4.25 kg of apples are being purchased.

Step 2

Decide on the strategy or operation to use.
Keyword: of
Multiplication is the operation to use.

Step 3

Apply the strategy or operation.

$$4.25 \text{ (2 decimal places)}$$
$$\times 2.2 \text{ (1 decimal place)}$$
$$850$$
$$+8500$$
$$9350 \xrightarrow{\text{move decimal 3 places to the left}} 9.350$$

It costs \$9.35 to buy 4.25 kg of apples.

Step 4

Check the solution.
$9.35 \div 4.25 = 2.2$
Therefore, 4.25 kg of apples cost \$9.35.

PRACTICE EXERCISES
ANSWERS AND SOLUTIONS

1.   12   (0 digits behind decimal)
   $\times 3.4$ (1 digit behind decimal)
      48
     360
   $\overline{408}$ ──move decimal 1 place to the left──→ 40.8

3.   125.2   (1 digit behind decimal)
   $\times 0.42$ (2 digits behind decimal)
     2504
   50 080
   $\overline{52\ 584}$ ──move decimal 3 places to the left──→ 52.584

5.   0.36   (2 digits behind decimal)
   $\times 0.81$ (2 digits behind decimal)
      36
    2880
   $\overline{2916}$ ──move decimal 4 places to the left──→ 0.2916

7. Enter the values into a calculator.
   [2][.][2][×][4][.][1][=]

   The product of 2.2×4.1 is 9.02.

9. **Step 1**
   Identify the given information.
   Cost of each camera: $138.50
   Number of cameras: 3

   Step 2
   Decide on the strategy or operation to use.
   Keyword: of
   Multiplication is the operation to use.

   Step 3
   Apply the strategy or operation.
   138.50   (2 decimal places)
   $\times\ 3$ (0 decimal place)
   $\overline{415.50}$

   Jill will need $415.50 to buy three cameras.

Lesson 5—Dividing Decimals

YOUR TURN
ANSWERS AND SOLUTIONS

1. **Step 1**
   Move the decimal over one place in the divisor and dividend to get a whole number divisor.
   $2.6)\overline{6.24} \rightarrow 26)\overline{62.4}$

   Step 2
   Divide using long division.

   ```
        24
   26) 62.4
      -52
      104
     -104
        0
   ```

   Step 3
   Place a decimal point directly above the decimal point in the dividend.

   ```
        2.4
   26) 62.4
      -52↓
      104
     -104
        0
   ```

   Therefore, $6.24 \div 2.6 = 2.4$.

2. Enter the expression into your calculator.
   [6][8][.][1][÷][3][.][2][=]

   The answer that appears on the screen is 21.281 25.

3. **Step 1**
   Identify the given information.
   There are 12 pencils in a box.
   Regular price: $9.99
   Sale price: $8.50

   Step 2
   Decide on the strategy or operation to use.
   Keyword: each

   Division is the operation to use.

   Step 3
   Apply the strategy or operation.
   $9.99 \div 12 = 0.8325$
   $8.5 \div 12 = 0.708\overline{3}$

Because both answers are money, the numbers are rounded to the hundredths place.
Regular price: $0.83/pencil
Sale price: $0.71/pencil

Step 4
Check the answer.
Doing the inverse operation is a good way to check.
$12 \times 0.83 = 9.96$
$12 \times 0.71 = 8.52$

Both answers are close but not exactly the price for the box of pencils because the individual prices were rounded.

The regular price for each pencil is $0.83. The sale price for each pencil is $0.71.

PRACTICE EXERCISES
ANSWERS AND SOLUTIONS

1.

$$\begin{array}{r} 30 \\ 42\overline{)126} \\ -126 \\ \hline 0 \end{array}$$

3.

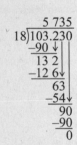

$$\begin{array}{r} 5\ 735 \\ 18\overline{)103.230} \\ -90 \downarrow \\ \hline 13\ 2 \\ -12\ 6\downarrow \\ \hline 63 \\ -54\downarrow \\ \hline 90 \\ -90 \\ \hline 0 \end{array}$$

5.

$$\begin{array}{r} 12.5 \\ 5\overline{)62.5} \\ -5\downarrow \\ \hline 12 \\ -10\downarrow \\ \hline 2\ 5 \\ -2\ 5 \\ \hline 0 \end{array}$$

7. Enter the expression into your calculator.
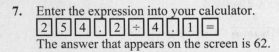
The answer that appears on the screen is 62.

---

9. **Step 1**
Use front-end estimation.
$33.99 \rightarrow 30$
$2.5 \rightarrow 2$
$30 \div 2 = 15$

Step 2
Enter the expression into your calculator.
$\boxed{3}\boxed{3}\boxed{.}\boxed{9}\boxed{9}\boxed{\div}\boxed{2}\boxed{.}\boxed{5}\boxed{=}$
The answer that appears on the screen is 13.596.

Lesson 6—Order of Operations with Decimal Numbers

YOUR TURN
ANSWERS AND SOLUTIONS

1. **Step 1**
Complete the operations inside the brackets.
$86.8 \div (5.6 \times 6.2) - 1.7$
$= 86.8 \div (34.72) - 1.7$

Step 2
Multiply and divide in order from left to right.
$\underline{86.8 \div 34.72} - 1.7$
$= 2.5 - 1.7$

Step 3
Add and subtract in order from left to right.
$2.5 - 1.7$
$= 0.8$

2. a) **Step 1**
Read the problem from the beginning, and write down each number and operation as it appears in the question.
2×3.99
5×15.99
3×52.99
Step 2
Write the expression.
$2 \times 3.99 + 5 \times 15.99 + 3 \times 52.99$

b) **Step 1**
Follow the order of operations.
Since there are no brackets, perform multiplication starting from the left and working right.
$\underline{2 \times 3.99} + 5 \times 15.99 + 3 \times 52.99$
$= 7.98 + \underline{5 \times 15.99} + 3 \times 52.99$
$= 7.98 + 79.95 + \underline{3 \times 52.99}$
$= 7.98 + 79.95 + 158.97$

Step 2
Add and subtract in order from left to right.
$7.98 + 79.95 + 158.97$
$= 87.93 + 158.97$
$= 246.90$

Nicholas paid $246.90 for his clothes.

PRACTICE EXERCISES
ANSWERS AND SOLUTIONS

1. **Step 1**
    Complete the operations in the brackets.
    $12.35 \div 1.3 \times 2.6 + (\underline{6.8 - 1.2})$
    $= 12.35 \div 1.3 \times 2.6 + 5.6$

    Step 2
    Multiply or divide in the order from left to right.
    $\underline{12.35 \div 1.3} \times 2.6 + 5.6$
    $= \underline{9.5 \times 2.6} + 5.6$
    $= 24.7 + 5.6$

    Step 3
    Complete the addition.
    $24.7 + 5.6$
    $= 30.3$

3. **Step 1**
    Complete the operations in the brackets.
    $4.5 - 7.6 \div 2 + 5.6 \times (\underline{12.2 - 2.2})$
    $= 4.5 - 7.6 \div 2 + 5.6 \times 10$

    Step 2
    Multiply or divide from left to right.
    $4.5 - \underline{7.6 \div 2} + 5.6 \times 10$
    $= 4.5 - 3.8 + \underline{5.6 \times 10}$
    $= 4.5 - 3.8 + 56$

    Step 3
    Add or subtract from left to right.
    $\underline{4.5 - 3.8} + 56$
    $= \underline{0.7 + 56}$
    $= 56.7$

5. **Step 1**
    Complete the operations inside the brackets.
    $(\underline{550 - 220}) \div 3$
    $= 330 \div 3$

Step 2
Multiply or divide from left to right.
$\underline{330 \div 3}$
$= 110$

Step 3
Check the answer.
It makes sense to first figure out the profit and then divide that by 3. Review all the calculations by working backward to make sure there is no error.
$3 \times 110 = 330$
$330 + 220 = 550$

Each charity receives $110.

7. **Step 1**
    Complete the operations in the brackets.
    $(\underline{1\,800 - 645}) \div 231$
    $= 1\,155 \div 231$

    Step 2
    Divide.
    $1\,155 \div 231$
    $= 5$

    Step 3
    Check the answer.
    It makes sense to first figure out how much money she needs to save and then divide that by 213. Review all the calculations by working backward to make sure there is no error.
    $5 \times 231 = 1\,155$
    $1\,155 + 645 = 1\,800$

    Anna has to work five more weeks before she will have enough money saved up.

9. $64.8 \div 8 - 2.5$
    $= 8.1 - 2.5$
    $= 5.6$

Practice Test

ANSWERS AND SOLUTIONS

1. $\overset{1\ \ 1\ 1}{6.428}$
    $+12.596$
    $\overline{19.024}$

3.

$$\overset{2}{}215.00$$
$$6.02$$
$$49.47$$
$$\underline{+109.5}$$
$$379.99$$

5.

$$17.04$$
$$\underline{\times6.1}$$
$$1704$$
$$\underline{102240}$$
$$103944 \xrightarrow{\text{move decimal 3 places to the left}} 103.944$$

7. $48.96 \div 5.1 \rightarrow 40 \div 5 = 8$

9. $5.7 + \underline{4.9 \times 2.1}$
$= \underline{5.7 + 10.29}$
$= 15.99$

11.

Tens	Ones	.	Tenths	Hundreds	Thousandths
3	9	.	4	2	3
2	1	.	6	3	0
1	7	.	7	9	3

13. Enter the expression into your calculator.

5 8 3 2 ÷ 1 0 . 8 =

The answer that appears on the screen is 540.

OPERATIONS WITH INTEGERS

Lesson 1—Introduction to Integers

YOUR TURN
ANSWERS AND SOLUTIONS

1. a)

−3 is to the right of −5.
−3 is greater than −5, or −5 is less than −3.

−3 > −5

b)

−3 is to the left of +5.
−3 is less than +5, or +5 is greater than −3.

−3 < +5

2. a) Unshaded tiles represent negative integers.

Draw six unshaded tiles.

☐☐☐☐☐☐

b) Shaded tiles represent positive integers.

Draw five shaded tiles.

■■■■■

3.

The opposite of −8 is +8 because both numbers are eight steps away from 0.

4.

5.

PRACTICE EXERCISES
ANSWERS AND SOLUTIONS

1. The positive and negative signs are integer signs indicating where the number is on the number line. The plus and minus signs are operation signs indicating adding and subtracting.

3. The arrow moves 10 steps to the right. Arrows in the right direction are positive, so the integer is +10.

5. Unshaded tiles are negative. There are three tiles, so the integer is –3.

7.

   –3 is to the right of –6.
   –3 is greater than –6, or –6 is less than –3.

   $-3 > -6$ or $-6 < -3$

9. The opposite integer of –18 is +18.

11. The zero principle is based on the sum of opposites. By walking to the back of the classroom, Mrs. Dean is modeling –1. Doing the opposite, or walking to the front of the classroom, she is modeling +1. Her position did not change. The sum of her actions is equal to 0. This models the zero principle.

Lesson 2—Adding Integers

YOUR TURN
ANSWERS AND SOLUTIONS

1. Twelve shaded tiles represent +12. Six unshaded tiles represent –6.

   There are six zero pairs. Six positive tiles remain.
   $(+12)+(-6)=(+6)$

2. Position your pencil on +3. Move six steps in the negative direction.

   $(+3)+(-6)=-3$

3. a) $(+14)+(+36)=+50$

   b) $(-12)+(-57)=(-69)$

4. a) The numerical value of +12 is 12.
      The numerical value of –30 is 30.
      Subtract 12 from 30.
      $30-12=18$

      Since 30 is the larger numerical value, place a negative integer sign in front of the answer
      $(+12)+(-30)=(-18)$

   b) The numerical value of +61 is 61.
      The numerical value of –21 is 21.
      Subtract 21 from 61.
      $61-21=40$

      Since 61 is the larger numerical value, place a positive integer sign in front of the answer.
      $(+61)+(-21)=40$

PRACTICE EXERCISES
ANSWERS AND SOLUTIONS

1. $(+31)+(-19)=(+12)$

3. $(+13)+(+40)=53$

5.

   The answer is +5.

7. Position your pencil on +9 Move eleven steps in the negative direction.

   $(+9)+(-11)=-2$

9. The statement does not match the diagram. There are 9 unshaded tiles that represent –9. There are 5 shaded tiles that represent +5. This is the opposite of the addition statement $(+9)+(-5)$. In order to correct the diagram, there must be 9 shaded tiles and 5 unshaded tiles.

Lesson 3—Subtracting Integers

YOUR TURN
ANSWERS AND SOLUTIONS

1. **Step 1**
    Draw integer tiles to represent the first term.
    Draw seven unshaded tiles to represent –7.

    ☐☐☐☐☐☐☐

    Step 2
    Subtract the number of tiles equal to the second term.

    Take away four unshaded tiles to represent $-(-4)$.

    ☐☐☐

    There are three unshaded tiles left over.
    The answer is –3.

2. **Step 1**
    Draw integer tiles to represent the first term.
    Draw one shaded tile to represent +1.

    ■

    Step 2
    Add zero pairs until there are enough tiles to represent the second term.
    Add five zero pairs.

    ■■■■■
    ☐☐☐☐☐

    Step 3
    Subtract the tiles that represent the second term.
    The second term is +6. Take away six shaded tiles.

    ☐☐☐☐☐

    There are five negative tiles left over. The answer is –5.

    $$(+1)-(+6)=(-5)$$

3. **Step 1**
    Place a pencil on the second term +9.

    Step 2
    Move the pencil to the point representing the

first term.

Step 3
Determine the length and direction of the movement.

The arrow moves 11 spaces to the left. This gives an answer of (–11).
$$(-2)-(+9)=(-11)$$

4. a) $(+8)-(-4) \rightarrow (+8)+(+4)$

    b) $(+6)-(+4) \rightarrow (+6)+(-4)$

    c) $(-5)-(-3) \rightarrow (-5)+(+3)$

    d) $(-7)-(+3) \rightarrow (-7)+(-3)$

PRACTICE EXERCISES
ANSWERS AND SOLUTIONS

1. **Step 1**
    Draw one shaded tile to represent +1.

    ■

    Step 2
    Add zero pairs until there are enough tiles to represent the second term Add four zero pairs..

    ■■■■■
    ☐☐☐☐

    Step 3
    Subtract the tiles that represent the second term.
    The second term is –4. Take away four unshaded tiles.

    ■■■■■

    There are five positive tiles left over. The answer is +5.
    $$(+1)-(-4)=(+5)$$

3. **Step 1**
    Place a pencil on the second term (+2).

Step 2
Move the pencil to the point representing the first term.

The arrow moves 7 spaces to the left. This gives an answer of (-7).

$$(-5)-(+2)=(-7)$$

5. $(-45)-(+3) \rightarrow (-45)+(-3)$

7. $(-3)-(-5) \rightarrow (-3)+(+5)$

9. $(+35)-(+27)$
   $(-35)+(-27)=+8$
   $(+35)+(-27)=+8$

Lesson 4—Problem Solving with Integers

YOUR TURN
ANSWERS AND SOLUTIONS

1. Write the opposite of the addition expression.
   $(\$20)-(+\$11)$

2. **Step 1**
   Identify integer and operation keywords.
   The first integer is given: $-218°C$
   The second integer is given: $+35°C$
   Keyword: *higher* indicates addition

   Step 2
   Write an expression representing the problem.
   The expression is $(-218)+(+35)$.

   Step 3
   Solve.
   $(-218)+(+35)=(-183)$

   The boiling point of oxygen is $-183°C$.

3. $(+\$250)-(+\$120)=\$250-\$120$
   $\qquad\qquad\qquad\qquad = \$130$

   The stock was worth $130 less on Friday.

PRACTICE EXERCISES
ANSWERS AND SOLUTIONS

1. The keyword *over* indicates positive: +4

3. The keyword *win* indicates positive: +10

5. The keyword *below* indicates negative: −242
   The keyword *ascends* indicates positive: +75

   The expression is $(-242)+(+75)$.

   Calculate: $(-242)+(+75)=(-167)$

   The final position of the submarine is 167 m below sea level.

7. The keyword *above* indicates positive: +17.
   The keyword *below* indicates negative: −5.

   Calculate the distance by finding the difference in the floors.
   $(-5)-(+17)$

   Calculate: $(-5)-(+17)=(-22)$

   Jimmy rides 22 floors down to get to his car.

9. **Strategy 1**
   Add up all the negative transactions, and add them to the leftover money.
   $(-20)+(-9)+(-10)=(-39)$

   Jinny spent $39.00.

   Now the equation is $(\underline{\quad})+(-39)=(+30)$
   Add 39 to +30.
   $(+30)+(+39)=(+69)$

   Jinny had $69 to begin with.

   Strategy 2
   Work backward.

   Start with $30.00. Every time Jinny spends money, add a positive integer.
   $(+30)+(+10)+(+9)+(+20)=(+69)$

Practice Test

ANSWERS AND SOLUTIONS

1. **a)** (-3) **c)** plus

    b) $(+3)$ **d)** minus

    c) $(+3)+(3)$ **b)** positive

    d) $(-3)-(-3)$ **a)** negative

3.

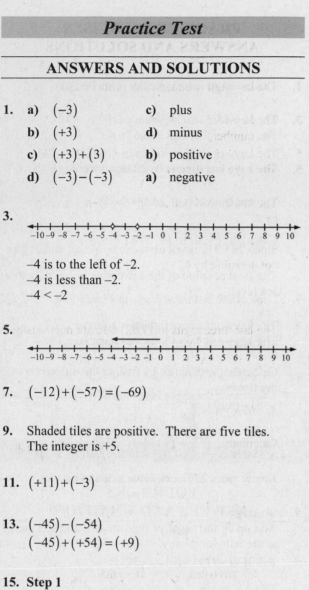

   −4 is to the left of −2.
   −4 is less than −2.
   $-4 < -2$

5.

7. $(-12)+(-57)=(-69)$

9. Shaded tiles are positive. There are five tiles.
    The integer is +5.

11. $(+11)+(-3)$

13. $(-45)-(-54)$
     $(-45)+(+54)=(+9)$

15. **Step 1**
     Identify what the problem is asking.

     The problem is asking you to find the difference in
     the stock.

     Step 2
     Identify the given information.

     The stock is worth $320 on Monday.
     The stock is worth $185 on Friday.

     Step 3
     Identify the strategy or operation to use.

     Subtraction

     Step 4
     Apply the strategy or operation.
     $(+320)-(+185)=(+135)$

Step 5
Check the answer.

Use the inverse operation to check the answer.
$(+135)+(+185)=(+320)$

The stock was worth $135 less on Friday.

WORKING WITH FRACTIONS, DECIMALS, AND PERCENTAGES

Lesson 1—Divisibility Rules

YOUR TURN
ANSWERS AND SOLUTIONS

1. a) Only 2 is a factor of numbers ending with the digit 2, 4, 6, or 8.

   b) Only 5 is a factor numbers ending with the digit 5.

   c) 2, 5, and 10 are factors of numbers ending with the digit 0.

2. Add the digits of the number.
   $$4+7+8+3+7+4+2+9+7=51$$
   $$5+1=6$$
   6 is divisible by 3 but not 9.

   478 374 297 is divisible by 3 but not 9.

3. Because 2 and 3 are factors of 6, the number must also have 2 and 3 as factors.

4. a) Because 4 is a factor of 8, any number that is divisible by 8 is divisible by 4. The quotient will be twice as large from dividing by 4 because 4 is half of 8.
   $$256 \div 8 = 32$$
   $$256 \div 4 = 64$$

   b) Because 2 is a factor of 4 and 8, the last digit must be even. If the last digit in any of the numbers is odd, you can assume the number is not divisible by 4 or 8.

5. a) The last two digits are 60. Since 60 is a multiple of 4, she could evenly divide the dirt up in 4 L pots. $60 \div 4 = 15$

   b) Since the last digit is a 0, which means the number can be divided by 5, she could evenly divide the dirt up in 5 L pots.

PRACTICE EXERCISES
ANSWERS AND SOLUTIONS

1. The last digit is odd, so 239 is not divisible by 2.

3. $72 \div 4 = 18$
   The number 72 is divisible by 4.

5. Since the last digit is 0, 3 330 is divisible by 5.

7. The last digit is odd, so 283 945 is not divisible by 2.

   Since 283 945 is not divisible by both 2 and 3, it is not divisible by 6.

9. Look at the last three digits in 17 921 930.

   The last three digits in 17 921 930 are not divisible by 8, so 17 921 930 is not divisible by 8.

11. $1 + 8 + 7 + 2 = 18$
    The sum of the digits is divisible by 9, so 1 872 is divisible by 9.

Lesson 2—Using Divisibility Rules

YOUR TURN
ANSWERS AND SOLUTIONS

1.

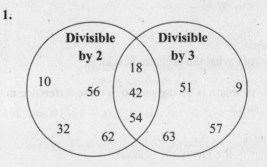

2. Determine if each number is divisible by 4 and 6, and place that number in the appropriate cell in the table.

   $10 \rightarrow$ is not divisible by 4, since $10 \div 4 = 2.5$.
   It is not divisible by 6, since $10 \div 6 = 1.\overline{6}$.

   $12 \rightarrow$ is divisible by 4, since $12 \div 4 = 3$.
   It is divisible by 6, since $12 \div 6 = 2$.

   $18 \rightarrow$ is not divisible by 4, since $18 \div 4 = 4.5$.

It is divisible by 6, since $18 \div 6 = 3$.

$20 \rightarrow$ is divisible by 4, since $20 \div 4 = 5$.
It is not divisible by 6, since $20 \div 6 = 3.\overline{3}$.

$30 \rightarrow$ is not divisible by 4, since $30 \div 4 = 7.5$.
It is divisible by 6, since $30 \div 6 = 5$.

$36 \rightarrow$ is divisible by 4, since $36 \div 4 = 9$.
It is divisible by 6, since $36 \div 6 = 6$.

Complete the Carroll diagram.

	Divisible by 4	Not Divisible by 4
Divisible by 6	12 36	18 30
Not divisible by 6	20	10

3. 1 and 36 are factors.

$2 \rightarrow$ the number is even, so 36 is divisible by 2.

$3 \rightarrow$ the sum of the digits is a multiple of 3:
$3 + 6 = 9$

$4 \rightarrow$ 36 is divisible by 4: $36 \div 4 = 9$.

$5 \rightarrow$ the number does not end in a 0 or 5, so 36 is not divisible by 5.

$6 \rightarrow$ the number is divisible by 2 and 3, so it is divisible by 6.

$8 \rightarrow$ 36 is not divisible by 8.

$9 \rightarrow$ the sum of the digits is a multiple of 9 $(3 + 6 = 9)$, so 36 is divisible by 9.

The factors of 36 are 1, 2, 3, 4, 6, 9, 12, 18, and 36.

4. Use divisibility rules to determine the factors of each number.
Factors of 28 are 1, 2, 4, 7, 14, and 28.
Factors of 32 are 1, 2, 4, 8, 16, and 32.

Draw a Carroll or Venn diagram, and place the factors into the correct circle or cell.

	Factors of 28	Not Factors of 28
Factors of 32	1, 2, 4	8, 16, 32
Not Factors of 32	7, 14, 28	

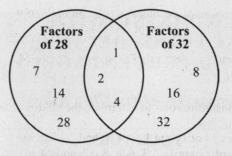

The common factors of 28 and 32 are 1, 2, and 4.
The greatest common factor is 4.

5. **Step 1**
List the factors of both numbers.
Factors of 32: 1, 2, 4, 8, 16, 32
Factors of 48: 1, 2, 3, 4, 6, 8, 12, 16, 24, 48

Step 2
Determine the GCF that both numbers share.
The GCF is 16.

Step 3
Divide both terms by the GCF.

$$\frac{32 \div 16}{48 \div 16} = \frac{2}{3}$$

In lowest terms, $\frac{32}{48}$ is $\frac{2}{3}$.

PRACTICE EXERCISES
ANSWERS AND SOLUTIONS

1. 1 and 48 are factors.

$2 \rightarrow$ the number is even, so 48 is divisible by 2.

$3 \rightarrow$ the sum of the digits is a multiple of 3 $(4 + 8 = 12)$, so the number is divisible by 3.

$4 \rightarrow$ the number is even, and 48 is divisible by 4.
$48 \div 4 = 12$

$5 \rightarrow$ the number does not end in a 0 or 5, so 48 is not divisible by 5.

$6 \rightarrow$ the number is divisible by 2 and 3, so it is divisible by 6.

$8 \rightarrow$ 48 is divisible by 8: $48 \div 8 = 6$.

9 → the sum of the digits is not a multiple of 9 (4 + 8 = 12), so 48 is not divisible by 9.

The factors of 48 are 1, 2, 3, 4, 6, 8, 12, 16, 24, and 48.

3. Use divisibility rules to determine the factors of each number.
The factors of 16 are 1, 2, 4, 8, and 16, and the factors of 24 are 1, 2, 3, 4, 6, 8, 12, and 24.

The greatest common factor is 8.

5. **Step 1**
List the factors of both numbers.
Factors of 18: 1, 2, 3, **6**, 9, 18
Factors of 30: 1, 2, 3, 5, **6**, 10, 15, 30

Step 2
Determine the GCF that both numbers share.
The GCF is 6.

Step 3
Divide both terms by the GCF.
$$\frac{18 \div 6}{30 \div 6} = \frac{3}{5}$$

The lowest term is $\frac{3}{5}$.

7. **Step 1**
List the factors of both numbers.
Factors of 28: 1, 2, **4**, 7, 14, 28
Factors of 36: 1, 2, 3, **4**, 6, 9, 12, 18, 36

Step 2
Determine the GCF that both numbers share.
The GCF is 4.

Step 3
Divide both terms by the GCF.
$$\frac{28 \div 4}{36 \div 4} = \frac{7}{9}$$

The lowest term is $\frac{7}{9}$.

9. **Step 1**
List the factors of 24 and 28.
Factors of 24: 1, 2, 3, 4, 6, 8, 12, 24
Factors of 28: 1, 2, 4, 7, 14, 28

Step 2
Place the numbers in a Venn diagram.

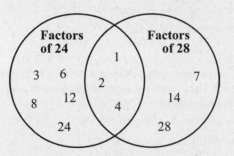

Step 3
List the common factors of 24 and 28.
The common factors of 24 and 28 are 1, 2, and 4.

Step 4
Determine the GCF.
The greatest common factor is 4.

Lesson 3—Converting Fractions into Decimals

YOUR TURN
ANSWERS AND SOLUTIONS

1. a) $\boxed{2}\boxed{3}\boxed{\div}\boxed{2}\boxed{5}\boxed{=}$
0.92

b) $\boxed{1}\boxed{8}\boxed{\div}\boxed{2}\boxed{7}\boxed{=}$
$0.\overline{6}$

2. a) Determine whether 3 is a factor of 45.
$4 + 5 = 9$

Because 3 is a factor of 45, $\frac{22}{45}$ is equivalent to a repeating decimal.

$\frac{22}{45} = 22 \div 45$
$= 0.4\overline{8}$

b) Determine whether 3 is a factor of 20.
$2 + 0 = 2$

Because 3 is not a factor of 20, $\frac{17}{20}$ is equivalent to a terminating decimal.

$\frac{17}{20} = 17 \div 20$
$= 0.85$

3. a) Convert the first few fractions into their decimal equivalents.

$$\frac{1}{9} = 1 \div 9 \qquad \frac{2}{9} = 2 \div 9 \qquad \frac{3}{9} = 3 \div 9$$
$$= 0.\overline{1} \qquad\qquad = 0.\overline{2} \qquad\qquad = 0.\overline{3}$$

The pattern is that as the numerator increases by 1, the repeating decimal increases by one tenth repeating.

b) Multiply the numerator by $0.\overline{1}$.

$$8 \times 0.\overline{1} = 0.\overline{8}$$

The decimal equivalent of $\frac{8}{9}$ will be $0.\overline{8}$.

c) Convert the first few fractions into their decimal equivalents.

$$\frac{1}{9} = 1 \div 9 \qquad \frac{1}{99} = 1 \div 99 \qquad \frac{1}{999} = 1 \div 999$$
$$= 0.\overline{1} \qquad\quad = 0.\overline{01} \qquad\quad = 0.\overline{001}$$

The pattern is that when the denominator is multiplied by a tenth, the equivalent repeating decimal is made smaller by a tenth.

d) The smallest place value in the denominator is hundred thousandths. Multiply $\overline{1}$ by the place value.

$$1 \div 99\ 999 = 0.\overline{000\ 01}.$$

PRACTICE EXERCISES
ANSWERS AND SOLUTIONS

1. $\boxed{3}\,\boxed{6}\,\boxed{\div}\,\boxed{4}\,\boxed{0}\,\boxed{=}$
0.9

3. $\boxed{1}\,\boxed{8}\,\boxed{\div}\,\boxed{3}\,\boxed{3}\,\boxed{=}$
$0.\overline{54}$

5. $\frac{12}{50} = 0.24$

7. $\frac{13}{5} = 2.6$

9. $1\frac{3}{8} = 1.375$

Lesson 4—Converting Decimals into Fractions

YOUR TURN
ANSWERS AND SOLUTIONS

1. a) Step 1
Determine the denominator, using the place value of the last digit.
Since 1 is in the thousandths place of $0.76\underline{1}$, the denominator is 1 000.

Step 2
Determine the numerator, by removing the decimal point.
Remove the decimal point. The numerator is 761. The resulting fraction is $\frac{761}{1\ 000}$.

Step 3
Reduce the fraction to lowest terms.
There is no number that will divide evenly into both numbers, so the fraction is in lowest terms.

Expressed as a fraction in lowest terms, 0.761 is $\frac{761}{1\ 000}$.

b) Step 1
Determine the denominator, using the place value of the last digit.
Since 8 is in the hundredths place of $0.9\underline{8}$, the denominator is 100.

Step 2
Determine the numerator, by removing the decimal point.
Remove the decimal point. The numerator is 98. The resulting fraction is $\frac{98}{100}$.

Step 3
Reduce the fraction to lowest terms.
Use divisibility rules to determine the GCF.

$$\frac{98 \div 2}{100 \div 2} = \frac{49}{50}$$

Expressed as a fraction in lowest terms, 0.98 is $\frac{49}{50}$.

c) The digits represent the value of the numerator. The smallest place value represents the value of the denominator.

2. **Step 1**
Determine the denominator using the number of repeating digits.
One digit repeats, so the denominator is 9.

Step 2
Determine the numerator by removing the decimal point and the bar notation. The numerator becomes 3.

Step 3
Reduce the fraction to lowest terms by dividing the numerator and denominator by the GCF.

$$\frac{3 \div 3}{9 \div 3} = \frac{1}{3}$$

The resulting fraction is $\frac{1}{3}$.

3. **Step 1**
Determine the denominator using the number of repeating digits. Two digits repeat, so the denominator is 99.

Step2
Determine the numerator by removing the decimal point and the bar. The numerator becomes 24.

Step 3
Reduce the fraction to lowest terms by dividing the numerator and denominator by the GCF.

$$\frac{24 \div 3}{99 \div 3} = \frac{8}{33}$$

The resulting fraction is $\frac{8}{33}$.

4. **Step 1**
Determine the denominator using the number of repeating digits. Three digits repeat, so the denominator is 999.

Step 2
Determine the numerator by removing the decimal point and bar. The number becomes 321.

Step 3
Reduce the fraction to lowest terms by dividing the numerator and denominator by the GCF.

$$\frac{321 \div 3}{999 \div 3} = \frac{107}{333}$$

1. **Step 1**
Determine the denominator, using the place value of the last digit.

Since 7 is in the thousandths place of 0.437, the denominator is 1 000.

Step 2
Determine the numerator, by removing the decimal point.
Remove the decimal point. The numerator is 437.

The resulting fraction is $\frac{437}{1\,000}$.

Step 3
Reduce the fraction to lowest terms.
There is no number that will divide evenly into both numbers. The fraction is in lowest terms.
Expressed as a fraction in lowest terms, 0.437 is $\frac{437}{1\,000}$.

3. The decimal number 3.4 has a definite end point, therefore it is a terminating decimal.

5. The decimal number $0.\overline{69}$ has a bar on the digits 6 and 9 which indicate that those two numbers continue on indefinitely, therefore it is a repeating decimal.

7. **Step 1**
Determine the denominator, using the place value of the last digit.
Since 5 is in the thousandths place of 0.275, the denominator is 1000.

Step 2
Determine the numerator, by removing the decimal point.

Remove the decimal point. The numerator is 275.

The resulting fraction is $\frac{275}{1\,000}$.

Step 3
Reduce the fraction to lowest terms.
Use divisibility rules to determine the GCF.

Both numbers end in a 5 or 0 and are divisible by 5, so 5 is a factor of 275 and 1 000.

$$\frac{275 \div 5}{1000 \div 5} = \frac{55 \div 5}{200 \div 5}$$
$$= \frac{11}{40}$$

Expressed as a fraction in lowest terms,

0.275 is $\frac{11}{40}$.

9. $1.4 = 1\frac{4}{10}$
$= 1\frac{2}{5}$

Lesson 5—Equivalent Fractions

YOUR TURN
ANSWERS AND SOLUTIONS

1. **Step 1**
Use divisibility rules to find factors of both numbers.
Factors of 12: 1, 2, 3, 4, 6, 12
Factors of 16: 1, 2, 4, 8, 16

Step 2
Divide both numbers by a factor to create an equivalent fraction.
$$\frac{12 \div 2}{16 \div 2} = \frac{6}{8} \qquad \frac{12 \div 4}{16 \div 4} = \frac{3}{4}$$

The fractions $\frac{3}{4}$ and $\frac{6}{8}$ are equivalent to $\frac{12}{16}$.

2. Answers may vary. Choose two factors. Multiply the numerator and denominator by the factors.
$$\frac{1 \times 2}{3 \times 2} = \frac{2}{6} \qquad \frac{1 \times 3}{3 \times 3} = \frac{3}{9}$$

3. **Step 1**
List the multiples of both denominators until a common multiple appears.
Multiples of 6: → 6, 12, 18, <u>24</u>
Multiples of 8: → 8, 16, <u>24</u>
Step 2
Multiply the numerator and denominator by a factor that results in the denominator equaling 24.
$$\frac{5 \times 4}{6 \times 4} = \frac{20}{24} \qquad \frac{7 \times 3}{8 \times 3} = \frac{21}{24}$$

Step 3
Compare the numerators.
$$\frac{20}{24} < \frac{21}{24}$$
Since 20 is smaller than 21, $\frac{5}{6} < \frac{7}{8}$.

4. **Step 1**
Find the LCD.
15 is a multiple of 5.

Step 2
Multiply the numerator and denominator of $\frac{3}{5}$ by 3 to create an equivalent fraction with a denominator of 15.
$$\frac{3 \times 3}{5 \times 3} = \frac{9}{15}$$

Step 3
Compare the numerators.
$$\frac{7}{15} < \frac{9}{15}$$
Since 9 is larger than 7, $\frac{7}{15} < \frac{3}{5}$.

5. The whole numbers are different. Since 5 is greater than 4, $5\frac{7}{8} > 4\frac{8}{9}$.

6. **Step 1**
List the multiples of both denominators until a common multiple appears.
Multiples of 3: 3, 6, 9, 12, 15, 18, <u>21</u>
Multiples of 7: 7, 14, <u>21</u>
Step 2
Make equivalent fractions with a denominator of 21.
$$\frac{2 \times 7}{3 \times 7} = \frac{14}{21} \qquad \frac{4 \times 3}{7 \times 3} = \frac{12}{21}$$

Step 3
Compare the numerators.
$$\frac{14}{21} > \frac{12}{21}$$
Since 14 is larger than 12, $2\frac{2}{3} > 2\frac{4}{7}$.

7. **Step 1**
Determine what the problem is asking.
Which label has the least amount of vitamin C?

Step 2
Determine the given information.

label A: $\dfrac{2}{4}$, label B: $\dfrac{2}{6}$, label C: $\dfrac{3}{8}$

Step 3
Identify the strategy or operation to use.
Use equivalent fractions.

Step 4
Apply the strategy or operation.
Multiples of 4: 4, 8, 12, 16, 20, <u>24</u>
Multiples of 6: 6, 12, 18, <u>24</u>
Multiples of 8: 8, 16, <u>24</u>

$$\dfrac{2\times6}{4\times6}=\dfrac{12}{24} \qquad \dfrac{2\times4}{6\times4}=\dfrac{8}{24} \qquad \dfrac{3\times3}{8\times3}=\dfrac{9}{24}$$

The smallest numerator is 8. $\dfrac{8}{24}=\dfrac{2}{6}$ is the

smallest fraction.

Label B has the least amount of vitamin C.

PRACTICE EXERCISES
ANSWERS AND SOLUTIONS

1. Answers may vary.

Step 1
Use divisibility rules to find factors of both numbers.
Factors of 15: 1, 3, 5, 15
Factors of 30: 1, 2, 3, 5, 6, 10, 15, 30.

Step 2
Divide both numbers by a factor to create an equivalent fraction.

$$\dfrac{15\div15}{30\div15}=\dfrac{1}{2} \qquad \dfrac{15\div3}{30\div3}=\dfrac{5}{10}$$

The fractions $\dfrac{1}{2}$ and $\dfrac{5}{10}$ are equivalent to $\dfrac{15}{30}$.

3. Answers may vary. Choose two factors. Multiply the numerator and denominator by the factors.

$$\dfrac{4\times2}{6\times2}=\dfrac{8}{12} \qquad \dfrac{4\times3}{6\times3}=\dfrac{12}{18}$$

The fractions $\dfrac{8}{12}$ and $\dfrac{12}{18}$ are equivalent to $\dfrac{4}{6}$.

5. **Step 1**
List the multiples of both denominators until a common multiple appears.
Multiples of 6: 6, 12, 18, 24, 30, <u>36</u>
Multiples of 18: 18, <u>36</u>

Step 2
Multiply the numerator and denominator of each fraction by factors that result in both denominators equaling 36.

$$\dfrac{2\times6}{6\times6}=\dfrac{12}{36} \text{ and } \dfrac{3\times2}{18\times2}=\dfrac{6}{36}$$

Step 3
Compare the numerators.

$\dfrac{12}{36}>\dfrac{6}{36}$.

Since 12 is greater than 6, $\dfrac{2}{6}>\dfrac{3}{18}$.

7. **Step 1**
List the multiples of both denominators until a common multiple appears.
Multiples of 5: 5, 10, 15, 20, 25, <u>30</u>
Multiples of 6: 6, 12, 18, 24, <u>30</u>

Step 2
Multiply the numerator and denominator of each fraction by factors that result in both denominators equaling 30.

$$\dfrac{4\times6}{5\times6}=\dfrac{24}{30} \text{ and } \dfrac{5\times5}{6\times5}=\dfrac{25}{30}$$

Step 3
Compare the numerators.

$\dfrac{24}{30}<\dfrac{25}{30}$

Since 24 is less than 25, $\dfrac{4}{5}<\dfrac{5}{6}$.

9. **Step 1**
Change each fraction into a mixed number.

$\dfrac{4}{3}=1\dfrac{1}{3}, \dfrac{6}{4}=1\dfrac{2}{4}, \dfrac{7}{2}=3\dfrac{1}{2}, \dfrac{8}{5}=1\dfrac{3}{5}$

Step 2

Compare the whole numbers.

The whole number for $3\frac{1}{2}$ is greater than the whole number for $1\frac{1}{3}$, $1\frac{2}{4}$, and $1\frac{3}{5}$. The whole numbers for $1\frac{1}{3}$, $1\frac{2}{4}$, and $1\frac{3}{5}$ are the same.

Step 3

Make equivalent fractions of the fraction part of the mixed numbers.

List the multiples of each denominator until a common multiple appears.
Multiples of 3: 3, 6, 9, **12**
Multiples of 4: 4, 8, **12,** 16, <u>20</u>
Multiples of 5: 5, 10, 15, <u>20</u>

Step 4

Compare $\frac{1}{3}$ and $\frac{2}{4}$ first as they have a common multiple of 12.

Multiply the numerator and denominator of both fractions by factors that result in the denominators equaling 12.
$$\frac{1\times4}{3\times4}=\frac{4}{12},\ \frac{2\times3}{4\times3}=\frac{6}{12}$$

Compare the numerators.

Since 4 is less than 6, $\frac{4}{3}<\frac{6}{4}$.

Step 5

Compare $\frac{2}{4}$ and $\frac{3}{5}$ as they both have a common multiple of 20. Multiply the numerator and denominator of each fraction by a factor that results in the denominators both equaling 20.
$$\frac{2\times5}{4\times5}=\frac{10}{20}\text{ and }\frac{3\times4}{5\times4}=\frac{12}{20}$$

Compare the numerators.
Since 10 is less than 12, $\frac{2}{4}<\frac{3}{5}$.

Arranged in order from smallest to largest, the fractions are $\frac{4}{3}$, $\frac{6}{4}$, $\frac{8}{5}$, and $\frac{7}{2}$.

Lesson 6—Comparing and Ordering Numbers

YOUR TURN
ANSWERS AND SOLUTIONS

1. Start with the numbers greater than 1: 1.7, $\frac{16}{9}$, and $1\frac{3}{4}$. The fraction $1\frac{3}{4}$ falls on a benchmark.
Convert the improper fraction to a mixed number.
$16\div9=1\ \text{R}7$
$$=1\frac{7}{9}$$
$\frac{7}{9}=0.\overline{7}$, so $1\frac{7}{9}$ is greater than $1\frac{3}{4}$.
Look for fractions that can be reduced to lowest terms. $\frac{8\div2}{18\div2}=\frac{4}{9}$

The fraction $\frac{2}{9}$ is less than $\frac{4}{9}$ but greater than 0.2 because it is a repeating decimal.

In descending order, the numbers are
$$\frac{16}{9},\ 1\frac{3}{4},\ 1.7,\ \frac{8}{18},\ \frac{2}{9},\ 0.2$$

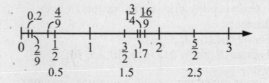

2. If the numerator is less than half the value of the denominator, it is less than $\frac{1}{2}$. If the numerator is exactly half the value of the denominator, it is equal to $\frac{1}{2}$. If the numerator is greater than half the value of the denominator, it is greater than $\frac{1}{2}$.

3. **Step 1**
Change all fractions to their decimal equivalents.
$$\frac{1}{2}=0.5 \qquad \frac{3}{9}=0.\overline{3} \qquad \frac{4}{16}=0.25$$

Step 2
In a place value chart, rank each value based on its place value.

Value	Ones		Tenths	Hundredths	Thousandths	Rank
3.45	3	.	4	5	0	4
$3\frac{1}{2}$	3	.	5	0	0	5
0.4	0	.	4	0	0	2
$3\frac{3}{9}$	3	.	3	3	3	3
$\frac{4}{16}$	0	.	2	5	0	1

The numbers ordered from least to greatest are $\frac{4}{16}$,

0.4, $3\frac{3}{9}$, 3.45, and $3\frac{1}{2}$.

4. Place value tables are a good strategy to use when there are many different denominators in the fractions.

5. **Step 1**
Change the decimal into a fraction with a denominator of 10.

$0.3 = \frac{3}{10}$

Step 2
Change mixed numbers into improper fractions.

$1\frac{2}{10} = \frac{1 \times 10 + 2}{10}$ $1\frac{2}{5} = \frac{1 \times 5 + 2}{5}$

$\quad = \frac{12}{10}$ $\quad = \frac{7}{5}$

Step 3
Make an equivalent fraction of the fractions without a denominator of 10.

$\frac{3 \times 2}{5 \times 2} = \frac{6}{10}$ $\frac{7 \times 2}{5 \times 2} = \frac{14}{10}$

Step 4
Compare the numerators.

$\frac{4}{10}, \frac{12}{10}, \frac{6}{10}, \frac{14}{10}, \frac{3}{10}$

The numbers ordered from smallest to largest are

0.3, $\frac{4}{10}$, $\frac{3}{5}$, $1\frac{2}{10}$, and $1\frac{2}{5}$.

PRACTICE EXERCISES
ANSWERS AND SOLUTIONS

1. Since both denominators are the same, compare the denominators.

$\frac{4}{5}, \frac{1}{5}$

4 is greater than 1, so $\frac{4}{5} > \frac{1}{5}$

3. $0.45 > \frac{7}{16} > \frac{3}{7}$

5. $\frac{7}{8} = 0.875$

$\frac{8}{9} = 0.888\,8888\ldots$

Therefore, $\frac{8}{9} > \frac{7}{8}$.

7. $\frac{4}{3} > \frac{35}{28} > \frac{6}{5}$

Practice Test

ANSWERS AND SOLUTIONS

1. A number is divisible by 6 if the number is divisible by both 2 and 3.

3. A number is divisible by 5 if the last digit in the number is 0 or 5.

5. $1 + 2 + 9 = 12$
$12 \div 3 = 4$
The number 129 is divisible by 3.

7. $1 + 2 + 8 + 3 + 7 = 21$
$21 \div 3 = 7$
The number 12 837 is divisible by 3.

9. $5 + 4 + 9 + 3 + 0 = 21$
$21 \div 3 = 7$
The number 54 930 is divisible by 3.

11. $3 + 6 + 9 = 18$
    $18 \div 9 = 2$
    The number 369 is divisible by 9.

13. $1 + 8 + 7 + 2 = 18$
    $18 \div 9 = 2$
    The number 1872 is divisible by 9.

15. $4 + 8 + 2 + 3 + 0 + 0 + 2 + 3 = 22$
    $22 \div 9 = 2.\overline{4}$
    The number 48 230 023 is not divisible by 9.

17. $0.8 = \dfrac{8}{10}$
    $ = \dfrac{4}{5}$

19. $1.7 = 1\dfrac{7}{10}$

21. $10.25 = 10\dfrac{25}{100}$
    $ = 10\dfrac{1}{4}$

23. $\dfrac{12}{50} = 12 \div 50$
    $\phantom{\dfrac{12}{50}} = 0.24$

25. $\dfrac{4}{9} = 0.\overline{4}$

27. $\dfrac{45}{55} = 0.\overline{81}$

29. $\dfrac{15}{4} > \dfrac{28}{9}$

WORKING WITH PERCENTS

Lesson 1—Expressing Percentages as Fractions and Decimals

YOUR TURN
ANSWERS AND SOLUTIONS

1. **Step 1**
    Write the percentage over a denominator of 100.
    40% means 40 out of 100, so write it as $\dfrac{40}{100}$

    Step 2
    Simplify the fraction.
    Divide the numerator and the denominator by 20.
    $\dfrac{40 \div 20}{100 \div 20} = \dfrac{2}{5}$

    Therefore, 40% can be written as $\dfrac{2}{5}$.

2. Move the decimal point two places to the left, and remove the percent symbol.
    $40\% = 0.40$

    Therefore, 40% can be written as 0.40.

3. **Step 1**
    Determine the fraction.
    The number of questions Chen got correct (16) represents the part. The total number of questions on the test (22) represents the whole.

    The fraction is $\dfrac{16}{22}$.

    Step 2
    Calculate the decimal equivalent of the fraction.
    Divide the numerator by the denominator.
    $16 \div 22 \doteq 0.73$

    Step 3
    Write the percentage.
    Multiply the result by 100, and place a percent sign after the answer.
    $0.73 \times 100 = 73\%$
    Chen got approximately 73% on his math quiz.

4. **Step 1**
    Determine the fraction.
    The increase is the numerator. The original price is the denominator.

The increase in the amount of the first shampoo is 250 mL.

The original amount of the first shampoo was 500 mL.

The fraction is $\dfrac{250}{500}$.

The increase in the amount of the second shampoo is 100 mL.

The original amount of the second shampoo was 650 mL.

The fraction is $\dfrac{100}{650}$.

Step 2
Calculate the decimal equivalent of the fractions. Divide the numerator by the denominator.
First shampoo: $250 \div 500 = 0.50$
Second shampoo: $100 \div 650 \doteq 0.15$

Step 3
Write the percentage.

Multiply the result by 100, and place a percent sign after the answer.

First shampoo: $0.50 \times 100 = 50\%$
Second shampoo: $0.15 \times 100 = 15\%$

The first shampoo is the better buy because it has the greater percentage increase.

PRACTICE EXERCISES
ANSWERS AND SOLUTIONS

1. **Step 1**
   Calculate the decimal equivalent of the fraction. Divide the numerator by the denominator.
   $3 \div 25 = 0.12$

   Step 2
   Write the percentage.
   Multiply the result by 100, and place a percent sign after the answer.
   $0.12 \times 100 = 12\%$

3. **Step 1**
   Determine the fraction.
   The numerator is 24.
   The denominator is 52.

The fraction is $\dfrac{24}{52}$.

Step 2
Calculate the decimal equivalent of the fraction. Divide the numerator by the denominator.
$24 \div 52 \doteq 0.46$

Step 3
Write the percentage.
Multiply the result by 100, and place a percent sign after the answer.
$0.46 \times 100 = 46\%$

5. Move the decimal point two places to the left, and remove the percent symbol.
   $50\% = 0.50$

   Therefore, 50% can be written as 0.50.

7. **Step 1**
   Determine the fraction.
   The additional tax is the numerator. The original price is the denominator.

   The fraction is $\dfrac{4.50}{75.00}$.

   Step 2
   Calculate the decimal equivalent of the fraction. Divide the numerator by the denominator.
   $4.5 \div 75 = 0.06$

   Step 3
   Write the percentage.
   Multiply the result by 100, and place a percent sign after the answer.
   $0.06 \times 100 = 6\%$

   The tax was 6%.

9. **Step 1**
   Determine the fraction.
   The number of seats that are full (150) represent the part. The total number of seats (250) represent the whole.

   The fraction is $\dfrac{150}{250}$.

   Step 2
   Calculate the decimal equivalent of the fraction. Divide the numerator by the denominator.
   $150 \div 250 = 0.60$

Step 3
Write the percentage.
Multiply the result by 100, and place a percent sign after the answer.
$0.60 \times 100 = 60\%$

The theatre is 60% full on Wednesday evening.

Lesson 2—Percent of a Number

YOUR TURN
ANSWERS AND SOLUTIONS

1. **Step 1**
    Set up equivalent fractions.
    Write the percentage as the first fraction.
    The numerator of the second fraction is represented with a variable and the denominator is the given number.
    $$\frac{18}{100} = \frac{x}{50}$$

    Step 2
    Determine the number used to create the equivalent denominator.
    The denominator is divided by 2 to get 50.
    $100 \div 2 = 50$

    Step 3
    Divide the numerator by the same divisor.
    $$\frac{18 \div 2}{100 \div 2} = \frac{9}{50}$$
    18% of 50 is 9.

2. **Step 1**
    Convert the percentage to a decimal.
    $45\% = 0.45$

    Step 2
    Multiply the decimal number by the given number.
    $0.45 \times 400 = 180$
    45% of 400 is 180.

3. **Step 1**
    Set up equivalent fractions.
    The percent is written as the first fraction.
    Since 45 represents the part, it will go in the numerator of the second fraction.
    $15 \times 3 = 45$

    Step 2

Determine the number used to create the equivalent numerator.
The numerator is multiplied by 3 to get 45.
$15 \times 3 = 45$

Step 3
Multiply the denominator by the same multiplier.
$$\frac{15 \times 3}{100 \times 3} = \frac{45}{300}$$

45 is 15% of 300.

PRACTICE EXERCISES
ANSWERS AND SOLUTIONS

1. **Method 1: Equivalent fractions**
    Step 1
    Set up equivalent fractions.
    Write the percentage as the first fraction.
    The numerator of the second fraction is represented by a variable. The denominator is the given number.
    $$\frac{42}{100} = \frac{x}{300}$$

    Step 2
    Determine the number used to create the equivalent denominator.
    The denominator is multiplied by 3 to get 300.
    $100 \times 3 = 300$

    Step 3
    Multiply the numerator by the same multiplier.
    $$\frac{42 \times 3}{100 \times 3} = \frac{126}{300}$$

    42% of 300 is 126.

    Method 2: Multiplying by a decimal number
    Step 1
    Convert the percentage to a decimal.
    $42\% = 0.42$

    Step 2
    Multiply the decimal number by the given number.
    $0.42 \times 300 = 126$

    42% of 300 is 126.

3. **Step 1**
Set up equivalent fractions.
The percent is written as the first fraction.
Since 60 represents the part, it will go in the numerator of the second fraction.

$$\frac{20}{100} = \frac{60}{x}$$

Step 2
Determine the number used to create the equivalent numerator.
The numerator is multiplied by 3 to get 60.
$20 \times 3 = 60$

Step 3
Multiply the denominator by the same multiplier.

$$\frac{20 \times 3}{100 \times 3} = \frac{60}{300}$$

60 is 20% of 300.

5. **Step 1**
Determine the percentage of the original price that is being paid. Since 15% off means 85% of the original price, the discounted DVD cost is 85% of $29.95.

Step 2
Convert 85% to a decimal.
$85\% = 0.85$

Step 3
Multiply this number by the original price.
$0.85 \times 29.95 = 25.4575$
Since this is a monetary value, the number is rounded to the hundredths place.

The cost of the discounted DVD is $25.46.

7. **Step 1**
Calculate the GST.
Multiply the price by the decimal equivalent of the GST. The decimal equivalent of 5% is 0.05.
$0.05 \times 19.99 = 0.9995$
$\doteq \$1.00$

Step 2
Add the GST to the price of the CD.
$19.99 + 1.00 = 20.99$

The total cost of the CD after tax is $20.99.

9. **Step 1**
Convert the percentage to a decimal.
$20\% = 0.20$

Step 2
Multiply the decimal by the given number.
$0.20 \times 420 = 84$

20% of 420 is 84.

Practice Test

ANSWERS AND SOLUTIONS

1. **Step 1**
Calculate the decimal equivalent of the fraction.
Divide the numerator by the denominator.
$12 \div 40 = 0.3$

Step 2
Write the percentage.
Multiply the result by 100, and place a percent sign after the answer.
$0.3 \times 100 = 30\%$

The fraction $\frac{12}{40}$ is equal to 30%.

3. Move the decimal point two places to the left and remove the percent symbol.
$30\% = 0.30$

The percentage 30% is equal to 0.30.

5. **Step 1**
Calculate the decimal equivalent of the fraction.
Divide the numerator by the denominator.
$3 \div 8 = 0.375$

Step 2
Write the percentage.
Multiply the result by 100, and place a percent sign after the answer.
$0.375 \times 100 = 37.5\%$

The fraction $\frac{3}{8}$ is equal to 37.5%.

7. Move the decimal point two places to the left and remove the percent symbol.
$42\% = 0.42$

The percentage 42% is equal to 0.42.

9. **Step 1**
Place the value of the percentage over a denominator of 100.

$$\frac{78}{100}$$

Step 2
Reduce the fraction to lowest terms.
Divide the numerator and denominator by the GCF.

$$\frac{78 \div 2}{100 \div 2} = \frac{39}{50}$$

78% is equivalent to the fraction $\frac{39}{50}$.

11. **Method 1: Find the discount amount, and subtract it from the original price.**
Step 1
Calculate the discount (20% of $149.95).

Convert the percentage to a decimal.
20% = 0.20

Multiply the decimal by the given number.
0.20 × 149.95 = 29.99
20% of $149.95 is $29.99.

The discount is $29.99

Step 2
Determine the sale price.
Subtract the discount from the original price.
original price – discount = sales price
149.95 – 29.99 = 119.96

On sale, the jacket will cost $119.96.

Method 2: Find the percentage of the original price left to pay.
Step 1
Determine the percentage of the original price.
20% off means 80% of the original price.

The sale price is 80% of $149.95.

Step 2
Convert 80% to a decimal.
80% = 0.80

Step 3
Multiply the decimal number by the original price.
0.80 × 149.95 = 119.96

On sale, the jacket will cost $119.96.

13. **Step 1**
Set up equivalent fractions.
Write the percentage as the first fraction.
The numerator of the second fraction is represented with a variable. The denominator is the given number.

$$\frac{6}{100} = \frac{x}{18\ 700}$$

Step 2
Determine the number used to create the equivalent numerator.
The denominator is multiplied by 187 to get 18 700.
$100 \times 187 = 18\ 700$

Step 3
Multiply the numerator by the same multiplier.

$$\frac{6 \times 187}{100 \times 187} = \frac{1\ 122}{18\ 700}$$

6% of $18 700.00 is $1 122.

Harry earned $1 122 commission in November.

15. **Step 1**
Calculate the tax (12% of $8 000).

Set up the equivalent fractions.

$$\frac{12}{100} = \frac{x}{8\ 000}$$

Convert the percentage into a decimal.
12% = 0.12
Multiply the percentage as a decimal by the given number.
$0.12 \times 8\ 000 = 960$

The tax on the cost of the car is $960.

Step 2
Determine the total purchase price, including tax.

Add the tax to the original cost.
$8000 + $960 = $8960

The total purchase price of the car including tax is $8 960.

FRACTION OPERATIONS

Lesson 1—Adding and Subtracting Fractions with Like and Unlike Denominators

YOUR TURN
ANSWERS AND SOLUTIONS

1. Step 1
Draw a grid based on the factors on the denominator. The factors of the denominator are 1, 2, 4, and 8. Use $4 \times 2 = 8$

Step 2
Colour in the parts equivalent to each numerator. The numerators are 4 and 3. Use a different shade for each number.

Step 3
Count the total number of shaded parts. 4 light grey squares plus 3 dark grey squares is a total of 7 shaded squares.

$$\frac{4}{8} + \frac{3}{8} = \frac{7}{8}$$

2. Step 1
Add the numerators of the fractions while keeping the denominators the same.

$$\frac{2}{6} + \frac{1}{6} = \frac{2+1}{6}$$
$$= \frac{3}{6}$$

Step 2
Reduce the resulting fraction to lowest terms by dividing the numerator and denominator by the GCF.

The GCF is 3.

$$\frac{3 \div 3}{6 \div 3} = \frac{1}{2}$$

$$\frac{2}{6} + \frac{1}{6} = \frac{1}{2}$$

3. Step 1
Draw a grid based on the factors of the denominator. The factors of the denominator are 1, 2, 4 and 8. Use $4 \times 2 = 8$

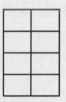

Step 2
Shade in the parts equivalent to the first numerator. The first numerator is 4.

Step 3
Cross out the shaded parts equivalent to the second numerator. The second numerator is 3.

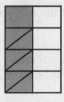

Step 4
Count the number of remaining shaded parts. There is 1 shaded square left.

The fraction $\frac{1}{8}$ is in lowest terms.

$$\frac{4}{8} - \frac{3}{8} = \frac{1}{8}$$

4. Subtract the numerators of the fractions while keeping the denominators the same.

$$\frac{3}{5}-\frac{1}{5}=\frac{3-1}{5}$$
$$=\frac{2}{5}$$

$\frac{2}{5}$ is in lowest terms.

The difference of $\frac{3}{5}-\frac{1}{5}$ is $\frac{2}{5}$.

5. **Step 1**
    Subtract the numerators of the fractions while keeping the denominators the same.

    $$\frac{7}{8}-\frac{3}{8}=\frac{7-3}{8}$$
    $$=\frac{4}{8}$$

    Step 2
    Reduce the resulting fraction to lowest terms.

    Divide the numerator and denominator by the GCF (4).

    $$\frac{4\div4}{8\div4}=\frac{1}{2}$$

    $\frac{1}{2}$ is in lowest terms.

    $$\frac{7}{8}-\frac{3}{8}=\frac{1}{2}$$

6. **Step 1**
    Rewrite the fractions using the LCD.

    Write the multiples of each denominator until a common one appears.
    Multiples of 3: 3, 6, 9, 12, **15**…
    Multiples of 5: 5, 10, **15**, 20…
    The lowest common denominator of 3 and 5 is 15.

    Multiply the numerator and the denominator of each fraction by the same factor.

    $$\frac{1\times5}{3\times5}=\frac{5}{15}\qquad\qquad\frac{2\times3}{5\times3}=\frac{6}{15}$$

    Step 2
    Add the numerators of the fractions while keeping the denominators the same.

$$\frac{5}{15}+\frac{6}{15}=\frac{5+6}{15}$$
$$=\frac{11}{15}$$

$$\frac{1}{3}+\frac{2}{5}=\frac{11}{15}$$

7. **Step 1**
    Rewrite the fractions using the LCD.

    Write the multiples of each denominator until a common one appears.
    Multiples of 3: 3, 6, 9, 12, **15**…
    Multiples of 5: 5, 10, **15**, 20…
    The lowest common denominator of 3 and 5 is 15.

    Multiply the numerator and the denominator of each fraction by the same factor.

    $$\frac{1\times5}{3\times5}=\frac{5}{15}\qquad\qquad\frac{2\times3}{5\times3}=\frac{6}{15}$$

    Step 2
    Subtract the numerators of the fractions while keeping the denominators the same.

    $$\frac{6}{15}-\frac{5}{15}=\frac{6-5}{15}$$
    $$=\frac{1}{15}$$

    $$\frac{2}{5}-\frac{1}{3}\text{ is }\frac{1}{15}$$

PRACTICE EXERCISES
ANSWERS AND SOLUTIONS

1. **Step 1**
    Draw a grid based on the factors of the denominator. Use 2×3.

    Step 2
    Colour in the parts of the grid that are equivalent to each numerator.

    The numerators are 4 and 1.

Step 3
Add the total number of coloured parts.
There are 5 coloured squares in total.

$$\frac{4}{6} + \frac{1}{6} = \frac{5}{6}$$

3.   **Step 1**
Add the numerators of the fractions while keeping the denominators the same.

$$\frac{23}{65} + \frac{32}{65} = \frac{23+32}{65}$$
$$= \frac{55}{65}$$

Step 2
Reduce the resulting fraction to lowest terms.
Divide the numerator and denominator by the GCF (5).

$$\frac{55 \div 5}{65 \div 5} = \frac{11}{13}$$

$$\frac{23}{65} + \frac{32}{65} = \frac{11}{13}$$

5.   **Step 1**
Rewrite the fractions using the LCD.

Write the multiples of each denominator until a common one appears.
Multiples of 2: 2, **4**, 6, 8…
Multiples of 4: **4**, 8, 12…
The lowest common denominator of 2 and 4 is 4.

Multiply the numerator and the denominator of each fraction by the same factor.

$$\frac{1}{4} = \frac{1}{4} \qquad \frac{1 \times 2}{2 \times 2} = \frac{2}{4}$$

Step 2
Add the numerators of the fractions while keeping the denominators the same.

$$\frac{1}{4} + \frac{2}{4} = \frac{1+2}{4}$$
$$= \frac{3}{4}$$

$\frac{3}{4}$ is the lowest term.
$$\frac{1}{4} + \frac{1}{2} = \frac{3}{4}$$

7.   **Step 1**
Rewrite the fractions using the LCD.

Write the multiples of each denominator until a common one appears.
Multiples of 3: 3, **6**, 9, 12, 15…
Multiples of 6: **6**, 12, 18…
The lowest common denominator of 3 and 6 is 6.

Multiply the numerator and the denominator of each fraction by the same factor.

$$\frac{5}{6} = \frac{5}{6} \qquad \frac{2 \times 2}{3 \times 2} = \frac{4}{6}$$

Step 2
Subtract the numerators of the fractions while keeping the denominators the same.

$$\frac{5}{6} - \frac{4}{6} = \frac{5-4}{6}$$
$$= \frac{1}{6}$$

$\frac{1}{6}$ is the lowest term.

$$\frac{5}{6} - \frac{2}{3} = \frac{1}{6}$$

9.   **Step 1**
Rewrite the fractions using the LCD.

Write the multiples of each denominator until a common one appears.
Multiples of 6: 6, **12**, 18, 24, 30…
Multiples of 12: **12**, 24…
The lowest common denominator of 6 and 12 is 12.
Multiply the numerator and the denominator of each fraction by the same factor.

$$\frac{5 \times 2}{6 \times 2} = \frac{10}{12} \qquad \frac{3}{12} = \frac{3}{12}$$

Step 2
Subtract the numerators of the fractions while keeping the denominators the same.

$$\frac{10}{12} - \frac{3}{12} = \frac{10-3}{12}$$
$$= \frac{7}{12}$$

$\frac{7}{12}$ is in lowest terms.

$$\frac{5}{6} - \frac{3}{12} \text{ is } \frac{7}{12}.$$

Lesson 2—Mixed Numbers

YOUR TURN
ANSWERS AND SOLUTIONS

1. **Step 1**
Change the mixed numbers to improper fractions.

$$2\frac{1}{8} = \frac{2\times8+1}{8} \qquad 3\frac{5}{8} = \frac{3\times8+5}{8}$$
$$= \frac{17}{8} \qquad\qquad = \frac{29}{8}$$

Step 2
Add the numerators of the fractions while keeping the denominators the same.

$$\frac{17}{8} + \frac{29}{8} = \frac{17+29}{8}$$
$$= \frac{46}{8}$$

Step 3
Reduce the resulting improper fraction to the lowest terms.

Divide the numerator and denominator by GCF (2).
$$\frac{46\div2}{8\div2} = \frac{23}{4}$$

Step 4
Change the improper fraction to a mixed number.
$23\div4 = 5\ \text{R}3$

$$\frac{23}{4} = 5\frac{3}{4}$$

$$2\frac{1}{8} + 3\frac{5}{8} = 5\frac{3}{4}$$

2 **Step 1**
Add the whole numbers.
$1+3 = 4$

Step 2
Add the fractions.
$$\frac{1}{4} + \frac{2}{4} = \frac{1+2}{4}$$
$$= \frac{3}{4}$$

Step 3
Combine the sum of the whole numbers and the sum of the fractions.

$$4 + \frac{3}{4} = 4\frac{3}{4}$$

$4\frac{3}{4}$ is in lowest terms.

$1\frac{1}{4} + 3\frac{2}{4}$ is $4\frac{3}{4}$

3. **Step 1**
Change the mixed numbers to an improper fractions.
$$3\frac{1}{4} = \frac{3\times4+1}{4} \qquad\qquad 2\frac{2}{3} = \frac{2\times3+2}{3}$$
$$= \frac{13}{4} \qquad\qquad\qquad = \frac{8}{3}$$

Step 2
Rewrite the fractions using the LCD.

Write the multiples of each denominator until a common one appears.
Multiples of 3: 3, 6, 9, **12**, 15…
Multiples of 4: 4, 8, **12**, 16, 20…
The lowest common denominator of 3 and 4 is 12.

Multiply the numerator and the denominator of each fraction by the same factor.
$$\frac{13\times3}{4\times3} = \frac{39}{12} \qquad\qquad \frac{8\times4}{3\times4} = \frac{32}{12}$$

Step 3
Add the numerators of the fractions while keeping the denominators the same.
$$\frac{39}{12} + \frac{32}{12} = \frac{39+32}{12}$$
$$= \frac{71}{12}$$

Step 4
Change the improper fraction to a mixed number.
$71\div12 = 5\ \text{R}11$
$$\frac{71}{12} = 5\frac{11}{12}$$

$$3\frac{1}{4} + 2\frac{2}{3} = 5\frac{11}{12}$$

4. **Step 1**
Change the mixed number to an improper fraction.

$$3\frac{5}{8} = \frac{3 \times 8 + 5}{8} \qquad 2\frac{1}{8} = \frac{2 \times 8 + 1}{8}$$

$$= \frac{29}{8} \qquad\qquad = \frac{17}{8}$$

Step 2
Subtract the numerators of the fractions while keeping the denominators the same.

$$\frac{29}{8} - \frac{17}{8} = \frac{29 - 17}{8}$$

$$= \frac{12}{8}$$

Step 3
Reduce the resulting improper fraction to lowest terms.

The GCF of 12 and 8 is 4. Divide both the numerator and denominator by 4.

$$\frac{12 \div 4}{8 \div 4} = \frac{3}{2}$$

Step 4
Change the reduced improper fraction to a mixed number. $3 \div 2 = 1$ R1.

$$\frac{3}{2} = 1\frac{1}{2}$$

$$3\frac{5}{8} - 2\frac{1}{8} = 1\frac{1}{2}$$

5. **Step 1**
Subtract the whole numbers.
$$4 - 1 = 3$$

Step 2
Subtract the numerators of the fractions while keeping the denominators the same.

$$\frac{3}{4} - \frac{1}{4} = \frac{3 - 1}{4}$$

$$= \frac{2}{4}$$

Step 3
Combine the whole number and the fraction.

$$3 + \frac{2}{4} = 3\frac{2}{4}$$

Reduce the fraction into lowest terms.

$$3\frac{2}{4} = 3\frac{2 \div 2}{4 \div 2}$$

$$= 3\frac{1}{2}$$

$$4\frac{3}{4} - 1\frac{1}{4} = 3\frac{1}{2}$$

6. **Step 1**
Change the mixed number to an improper fraction.

$$3\frac{4}{5} = \frac{3 \times 5 + 4}{5} \qquad 2\frac{1}{3} = \frac{2 \times 3 + 1}{3}$$

$$= \frac{19}{5} \qquad\qquad = \frac{7}{3}$$

Step 2
Rewrite the fractions using the LCD.

Write the multiples of each denominator until a common one appears.
Multiples of 3: 3, 6, 9, 12, **15**…
Multiples of 5: 5, 10, **15**, 20…
The lowest common denominator of 3 and 5 is 15.

Multiply the numerator and the denominator of each fraction by the same factor.

$$\frac{19 \times 3}{5 \times 3} = \frac{57}{15} \qquad \frac{7 \times 5}{3 \times 5} = \frac{35}{15}$$

Step 3
Subtract the numerators of the fractions while keeping the denominators the same.

$$\frac{57}{15} - \frac{35}{15} = \frac{57 - 35}{15}$$

$$= \frac{22}{15}$$

Step 4
Change the reduced improper fraction to a mixed number.
$$22 \div 15 = 1 \text{ R7}$$

$$\frac{22}{15} = 1\frac{7}{15}$$

$$3\frac{4}{5} - 2\frac{1}{3} = 1\frac{7}{15}$$

PRACTICE EXERCISES
ANSWERS AND SOLUTIONS

1. **Step 1**
    Add the whole numbers.
    $1 + 2 = 3$

    Step 2
    Add the fractions.
    $$\frac{1}{3} + \frac{1}{3} = \frac{1+1}{3}$$
    $$= \frac{2}{3}$$

    Step 3
    Combine the whole number and fraction.
    $$3 + \frac{2}{3} = 3\frac{2}{3}$$

    $$1\frac{1}{3} + 2\frac{1}{3} = 3\frac{2}{3}$$

3. **Step 1**
    Change the mixed numbers to improper fractions.
    $$2\frac{1}{2} = \frac{2 \times 2 + 1}{2} \qquad 2\frac{3}{6} = \frac{2 \times 6 + 3}{6}$$
    $$= \frac{5}{2} \qquad\qquad\qquad = \frac{15}{6}$$

    Step 2
    Rewrite the fractions using the LCD.

    Write the multiples of each denominator until a common one appears.

    Multiples of 2: 2, 4, **6,** 8, 10, 12…
    Multiples of 6: **6**, 12, 18…
    The lowest common denominator of 2 and 6 is 6.

    Multiply the numerator and the denominator of each fraction by the same factor.
    $$\frac{5 \times 3}{2 \times 3} = \frac{15}{6} \qquad \frac{15}{6} = \frac{15}{6}$$

    Step 3
    Add the numerators of the fractions while keeping the denominators the same.
    $$\frac{15}{6} + \frac{15}{6} = \frac{15 + 15}{6}$$
    $$= \frac{30}{6}$$

Step 4
Reduce the resulting improper fraction to lowest terms.

The common factor of 30 and 6 is 6. Divide both the numerator and denominator by 6.
$$\frac{30 \div 6}{6 \div 6} = \frac{5}{1}$$

Step 5
Change the improper fraction to a mixed number.
$5 \div 1 = 5$
$$2\frac{1}{2} + 2\frac{3}{6} = 5$$

5. **Step 1**
    Add the whole numbers.
    $5 + 2 = 7$

    Step 2
    Add the fractions.
    $$\frac{5}{8} + \frac{1}{8} = \frac{5 + 1}{8}$$
    $$= \frac{6}{8}$$

    Step 3
    Add the whole number and fraction.
    $$7 + \frac{6}{8} = 7\frac{6}{8}$$

    Reduce to lowest terms.
    The GCF of 6 and 8 is 2. Divide both the numerator and denominator by 2.
    $$7\frac{6 \div 2}{8 \div 2} = 7\frac{3}{4}$$

    $$5\frac{5}{8} + 2\frac{1}{8} = 7\frac{3}{4}$$

7. **Step 1**
    Change the mixed number to an improper fraction.
    $$2\frac{1}{2} = \frac{2 \times 2 + 1}{2} \qquad 2\frac{1}{6} = \frac{2 \times 6 + 1}{6}$$
    $$= \frac{5}{2} \qquad\qquad\qquad = \frac{13}{6}$$

    Step 2
    Rewrite the fractions using the LCD.

    Write the multiples of each denominator until a common one appears.
    Multiples of 2: 2, 4, **6**, 8…

Multiples of 6: **6**, 12, 18…
The lowest common denominator of 2 and 6 is 6.

Multiply the numerator and the denominator of each fraction by the same factor.

$$\frac{5\times 3}{2\times 3}=\frac{15}{6}\qquad\qquad\frac{13}{6}=\frac{13}{6}$$

Step 3
Subtract the numerators of the fractions while keeping the denominators the same.

$$\frac{15}{6}-\frac{13}{6}=\frac{15-13}{6}$$
$$=\frac{2}{6}$$

Step 4
Reduce the fraction into lowest terms.

$$\frac{2}{6}=\frac{2\div 2}{6\div 2}$$
$$=\frac{1}{3}$$

$$2\frac{1}{2}-2\frac{1}{6}=\frac{1}{3}$$

9. **Step 1**
Change the mixed number to an improper fraction.

$$1\frac{2}{3}=\frac{1\times 3+2}{3}$$
$$=\frac{5}{3}$$

Step 2
Rewrite the fractions using the LCD.

Write the multiples of each denominator until a common one appears.
Multiples of 3: 3, 6, 9, 12, 15, 18, **21**…
Multiples of 7: 7, 14, **21**, 28…
The lowest common denominator of 3 and 7 is 21.

Multiply the numerator and the denominator of each fraction by the same factor.

$$\frac{5\times 7}{3\times 7}=\frac{35}{21}\qquad\qquad\frac{6\times 3}{7\times 3}=\frac{18}{21}$$

Step 3
Subtract the numerators of the fractions while keeping the denominators the same.

$$\frac{35}{21}-\frac{18}{21}=\frac{35-18}{21}$$
$$=\frac{17}{21}$$

$$1\frac{2}{3}-\frac{6}{7}\ \text{is}\ \frac{17}{21}$$

Lesson 3—Problem Solving with Fractions

YOUR TURN
ANSWERS AND SOLUTIONS

1.　**Step 1**
Identify the fractions and the operational keywords.

Distance to friend's house is $9\frac{1}{4}$ km.

Rheanna drove $2\frac{3}{4}$ km.

Abdu drove $4\frac{2}{4}$ km.

"How much further do they have to drive?" means subtraction.

Step 2
Write an expression to represent the problem.

$$9\frac{1}{4}-\left(2\frac{3}{4}+4\frac{2}{4}\right)$$

Step 3
Solve the expression and reduce the answer to lowest terms if required.

Change the mixed numbers into improper fractions.

$$9\frac{1}{4}=\frac{37}{4}\qquad 2\frac{3}{4}=\frac{11}{4}\qquad 4\frac{2}{4}=\frac{18}{4}$$

Follow the order of operations.

$$\frac{37}{4}-\left(\frac{11}{4}+\frac{18}{4}\right)$$

Brackets first.

$$\frac{37}{4}-\left(\frac{11}{4}+\frac{18}{4}\right)=\frac{37}{4}-\left(\frac{11+18}{4}\right)$$
$$=\frac{37}{4}-\frac{29}{4}$$

Complete the subtraction.

$$\frac{37}{4} - \frac{29}{4} = \frac{37-29}{4}$$
$$= \frac{8}{4}$$
$$= 2$$

Rheanna and Abdu have 2 km further to drive.

2. **Step 1**
Identify the fractions and the operational keywords.

$3\frac{3}{4}$ m of blue fabric

$4\frac{1}{3}$ m of purple fabric

"In total" means addition.

Step 2
Write an expression to represent the problem.

$3\frac{3}{4} + 4\frac{1}{3}$

Step 3
Solve the expression and reduce the answer to lowest terms if required.

Change the mixed numbers into improper fractions.

$$3\frac{3}{4} = \frac{3 \times 4 + 3}{4} \qquad 4\frac{1}{3} = \frac{4 \times 3 + 1}{3}$$
$$= \frac{15}{4} \qquad\qquad = \frac{13}{3}$$

Rewrite the improper fractions using the LCD. The LCD of 3 and 4 is 12.

$$\frac{15}{4} + \frac{13}{3} = \frac{45}{12} + \frac{52}{12}$$
$$\frac{15 \times 3}{4 \times 3} = \frac{45}{12}$$
$$\frac{13 \times 4}{3 \times 4} = \frac{52}{12}$$

Add the numerators while keeping the denominator the same.

$$\frac{45}{12} + \frac{52}{12} = \frac{45+52}{12}$$
$$= \frac{97}{12}$$

Step 4
Change the improper fraction to a mixed number.
$97 \div 12 = 8$ remainder 1

$$\frac{97}{12} = 8\frac{1}{12}$$

Rachel bought a total of $8\frac{1}{12}$ m of fabric.

PRACTICE EXERCISES
ANSWERS AND SOLUTIONS

1. **Step 1**
Identify the fractions and the operational keywords.

Holly bought $4\frac{2}{7}$ gallons of paint.

She used $\frac{3}{4}$ of a gallon of paint on Monday and

$1\frac{1}{2}$ gallons on Tuesday.

"How much paint does she still have left?" means subtraction.

Step 2
Write an expression to represent the problem.

$4\frac{2}{7} - \frac{3}{4} - 1\frac{1}{2}$

Step 3
Solve the expression and reduce the answer to lowest terms if required.

Change the mixed numbers into improper fractions.

$$4\frac{2}{7} = \frac{30}{7} \qquad \frac{3}{4} = \frac{3}{4} \qquad 1\frac{1}{2} = \frac{3}{2}$$

Rewrite the improper fractions using the LCD. The LCD of 2, 4, and 7 is 28.

$$\frac{30}{7} - \frac{3}{4} - \frac{3}{2} = \frac{120}{28} - \frac{21}{28} - \frac{42}{28}$$

Complete the subtraction, working from left to right.

$$\frac{120}{28} - \frac{21}{28} - \frac{42}{28} = \frac{120 - 21 - 42}{28}$$
$$= \frac{57}{28}$$

Step 4
Change the improper fraction to a mixed number.
$57 \div 28 = 2$ remainder 1

$$\frac{57}{28} = 2\frac{1}{28}$$

Holly has $2\frac{1}{28}$ gallons of paint left.

3. **Step 1**
Identify the fractions and the operational keywords.

Ginny bought $2\frac{2}{3}$ kg of jellybeans and $3\frac{1}{6}$ kg of gummy bears.
"In total" means addition.

Step 2
Write an expression to represent the problem.

$$2\frac{2}{3} + 3\frac{1}{6}$$

Step 3
Solve the expression and reduce the answer to lowest terms if required.
Change the mixed numbers into improper fractions.

$$2\frac{2}{3} = \frac{8}{3} \qquad\qquad 3\frac{1}{6} = \frac{19}{6}$$

Rewrite the improper fractions using the LCD.
The LCD of 3 and 6 is 6.

$$\frac{8}{3} + \frac{19}{6} = \frac{16}{6} + \frac{19}{6}$$

Add the numerators while keeping the same denominator.

$$\frac{16}{6} + \frac{19}{6} = \frac{16+19}{16}$$
$$= \frac{35}{6}$$

Step 4
Change the improper fraction to a mixed number.
$35 \div 6 = 5$ remainder 5

$$\frac{35}{6} = 5\frac{5}{6}$$

In total, Ginny bought $5\frac{5}{6}$ kg of candy.

5. **Step 1**
Identify the fractions and the operational keywords.

Josh spent $2\frac{3}{4}$ hours on homework and $4\frac{2}{3}$ hours babysitting.

"How many more hours did he spend…" means subtraction.

Step 2
Write an expression to represent the problem.

$$4\frac{2}{3} - 2\frac{3}{4}$$

Step 3
Solve the expression and reduce the answer to lowest terms if required.

Change the mixed numbers into improper fractions.

$$4\frac{2}{3} = \frac{14}{3} \qquad\qquad 2\frac{3}{4} = \frac{11}{4}$$

Rewrite the improper fractions using the LCD.
The LCD of 3 and 4 is 12.

$$\frac{14}{3} - \frac{11}{4} = \frac{56}{12} - \frac{33}{12}$$

Subtract the numerators while keeping the same denominator.

$$\frac{56}{12} - \frac{33}{12} = \frac{56-33}{12}$$
$$= \frac{23}{12}$$

Step 4
Change the improper fraction to a mixed number.
$23 \div 12 = 1$ remainder 11

$$\frac{23}{12} = 1\frac{11}{12}$$

Josh spent $1\frac{11}{12}$ hours more babysitting than he did doing homework.

7. **Step 1**
Identify the fractions and the operational keywords.

Ms. Olsen bought $6\frac{9}{10}$ kg of cheese.

The first class used $2\frac{1}{6}$ kg and the second class used $3\frac{3}{5}$ kg.

"How much cheese is left?" means subtraction.

Step 2
Write an expression to represent the problem.

$$6\frac{9}{10} - \left(2\frac{1}{6} + 3\frac{3}{5}\right)$$

Step 3
Solve the expression and reduce the answer to lowest terms if required.

Change the mixed numbers into improper fractions.

$$6\frac{9}{10}=\frac{69}{10} \quad 2\frac{1}{6}=\frac{13}{6} \quad 3\frac{3}{5}=\frac{18}{5}$$

Rewrite the improper fractions using the LCD. The LCD of 10, 6, and 5 is 30.

$$\frac{69}{10}-\left(\frac{13}{6}+\frac{18}{5}\right)=\frac{207}{30}-\left(\frac{65}{30}+\frac{108}{30}\right)$$

Solve the expression.

$$\frac{207}{30}-\left(\frac{65}{30}+\frac{108}{30}\right)=\frac{207}{30}-\left(\frac{65+108}{30}\right)$$
$$=\frac{207}{30}-\frac{173}{30}$$
$$=\frac{34}{30}$$
$$=\frac{17}{15}$$

Step 4
Change the improper fraction to a mixed number.
$17\div15=1$ R2

$$\frac{17}{15}=1\frac{2}{15}$$

Ms. Olsen has $1\frac{2}{15}$ kg of cheese left for the third class.

9. **Step 1**
Identify the fractions and the operational keywords.

Ayden has to prepare $3\frac{1}{2}$ pages, Ben has to

prepare $4\frac{1}{9}$ pages, and Hirsh has to prepare

$4\frac{1}{3}$ pages.

"In total" means addition.

Step 2
Write an expression to represent the problem.
$$3\frac{1}{2}+4\frac{1}{9}+4\frac{1}{3}$$

Step 3
Solve the expression and reduce the answer to lowest terms if required.

Change the mixed numbers into improper fractions.

$$3\frac{1}{2}=\frac{7}{2} \quad 4\frac{1}{9}=\frac{37}{9} \quad 4\frac{1}{3}=\frac{13}{3}$$

Rewrite the improper fractions using the LCD. The LCD of 2, 3, and 9 is 18.

$$\frac{7}{2}+\frac{37}{9}+\frac{13}{3}=\frac{63}{18}+\frac{74}{18}+\frac{78}{18}$$

Add the numerators while keeping the same denominator.

$$\frac{63}{18}+\frac{74}{18}+\frac{78}{18}=\frac{63+74+78}{18}$$
$$=\frac{215}{18}$$

Step 4
Change the improper fraction to a mixed number.
$215\div18=11$ R17

$$\frac{215}{18}=11\frac{17}{18}$$

In total, the report will have $11\frac{17}{18}$ pages .

Practice Test

ANSWERS AND SOLUTIONS

1. **Step 1**
Draw a grid based on the factors of the denominator. Use $3\times4=12$.

Step 2
Colour in the parts of the grid that are equivalent to each numerator.

The numerators are 4 and 3. Use a different shade for each numerator.

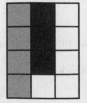

Step 3
Count the total number of shaded parts.

You have 7 shaded squares.

$$\frac{4}{12}+\frac{3}{12}=\frac{7}{12}$$

The sum of $\frac{4}{12}+\frac{3}{12}=\frac{7}{12}$.

3. **Step 1**
Draw a grid based on the factors of the denominator. Use $3\times4=12$.

Step 2
Shade in the parts of the grid that are equivalent to the first numerator.
The first numerator is 9.

Step 3
Cross out the shaded parts equivalent to the second numerator.
The second numerator is 3.

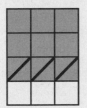

Step 4
Count the total number of remaining shaded parts.
There are 6 shaded squares left.

$$\frac{9}{12}-\frac{3}{12}=\frac{6}{12}$$

Notice that 2 out of 4 rows are left shaded.

The fraction $\frac{6}{12}$ can be reduced to $\frac{1}{2}$.

The difference of $\frac{9}{12}-\frac{3}{12}$ is $\frac{1}{2}$.

5. **Step 1**
Rewrite the fractions using the LCD.

Write the multiples of each denominator until a common one appears.
Multiples of 4: 4, 8, and **12**…
Multiples of 6: 6, **12**, 18…
The lowest common denominator of 4 and 6 is 12.

Multiply the numerator and the denominator of each fraction by the same factor.

$$\frac{3\times3}{4\times3}=\frac{9}{12} \qquad\qquad \frac{5\times2}{6\times2}=\frac{10}{12}$$

Step 2
Add the numerators of the fractions while keeping the denominators the same.

$$\frac{9}{12}+\frac{10}{12}=\frac{9+10}{12}$$
$$=\frac{19}{12}$$

Step 3
Reduce the fraction to lowest terms and convert to a mixed number.

$19\div12=1\ R7$

$$\frac{19}{12}=1\frac{7}{12}$$

$$\frac{3}{4}+\frac{5}{6}=1\frac{7}{12}$$

7. **Step 1**
Add the whole numbers.
$3+4=7$

Step 2
Add the fractions.

$$\frac{2}{12}+\frac{8}{12}=\frac{2+8}{12}$$
$$=\frac{10}{12}$$

Reduce to lowest terms.

The GCF of 10 and 12 is 2.

$$\frac{10\div2}{12\div2}=\frac{5}{6}$$

Step 3
Add the whole number and fraction.

$$7 + \frac{5}{6} = 7\frac{5}{6}$$

$$3\frac{2}{12} + 4\frac{8}{12} = 7\frac{5}{6}$$

9. **Step 1**
Change mixed numbers into improper fractions

$$4\frac{3}{10} = \frac{43}{10} \qquad\qquad 1\frac{1}{5} = \frac{6}{5}$$

Step 2
Rewrite the fractions using the LCD.

The LCD of 10 and 5 is 10.

$$\frac{43}{10} = \frac{43}{10} \qquad\qquad \frac{6 \times 2}{5 \times 2} = \frac{12}{10}$$

Step 3
Subtract the numerators of the fractions while keeping the denominators the same.

$$\frac{43}{10} - \frac{12}{10} = \frac{43 - 12}{10}$$
$$= \frac{31}{10}$$

Step 4
Change the improper fraction into a mixed number.

$$\frac{31}{10} = 31 \div 10$$
$$= 3\ \text{R}1$$
$$= 3\frac{1}{10}$$

$$4\frac{3}{10} - 1\frac{1}{5} = 3\frac{1}{10}$$

11. **Step 1**
Change mixed numbers into improper fractions.

$$5\frac{3}{4} = \frac{23}{4} \qquad\qquad 3\frac{2}{3} = \frac{11}{3}$$

Step 2
Rewrite the improper fractions with a common denominator.

$$\frac{23}{4} - \frac{11}{3} = \frac{69}{12} - \frac{44}{12}$$

Step 3
Subtract the numerators of the fractions while keeping the denominators the same.

$$\frac{69}{12} - \frac{44}{12} = \frac{69 - 44}{12}$$
$$= \frac{25}{12}$$

Step 4
Change the improper fraction into a mixed number.

$$\frac{25}{12} = 2\frac{1}{12}$$

$$5\frac{3}{4} - 3\frac{2}{3} = 2\frac{1}{12}$$

13. **Step 1**
Identify the fractions and the operational keywords.

Sam shovelled $\frac{2}{3}$ of the driveway yesterday and

$\frac{1}{6}$ of the driveway the day before.

Whole drive way is represented by 1, $\frac{1}{1}$.

"How much does he have left…"
means subtraction.

Step 2
Write an expression to represent the problem.

$$\frac{1}{1} - \left(\frac{2}{3} + \frac{1}{6} \right)$$

Step 3
Solve.

Follow the order of operations.
Rewrite the fractions using the LCD.
The LCD of 3 and 6 is 6.

$$\frac{2 \times 2}{3 \times 2} = \frac{4}{6} \qquad\qquad \frac{1 \times 1}{6 \times 1} = \frac{1}{6}$$

Brackets first.

$$\frac{6}{6} - \left(\frac{4}{6} + \frac{1}{6} \right) = \frac{6}{6} - \left(\frac{4 + 1}{6} \right)$$
$$= \frac{6}{6} - \frac{5}{6}$$

Complete the subtraction.

$$\frac{6}{6} - \frac{5}{6} = \frac{6 - 5}{6}$$
$$= \frac{1}{6}$$

Sam has $\frac{1}{6}$ of the driveway left to shovel.

15. **Step 1**
Identify fractions and key operation words.

Sports were chosen by $\frac{1}{3}$ of the students.

Band was chosen by $\frac{3}{10}$ of the students.

Art was chosen by $\frac{1}{6}$ of the students.

The class is equal to 1.

"What fraction of the class chose drama?" means subtraction.

Step 2
Write an expression to represent the problem.

$$\frac{1}{1} - \left(\frac{1}{3} + \frac{3}{10} + \frac{1}{6} \right)$$

Rewrite the fractions using the LCD.

$$\frac{30}{30} - \left(\frac{10}{30} + \frac{9}{30} + \frac{5}{30} \right)$$

Step 3
Solve.
Follow the order of operations.

$$\frac{30}{30} - \left(\frac{10}{30} + \frac{9}{30} + \frac{5}{30} \right) = \frac{30}{30} - \frac{24}{30}$$
$$= \frac{6}{30}$$
$$= \frac{1}{5}$$

$\frac{1}{5}$ of the class chose drama as their favourite activity.

THE CARTESIAN PLANE

Lesson 1—The Cartesian Plane

YOUR TURN
ANSWERS AND SOLUTIONS

1. **Step 1**
Determine the x-coordinate for each point.

To determine the x-coordinate, count horizontally from the origin. If the point is to the right of the origin, it is a positive count; if it is to the left of the origin, it is a negative count.

Point W is 1 unit to the right of the origin, so its x-coordinate is 1.
Point X is 4 units to the right of the origin, so its x-coordinate is 4.
Point Y is 5 units to the right of the origin, so its x-coordinate is 5.
Point Z is 8 units to the right of the origin, so its x-coordinate is 8.

Step 2
Determine the y-coordinate for each point.

To determine the y-coordinates, count vertically from the origin. If the point is above the origin, it is a positive count; if it is below the origin, it is a negative count.

Point W is 4 units above the origin, so its y-coordinate is 4.
Point X is 3 units above the origin, so its y-coordinate is 3.
Point Y is 7 units above the origin, so its y-coordinate is 7.
Point Z is 4 units above the origin, so its y-coordinate is 4.

Step 3
Write the ordered pairs.
Put brackets around the numbers, and separate them with a comma. The horizontal count (x-coordinate) goes first, and the vertical count (y-coordinate) goes second.

The coordinates of point W are (1, 4).
The coordinates of point X are (4, 3).
The coordinates of point Y are (5, 7).
The coordinates of point Z are (8, 4).

2. **Step 1**

Determine the placement of the *x*-coordinates. If the coordinate is positive, move to the right of the origin. If the coordinate is negative, move to the left of the origin.

For point *P*, move 2 spaces left of the origin (–2).

For point *Q*, move 2 spaces left of the origin (–2).

For point *R*, move 3 spaces right of the origin (3).

For point *S*, move 4 spaces right of the origin (4).

Step 2

Determine the placement of the *y*-coordinates. Count vertically from the *x*-axis. If the coordinate is positive, move up from the *x*-axis. If the coordinate is negative, move down from the *x*-axis.

For point *P*, move 3 spaces up from the *x*-axis (3).

For point *Q*, move 3 spaces down from the *x*-axis (–3).

For point *R*, move 4 spaces up from the *x*-axis (4).

For point *S*, move 2 spaces down from the *x*-axis (–2).

Step 3

Plot the points and label each point with its corresponding letter.

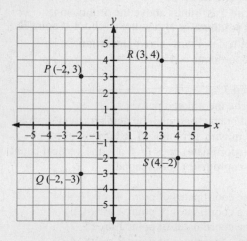

PRACTICE EXERCISES
ANSWERS AND SOLUTIONS

1. **Step 1**

Determine the *x*-coordinate for each point. To determine the *x*-coordinate, count horizontally from the origin. If the point is to the right of the origin, it is a positive count; if it is to the left of the origin, it is a negative count.

Point *A* is 3 spaces to the right of the origin, its *x*-coordinate is 3.
Point *B* is 2 spaces to the right of the origin, its *x*-coordinate is 2.
Point *C* is 3 spaces to the left of the origin, its *x*-coordinate is –3.
Point *D* is 2 spaces to the left of the origin, its *x*-coordinate is –2.

Step 2

Determine the *y*-coordinate for each point. To determine the *y*-coordinates, count vertically from the origin. If the point is above the origin, it is a positive count; if it is below the origin, it is a negative count.

Point *A* is on the *x*-axis, so its *y*-coordinate is 0.

Point *B* is 4 spaces above the origin, so its *y*-coordinate is 4.

Point *C* is 5 spaces below the origin, so its *y*-coordinate is –5.

Point *D* is 3 spaces above the origin, so its *y*-coordinate is 3.

Step 3

Write the ordered pairs. Put brackets around the numbers, and separate them with a comma. The *x*-coordinate goes first, and the *y*-coordinate goes second.

The coordinates of point *A* are (3, 0), of point *B* are (2, 4), of point *C* are (–3, –5), and of point *D* are (–2, 3).

3. **Step 1**

Determine the *x*-coordinate for each point. To determine the *x*-coordinate, count horizontally from the origin. If the point is to the right of the origin, it is a positive count; if it is to the left of the origin, it is a negative count.

Point *M* is 2 spaces to the right of the origin, so its *x*-coordinate is 2.

Point *N* is 4 spaces to the right of the origin, so its *x*-coordinate is 4.

Point *D* is 7 spaces to the right of the origin, so its *x*-coordinate is 7

Point *P* is 9 spaces to the right of the origin, so its *x*-coordinate is 9.

Step 2
Determine the *y*-coordinate for each point.
To determine the *y*-coordinates, count vertically from the origin. If the point is above the origin, it is a positive count; if it is below the origin, it is a negative count.

Point *M* is 3 spaces above the origin, so its *y*-coordinate is 3.

Point *N* is 4 is 6 spaces above the origin, so its *y*-coordinate is 6.

Point *D* is 4 spaces above the origin, so its *y*-coordinate is 4.

Point *P* is 8 spaces above the origin, so its *y*-coordinate is 8.

Step 3
Write the ordered pairs.
Put brackets around the numbers, and separate them with a comma. The *x*-coordinate goes first, and the *y*-coordinate goes second.

The coordinates of points *M*, *N*, *D*, and *P* are (2, 3), (4, 6), (7, 4), and (9, 8), respectively.

5. For the given coordinate pairs, the *x*-coordinates of the points are positive, and the *y*-coordinates are negative.

In quadrant I, both coordinates are positive.

In quadrant II, the *x*-coordinate is negative, and the *y*-coordinate is positive.

In quadrant III, both coordinates are negative.

In quadrant IV, the *x*-coordinate is positive, and the *y*-coordinate is negative.

The points represented by the coordinate pairs (5, −9) and (6, −3) are located in quadrant IV.

7. The following Cartesian plane shows the three points plotted correctly. It also shows the fourth vertex of the parallelogram.

The coordinates of the missing vertex are (3, 2).

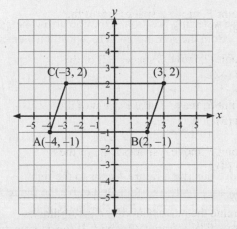

9. **A**
All four points are plotted in quadrant I on the Cartesian plane.

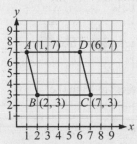

Line segments *AB* and *CD* are parallel and equal in length. Also, line segments *AD* and *BC* are parallel and equal in length. Consequently, the shape formed by joining the four points is a parallelogram.

10. The coordinates of Samuel's school at point *B* are (3, −5).

Lesson 2—Transformations

YOUR TURN
ANSWERS AND SOLUTIONS

1. Choose a starting position. Draw an arrow that moves from the starting point to a position 4 units right and 3 units down.

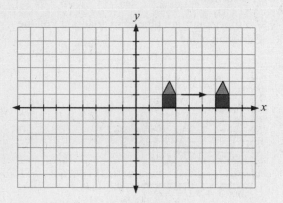

2. To move the given figure 4 units to the right, count each square as 1 unit, and move the figure 4 squares to the right. Draw the image in its new location.

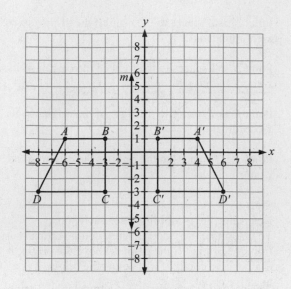

The coordinates of the reflected image are $A'(4, 1)$, $B'(1, 1)$, $C'(1, -3)$, and $D'(6, -3)$.

4. **a)** Trace the original figure, and rotate it 270° counterclockwise about the turn centre.

   b) Trace the original figure, and rotate it 180° clockwise about the turn centre.

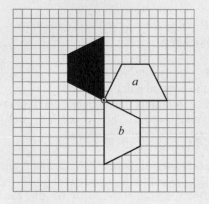

Images *a* and *b* show the required rotations of the original figure.

3. Vertex *A* is 5 units to the left of the mirror line, so *A'* will be 5 units to the right of the mirror line.

   Vertex *B* is 2 units to the left of the mirror line, so *B'* will be 2 units to the right of the mirror line.

   Vertex *C* is 2 units to the left of the mirror line, so *C'* will be 2 units to the right of the mirror line.

   Vertex *D* is 7 units to the left of the mirror line, so *D'* will be 7 units to the right of the mirror line.

   Plotting these points on the coordinate plane and connecting the points results in the following reflection.

5. **Step 1**
   Perform the first transformation using the original shape *ABCD*.

   The first transformation is a reflection about a line 1 unit to the right of the *y*-axis.

   Plot and label each new point. Then, connect the points with line segments to form quadrilateral A'B'C'D'.

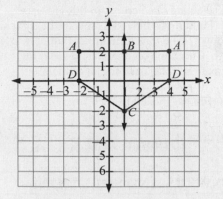

Step 2

Perform the second transformation using the transformed image.

The second transformation is a translation 2 units left and 3 units down.

Plot and label each new point, then connect these points with line segments to form the translated quadrilateral $A''B''C''D''$.

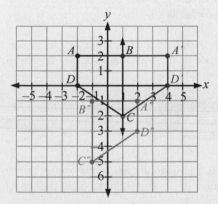

6. **Step 1**

Identify the coordinates of $M'N'O'$ after the first transformation is applied.

The first transformation is a reflection about the x-axis. The y-coordinates change to their opposite values while the x-coordinates stay the same.

$M'(1, 1)$ becomes $(1, -1)$

$N'(3, 1)$ becomes $(3, -1)$

$O'(2, 3)$ becomes $(2, -3)$

Step 2

Identify the coordinates of $M''N''O''$ after the second transformation is applied.

The second transformation is a translation of 4 units to the left and 2 units up. Subtract 4 from every x-coordinate, and add 2 to every y-coordinate.

$M''(1-4, -1+2)$ becomes $(-3, 1)$

$N''(3-4, -1+2)$ becomes $(-1, 1)$

$O''(2-4, -3+2)$ becomes $(-2, -1)$

The coordinates of triangle $M''N''O''$ are $M''(-3, 1)$, $N''(-1, 1)$, $O''(-2, -1)$.

PRACTICE EXERCISES
ANSWERS AND SOLUTIONS

1. Translate the figure 5 units to the right and 6 units down.

3. Move each vertex 2 units to the left and 5 units down.
   $A'(-4, 0)$, $B'(0, 0)$, $C'(1, -2)$, $D'(-3, -2)$

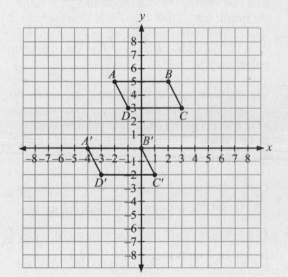

5. Each vertex of the image is plotted on the grid the same distance from the mirror line as each vertex in the original figure.

The coordinates are $W'(7, 4)$, $X'(4, 1)$, $Y'(7, -2)$, and $Z'(10, 1)$.

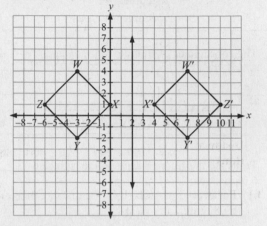

7. To draw the reflected image of the shaded figure, pick one vertex, and determine how far it is from the mirror line. Point C is 1 unit to the left of the line. That means the reflected image of point C, called C', must be placed 1 unit to the right of the reflection line.

Use the same process for locating each vertex on the opposite side of the reflection line. When you have marked each vertex, join them together to form a shape. The reflected shape should match the original shape.

Each vertex must be the same distance from the mirror line m.

The coordinates are $A'(9, 7)$, $B'(9, 2)$, and $C'(4, 7)$.

Each vertex must be the same distance from the mirror line m.

The coordinates are $A'(9, 7)$, $B'(9, 2)$, and $C'(4, 7)$.

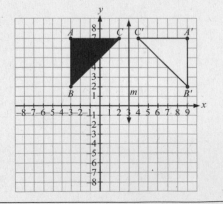

9. Start by selecting one vertex. In this case, use point A. Point A has moved 6 units to the right and 2 units down. The transformation of point A to A' is $[6, -2]$. Check the other points to see if the transformation is the same for all of them.

The hexagon has moved $[6, -2]$.

Practice Test

ANSWERS AND SOLUTIONS

1. D
The graph that represents the correct locations of the given points is graph **D**.

3. A
The graph that represents the correct locations of the two points is graph **A**.

5. Point U is 8 units to the left of the origin, so its x-coordinate is -8. It is 3 units below the origin, so its y-coordinate is -3.

Point V is 5 units to the left of the origin, so its x-coordinate is -5. It is 3 units below the origin, so its y-coordinate is -3.

Point X is 8 units to the left of the origin, so its x-coordinate is -8. It is 7 units below the origin, so its y-coordinate is -7.

Point W is 5 units to the left of the origin, so its x-coordinate is -5. It is 7 units below the origin, so its y-coordinate is -7.

The coordinates are $U(-8, -3)$, $V(-5, -3)$, $X(-8, -7)$, and $W(-5, -7)$.

7. Determine the slide rule being used. Since $A(4, 3)$ becomes $A'(8, 6)$, the slide rule is [4, 3].

Find the new coordinates by adding 4 to each x-coordinate and 3 to each y-coordinate.

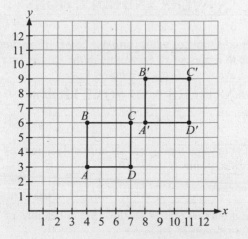

The coordinates of the translated image are $A'(8, 6)$, $B'(8, 9)$, $C'(11, 9)$, and $D'(11, 6)$.

9. Draw the mirror image of the given polygon.

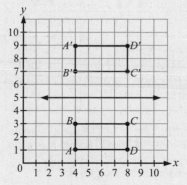

The vertices of the mirror image are $A'(4, 9)$, $B'(4, 7)$, $C'(8, 7)$, and $D'(8, 9)$.

11. The polygon is rotated 180° cw or ccw about the turn point located at (7, 7).

The image was then translated [8, 3] to position B.

13. The translation rule for the movement of the triangle from position 1 to position 2 is 5 right and 4 up or [5, 4].

PATTERNS

Lesson 1—Relating Patterns to Linear Relations

YOUR TURN
ANSWERS AND SOLUTIONS

1. a)

Time (h)	1	2	3	4	5	6
Distance (km)	80	160	240	320	400	480

b) For every hour travelled, the distance increases by 80 km.

c) $d = 80t$

d) $d = 80t$
$= 80(12)$
$= 960$ km

In 12 h, the car will travel 960 km.

2. **Step 1**
Determine what the first term could represent. Assuming the variable letter is meaningful, h could represent an hour; h is multiplied by 17.50.

Step 2
Determine what the constant could mean. 10 is subtracted from the product. It could represent a discount.

Step 3
Create a context that fits with the terms. A housecleaner charges $17.50 an hour and gives a $10.00 discount for booking in advance.

PRACTICE EXERCISES
ANSWERS AND SOLUTIONS

1.

Diagram 5

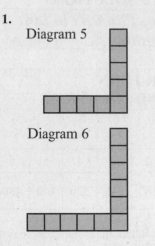

Diagram 6

3. $n = 2d + 1$

5.

x	y
1	5
2	10
3	15
4	20
5	25
6	30
7	35

7. $y = 5x$

9. Answers may vary.
Step 1
Determine what the first term could represent.
Assuming the variable letter is meaningful, l could represent length; l is multiplied by 0.25.

Step 2
Determine what the constant could mean.
1 is added to the product. It could represent the original length.

Step 3
Create a context that fits with the terms.
A lodgepole pine was 1 m tall before it was planted in the ground. The tree grows 0.25 m every year.

Lesson 2—Table of Values and Graphing

YOUR TURN
ANSWERS AND SOLUTIONS

1. Set up a table of values and use any numbers you like to represent x. Substitute in the values for x and evaluate the linear relation for y.

x	y
1	$5(1) - 7 = -2$
2	$5(2) - 7 = 3$
3	$5(3) - 7 = 8$
4	$5(4) - 7 = 13$

2. **Step 1**
Identify the ordered pairs that will be used to graph the relation.

Time	Temperature (°C)	Ordered Pair
5 P.M.	30	(5, 30)
6 P.M.	25	(6, 25)
7 P.M.	20	(7, 20)
8 P.M.	15	(8, 15)

Step 2
Draw and label the x-axis and y-axis.

Plot the ordered pairs on the graph.

Give the graph a suitable title.

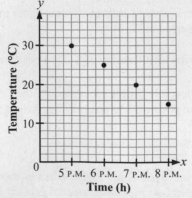

Recorded Temperature in Jasper

3. Since the points are rising to the right, the pattern indicates that the more time Tim works the more money he will earn.

PRACTICE EXERCISES
ANSWERS AND SOLUTIONS

1.

Number of chocolate bars (n)	Cost (C) ($\$$)
0	0
1	1.50
2	3.00
3	4.50
4	6.00
5	7.50
6	9.00

3. $C = 1.50n$
$= 1.50(10)$
$= 15.00$

It will cost $\$15.00$ to purchase 10 chocolate bars.

5.

Number of classes (n)	Cost (C) ($\$$)
0	0.00
1	14.00
2	28.00
3	42.00
4	56.00
5	70.00
6	84.00

7. $C = 14n$
$= 14(10)$
$= 140$

It will cost $\$140.00$ to attend 10 classes.

9. The points rise to the right, which indicates that the more watermelons in the crate, the greater the mass.

Practice Test

ANSWERS AND SOLUTIONS

1.

Number of DVDs rented	0	1	2	3	4
Rental fee ($\$$)	0	3.50	7.00	10.50	14.00

3. $r = 3.50n$

5.

Time (t) (h)	Cost (C) ($\$$)
0	0
1	60
2	120
3	180
4	240

7. Label the x-axis and y-axis, then plot ordered pairs.

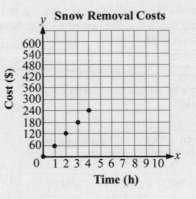

Snow Removal Costs

$Cost = 60 \times$ number of hours
$C = 60t$

9. $C = 60t$
$= 60(10)$
$= 600$
It will cost $\$600$ to complete 10 hours of snow removal.

11. Step 1
Create a table of values and identify a set of ordered pairs.

b	4b	Ordered Pair
1	4(1) = 4	(1, 4)
2	4(2) = 8	(2, 8)
3	4(3) = 12	(3, 12)
4	4(4) = 16	(4, 16)
5	4(5) = 20	(5, 20)

Step 2
Plot the ordered pairs on the graph.

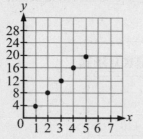

13. Step 1
Form an expression to represent the total cost. Let h represent the number of hours the hall is used.
The total cost is the sum of the booking fee and the cost for using the hall at the rate of $75 per hour. The expression is $50 + 75h$.

Step 2
Create a table of values and identify a set of ordered pairs.

h	50 + 75h	Ordered Pair
1	50 + 75(1) = 125	(1, 125)
2	50 + 75(2) = 200	(2, 200)
3	50 + 75(3) = 275	(3, 275)
4	50 + 75(4) = 350	(4, 350)
5	50 + 75(5) = 425	(5, 425)

Step 3
Plot the ordered pairs on the graph.

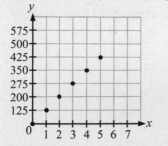

EXPRESSIONS AND EQUATIONS

Lesson 1—Evaluating Expressions

YOUR TURN
ANSWERS AND SOLUTIONS

1. Step 1
Substitute the value of the variable into the expression using brackets.
$$4(x-7)+2$$
$$=4(9-7)+2$$

Step 2
Evaluate the expression using BEDMAS.
$$=4(9-7)+2$$
$$=4(2)+2$$
$$=8+2$$
$$=10$$

2. There is an equal sign and the value of x can be solved. This matmatical statement is an equation.

PRACTICE EXERCISES
ANSWERS AND SOLUTIONS

When evaluating expressions, substitute the given value in for the variable, apply the order of operations, and evaluate the expression.

1. $3x-4$
$$=3(6)-4$$
$$=18-4$$
$$=14$$

3. $14z+11$
$$=14(5)+11$$
$$=70+11$$
$$=81$$

5. $3y-9z+13$
$$=3(10)-9(5)+13$$
$$=30-45+13$$
$$=-15+13$$
$$=-2$$

7. $4z - 9y - 12x + 21$
$= 4(5) - 9(10) - 12(6) + 21$
$= 20 - 90 - 72 + 21$
$= -70 - 72 + 21$
$= -142 + 21$
$= -121$

9. The constant term is 17.
The numerical coefficient is -12.
The variable is b.

Lesson 2—Preserving Equality

YOUR TURN
ANSWERS AND SOLUTIONS

1. Addition: $3r = 6$
$3r + 3 = 6 + 3$
$3r + 3 = 9$
Subtraction: $3r = 6$
$3r - 3 = 6 - 3$
$3r - 3 = 3$
Multiplication: $3r = 6$
$3r \times 3 = 6 \times 3$
$9r = 18$
Division: $3r = 6$
$3r \div 3 = 6 \div 3$
$r = 2$

2. **Step 1**
Draw a diagram using algebra tiles to represent the equation.

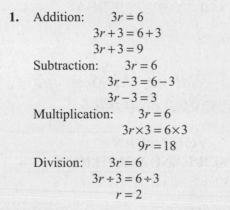

Step 2
Perform the opposite operation to both sides of the equation.

The opposite of adding 6 is to subtract 6. Subtract 6 squares from each side of the balance scale.

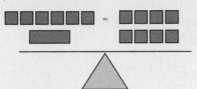

In this case, $n = 2$.

Step 3
Check the answer by substituting the value of n into the original equation.

$n + 6 = 8$
$(2) + 6 = 8$
$8 = 8$

PRACTICE EXERCISES
ANSWERS AND SOLUTIONS

1. **Step 1**
Draw a diagram using algebra tiles to represent the equation.

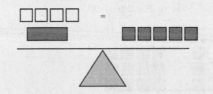

Step 2
Perform the opposite operation to both sides of the equation.

The opposite of subtracting 4 is adding 4.
Add 4 to each side of the equation.

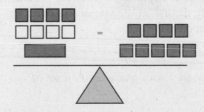

Remove equal numbers of positive and negative unit tiles from the left side of the equation.

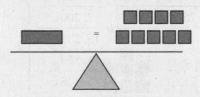

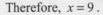

Therefore, $x = 9$.

3. **Step 1**
    Draw a diagram using algebra tiles to represent the equation.

    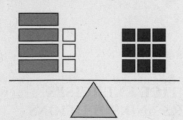

    Step 2
    Perform the opposite operation to both sides of the equation.

    Add 3 to each side of the equation.

    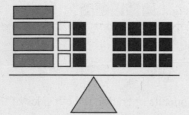

    Divide the right side of the equation into four equal parts.

    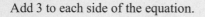

    Therefore, $n = 3$.

5   **Step 1**
    Draw a diagram using algebra tiles to represent the equation.

    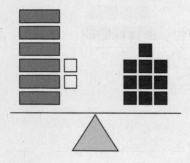

    Step 2
    Perform the opposite operation to both sides of the equation.

Add 2 to each side of the equation.

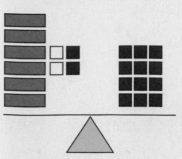

Divide the right side of the equation into six equal parts.

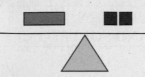

Therefore, $g = 2$.

Lesson 3—Solving One-Step and Two-Step Equations

YOUR TURN
ANSWERS AND SOLUTIONS

1. **Step 1**
    Perform the opposite operation to both sides of the equation.

    The opposite of subtracting 13 is adding 13.

    Add 13 to both sides of the equation.
    $$p - 13 = 54$$
    $$p - 13 + 13 = 54 + 13$$
    $$p = 67$$

    Step 2
    Check by substitution.
    $$p - 13 = 54$$
    $$(67) - 13 = 54$$
    $$54 = 54$$

2. **Step 1**
    Perform the opposite operation to both sides of the equation.

    The opposite operation of multiplying by 4 is dividing by 4.

Divide each side by 4.

$$4m = 16$$
$$\left(\frac{4m}{4}\right) = \frac{16}{4}$$
$$m = 4$$

Step 2
Check by substitution.

$$4m = 16$$
$$4(4) = 16$$
$$16 = 16$$

3. **Step 1**
    Perform the opposite operation to both sides of the equation.

    The opposite operation of dividing t by 8 is multiplying t by 8.

    Multiply each side by 8.

    $$\frac{h}{8} = 11$$
    $$\frac{8(h)}{8} = 8(11)$$
    $$h = 88$$

    Step 2
    Check by substitution.

    $$\frac{h}{8} = 11$$
    $$\frac{(88)}{8} = 11$$
    $$11 = 11$$

4. **Step 1**
    Perform the opposite operation of the constant to both sides of the equation.

    The opposite of subtracting 9 is adding 9.

    Add 9 to each side.

    $$5n - 9 = 21$$
    $$5n - 9 + 9 = 21 + 9$$
    $$5n = 30$$

    Step 2
    Perform the opposite operation of the variable to both sides of the equation.

    The opposite of multiplying n by 5 is to divide by 5.

Divide each side by 5.

$$\frac{5n}{5} = \frac{30}{5}$$
$$n = 6$$

Step 3
Check by substitution.

$$5n - 9 = 21$$
$$5(6) - 9 = 21$$
$$30 - 9 = 21$$
$$21 = 21$$

5. **Step 1**
    Define the variable.
    Let b equal the total number of beads.

    Step 2
    Write the equation.
    Since Raquel divides her beads into sets of 6 and there are exactly 20 beads in each group, the equation that represents this situation is $\frac{b}{6} = 20$.

    Step 3
    Isolate the variable to find the value of b.

    $$\frac{b}{6} = 20$$
    $$6\left(\frac{b}{6}\right) = (20)6$$
    $$b = 120$$

    Step 4
    Check by substitution.

    $$\frac{b}{6} = 20$$
    $$\frac{(120)}{6} = 20$$
    $$20 = 20$$

    Raquel has a total of 120 beads.

PRACTICE EXERCISES
ANSWERS AND SOLUTIONS

1. **Step 1**
    Isolate the variable by completing the opposite operation.

    The opposite of multiplying by 3 is dividing by 3.

Divide both sides of the equation by 3.
$$3r = 15$$
$$\frac{(3r)}{3} = \frac{15}{3}$$
$$r = 5$$

Step 2
Check by substitution.
$$3r = 15$$
$$3(5) = 15$$
$$15 = 15$$

3. **Step 1**
Perform the opposite operation to both sides of the equation.

The opposite of adding 8 is subtract 8.

Subtract 8 from both sides of the equation.
$$w + 8 = 2$$
$$w + 8 - 8 = 2 - 8$$
$$w = -6$$
Step 2
Check by substitution.
$$w + 8 = 2$$
$$(-6) + 8 = 2$$
$$2 = 2$$

5. **Step 1**
Perform the opposite operation of the constant to both sides of the equation.

The opposite of adding 5 is subtracting 5.

Subtract 5 from both sides of the equation.
$$3t + 5 = 23$$
$$3t + 5 - 5 = 23 - 5$$
$$3t = 18$$

Step 2
Isolate the variable by completing the inverse operation.

The inverse of multiplying by 3 is dividing by 3.
$$\frac{3t}{3} = \frac{18}{3}$$
$$t = 6$$

Step 3
Check by substitution.
$$3t + 5 = 23$$
$$3(6) + 5 = 23$$
$$18 + 5 = 23$$
$$23 = 23$$

7. **Step 1**
Perform the opposite operation of the constant to both sides of the equation.

The opposite of subtracting 4 is adding 4.

Add 4 to both sides of the equation.
$$7n - 4 = 31$$
$$7n - 4 + 4 = 31 + 4$$
$$7n = 35$$

Step 2
Isolate the variable by completing the inverse operation.

The inverse of multiplying by 7 is dividing by 7.

Divide both sides of the equation by 7.
$$\frac{7n}{7} = \frac{35}{7}$$
$$n = 5$$

Step 3
Check by substitution.
$$7n - 4 = 31$$
$$7(5) - 4 = 31$$
$$35 - 4 = 31$$
$$31 = 31$$

9. **Step 1**
Define the variable.
Let b equal the number of balloons.

Step 2
Write the equation.
Since Tina gave away 6 balloons and had 13 left, the equation that represents this situation is
$b - 6 = 13$.

Step 3
Isolate the variable to find the value of b.
$$b - 6 = 13$$
$$b - 6 + 6 = 13 + 6$$
$$b = 19$$

Step 4
Check by substitution.
$$b - 6 = 13$$
$$(19) - 6 = 13$$
$$13 = 13$$

Tina initially had 19 balloons.

Practice Test

ANSWERS AND SOLUTIONS

1. $7p+8r$
   $= 7(2)+8(7)$
   $= 14+56$
   $= 70$

3. The constant term is 36.
   The numerical coefficient is –9.
   The variable is g.

5. **Step 1**
   Draw a diagram using algebra tiles to represent the equation.

   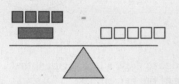

   Step 2
   Perform the opposite operation to both sides of the equation.

   Subtract 4 from each side of the equation.

   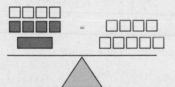

   Remove the zero pairs from the left side of the equation.

   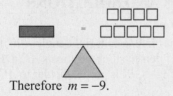

   Therefore $m = -9$.

7. Solve $\qquad$ Check
   $\qquad 45 = n-8 \qquad\qquad 45 = n-8$
   $45+8 = n-8+8 \qquad 45 = (53)-8$
   $\qquad 53 = n \qquad\qquad\quad 45 = 45$

9. Solve $\qquad\qquad$ Check
   $\quad 9h = 72$
   $\quad \dfrac{9h}{9} = \dfrac{72}{9} \qquad\qquad 9h = 72$
   $\qquad\qquad\qquad\quad 9(8) = 72$
   $\quad h = 8 \qquad\qquad\quad 72 = 72$

11. Solve $\qquad\qquad$ Check
    $\quad 5n-2 = 13$
    $5n-2+2 = 13+2 \qquad 5n-2 = 13$
    $\quad 5n = 15 \qquad\qquad 5(3)-2 = 13$
    $\quad \dfrac{5n}{5} = \dfrac{15}{5} \qquad\qquad 15-2 = 13$
    $\qquad\qquad\qquad\qquad 13 = 13$
    $\quad n = 3$

13. Solve $\qquad\qquad$ Check
    $\quad t-11 = 70 \qquad\qquad t-11 = 70$
    $t-11+11 = 70+11 \qquad (81)-11 = 70$
    $\qquad t = 81 \qquad\qquad\qquad 70 = 70$

15. Solve $\qquad\qquad$ Check
    $\quad 12h-6 = 30$
    $12h-6+6 = 30+6 \qquad 12h-6 = 30$
    $\quad 12h = 36 \qquad\qquad 12(3)-6 = 30$
    $\quad \dfrac{12h}{12} = \dfrac{36}{12} \qquad\qquad 36-6 = 30$
    $\qquad\qquad\qquad\qquad 30 = 30$
    $\quad h = 3$

17. Solve $\qquad\qquad$ Check
    $\quad 4k+6 = 34 \qquad\qquad 4k+6 = 34$
    $4k+6-6 = 34-6 \qquad 4(7)+6 = 34$
    $\quad 4k = 28 \qquad\qquad 28+6 = 34$
    $\quad \dfrac{4k}{4} = \dfrac{28}{4} \qquad\qquad 34 = 34$
    $\quad k = 7$

19. **Step 1**
    Define the variable. Let t equal the temperature in degrees Celsius.

    Step 2
    Write the equation. Since the temperature had risen 10°C since noon and ends up being –16°C by evening, the equation that represents this situation is $t+10 = (-16)$.

    Step 3
    Isolate the variable to find the value of t.
    $\quad t+10 = -16$
    $t+10-10 = -16-10$
    $\qquad t = -26$

    Step 4
    Check by substitution.
    $\quad t+10 = -16$
    $(-26)+10 = -16$
    $\qquad -16 = -16$

    The temperature at noon was –26°C.

GEOMETRIC CONSTRUCTIONS

Lesson 1—Line Segments

YOUR TURN
ANSWERS AND SOLUTIONS

1. **Step 1**
Draw line segment *JK* and place point *L* on it.

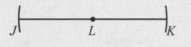

Step 2
Place a compass on point *L*, and draw two small arcs (with the same spread) that cut the line segment.

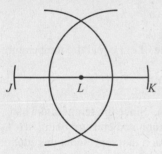

Step 3
Place the point of the compass on one arc. With a spread of about three-quarters of the distance between the two arcs, draw a semicircle. Repeat this procedure on the other small arc.

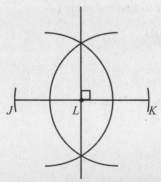

Step 4
Connect the two points of intersection.

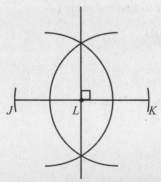

The new line is perpendicular to line segment *JK*.

2. **Step 1**
Draw the first line segment 5 cm long. Label each of the points at the ends of the line with a letter.

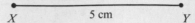

Step 2
Spread the two ends of a compass 1.5 cm apart. Place the point of the compass on one end of the line segment, and draw a circle. Repeat on the other end, keeping the same spread.

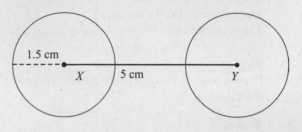

Step 3
Use a straight edge to draw a line segment that connects the top of the two circles.

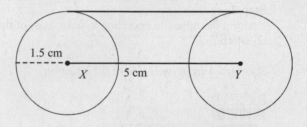

The new line is parallel to line segment *XY*.

PRACTICE EXERCISES
ANSWERS AND SOLUTIONS

1. Perpendicular lines intersect at right angles (90°). Line segment *BI* intersects line segments *AC*, *DE*, and *FG* at right angles, *BI* is perpendicular to *AC*, *DE*, and *FG*.
Line segment *BG* also intersects *AC*, *DE* and *FG* at right angles, *BG* is perpendicular to *AC*, *DE*, and *FG*.

3. **Step 1**
Draw the first line segment 12 cm long. Label the points at the ends of the line as *C* and *D*.

C ———— 12 cm ———— D

Step 2
Spread the two ends of the compass 3 cm apart.
Place the point of the compass on one end of the
line segment, and draw a circle. Repeat on the
other end, keeping the same spread.

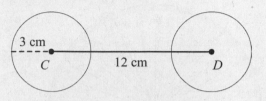

Step 3
Use a straight edge to draw a line segment
connecting the top of the two circles.

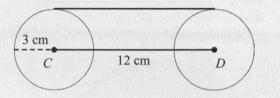

5. **Step 1**
Draw the line segment EF 1 cm long. Label each of
the points at the ends of the line with a letter.

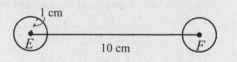

Step 2
Spread the two ends of the compass 0.1 dm, or
1 cm apart. Place the point of the compass on one
end of the line segment, and draw a circle.
Repeat on the other end, keeping the same spread.

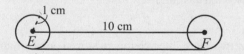

Step 3
Use a straight edge to draw a line segment that
connects the bottom or top of the two circles.

The new line is parallel to line segment EF.

7. Perpendicular lines are lines that intersect each
other at 90°. Since lines *p* and *m* intersect at 90°
and lines *p* and *l* intersect at 90°, they are
perpendicular.

9. **Step 1**

Draw line segment *FG*, and place point *H* on it.

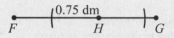

Step 2

Place a compass on point *H*, and draw two small
arcs (with the same spread) that cut the line
segment.

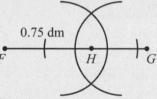

Step 3
Place the point of the compass on one arc.
With a spread of about three-quarters of the
distance between the two arcs, draw a semicircle.
Repeat this procedure on the other arc.

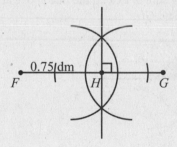

Step 4
Connect the two points of intersection using a
straight edge.

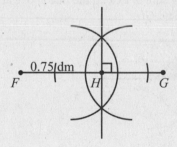

The new line is perpendicular to line segment *FG*.

Lesson 2—Perpendicular and Angle Bisectors

YOUR TURN
ANSWERS AND SOLUTIONS

1. **Step 1**
Draw line segment *JK* and label.

Step 2
Draw the first arc.
Place the compass point on point *J* and draw and arc on a circle that crosses the line segment close to point *K*.

Step 3
Draw the second arc.
Repeat the process from point *K*. Keep the same spread.

Step 4
Draw the perpendicular bisector.
Use a straight edge to draw a line segment connecting the two points where the two arcs or circles meet.

2. **Step 1**
Draw line segment *GH* 14 cm long.

G ——— 14 cm ——— *H*

Step 2
Divide the length by 2.
$14 \div 2 = 7$

Step 3
Plot point *I* 7 cm from either side. Place the corner of the right triangle at point *I*. Draw a line segment, making sure to extend the line above and below line segment *GH*.

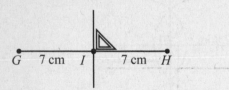

G 7 cm *I*   7 cm *H*

3. **Step 1**
Draw line segment *KL*. Use a protractor to add line segment MK at 66°.

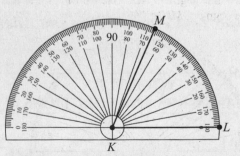

Step 2
Calculate the size of the bisected angle.
Divide the measure of the angle by 2.
$66° \div 2 = 33°$

Step 3
Use a protractor to mark this angle. Place the zero line on one of the line segments. Follow the inside numbers to 33. Plot point *J* at 33°.

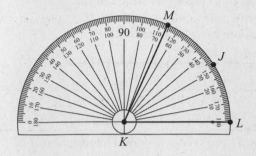

Step 4
Draw the angle bisector.
Use a straight edge to connect point *K* to point *J*.

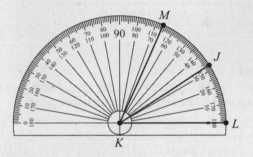

Line KJ is the angle bisector of ∠MKL

4. **Step 1**
Draw and label the angle.

Draw line segment *NO*. Use a protractor to add line segment *OP* at 128°.

Step 2
Draw an arc to intersect the two line segments of the angle. Place the point of the compass on point *O*. Draw an arc intersecting line segment NO and line segment *OP*. Label the points of intersection as *R* and *S*.

Step 3
Draw two more intersecting arcs from points *R* and *S*. Place the point of the compass on point *R*.

Draw an arc toward the middle of the angle. Repeat the process at point *S*, keeping the size of the compass opening the same. Label the point of intersection as *T*.

426

Step 4
Draw a line from the angle to the intersection point. Use a straight edge to connect point O to point T.

Step 5
Verify that the angles are equal. Use a protractor to measure the two new angles.

Line OT is the angle bisector of LNO.

PRACTICE EXERCISES
ANSWERS AND SOLUTIONS

1. **A**
A bisector is perpendicular if it intersects the line segment at a 90° angle.

3. **Step 1**
Draw line segment CD 12 cm long.

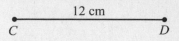

Step 2
Place the pointed end of the compass on point C of the line segment. Draw an arc that crosses the line segment at a distance greater than halfway between the two points.

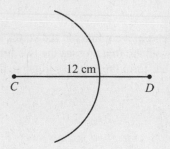

Step 3
Repeat the same process with the pointed end of the compass on point D of the line segment. Keep the spread of the compass the same. Label the points of intersection as A and B.

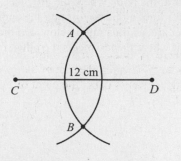

Step 4
Draw the perpendicular bisector. Use a straight edge to connect points A and B.

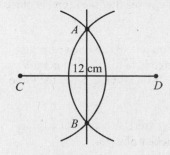

Line AB is the perpendicular bisector of line CD.

5. **Step 1**
Draw line segment AB 36 mm long.

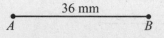

Step 2
Calculate the length of the bisected line segment. Divide the length by 2.
$36 \div 2 = 18$

Step 3
Plot point C 18 mm from either side. Place the corner of the right triangle at point C. Draw a line segment, making sure to extend the line above and below line segment AB.

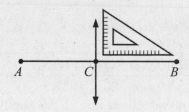

7. **Step 1**
Draw line segment NO. Use a protractor to add line segment MN at 140°.

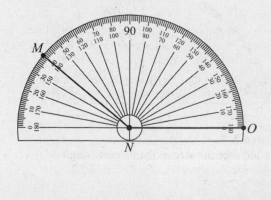

Step 2

Calculate the size of the bisected angle. Divide the measure of the angle by 2.

$140° \div 2 = 70°$

Step 3

Place the zero line on one of the line segments. Follow the inside numbers to 70. Plot point P at 70°.

Step 4

Draw the angle bisector. Use a straight edge to connect point N to point P.

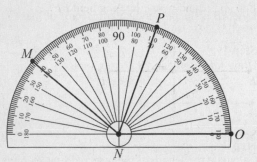

The angle bisector of $\angle LMO$ is line NP.

9. **A**

A perpendicular bisector intersects with another line to form a 90° angle. The post would be planted vertically, so it would be perpendicular to the horizontal plane of the ground.

Practice Test

ANSWERS AND SOLUTIONS

1. The line being drawn cuts the existing line exactly in half, so it is a bisector of some kind. Since there is a 90° angle that is formed from this construction, Terry constructed a perpendicular bisector.

3. **A**

An angle bisector divides an angle, not a line segment, into two equal parts at its vertex.

5. One method that Kelly can use to construct the perpendicular segments is as follows:

Step 1

Draw a line with the straight edge, and place a point where the perpendicular line will intersect it.

Step 2

Place the point of the compass on the point drawn. Draw two arcs that cut the line segment on both sides while keeping the same spread.

Step 3

Place the point of the compass on one of the arcs, where it intersects the line and draw a semicircle that cuts the line segment (ensure that the spread is more than half the distance between the two arcs).

Step 4

While keeping the same spread as before, place the point of the compass on the other arc where it intersects the line and draw a second semicircle.

Connect the two points of intersection using the straight edge.

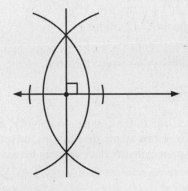

7. **Step 1**

Place the pointed end of a compass at the vertex of the angle and draw an arc that crosses the two lines or line segments that form the angle as illustrated below.

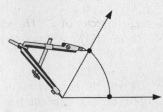

Step 2

lace the compass at the point where the arc meets one of the lines or line segments forming the angle and draw another arc, as illustrated below. Do the same at the point where the arc meets the other line.

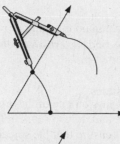

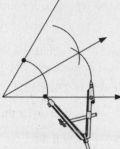

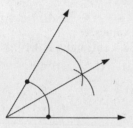

Step 3
Draw a ray starting at the vertex of the angle and passing through the point where the two arcs meet.

Step 2
Calculate the length of the bisected line segment.

Divide the length by 2.
$10 \div 2 = 5$

Step 3
Draw the perpendicular bisector.

Plot point D 5 cm from either side.

Place the corner of the right triangle at point D. Draw a line segment, making sure to extend the line above and below line segment EF.

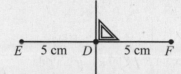

E 5 cm D 5 cm F

The ray is the angel bisector.

9. An angle bisector divides an existing angle in half, creating two equivalent angles.

Since line YW is the angle bisector of $\angle PYK$ and $\angle PYK$ measures 38°, then $\angle WYK$ will measure $\dfrac{38°}{2} = 19°$.

13. **Step 1**
Draw line segment GH 14 cm long.

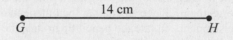

14 cm

G H

Step 2
Calculate the length of the bisected line segment.
Divide the length by 2.
$14 \div 2 = 7$

Step 3
Plot point 7 cm from either side. Place the corner of the right triangle at point I. Draw a line segment, making sure to extend the line above and below line segment GH.

11. **Step 1**
Draw line segment EF.

Plot point E. Measure 1 dm, which is equal to 10 cm. Then, plot point F.
Connect the two points.

10 cm

E F

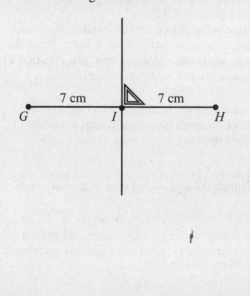

7 cm   7 cm

G I H

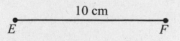

CIRCLES

Lesson 1—Introduction to Circles

YOUR TURN
ANSWERS AND SOLUTIONS

1. **Step 1**
Determine the value of r.

The radius of a circle is equal to half the diameter. If the diameter is 10 cm, the radius is 5 cm.
$10 \div 2 = 5$

Step 2
Draw a line segment 5 cm long using a ruler.

Step 3
Draw the circle using a compass.

Place the pointed end of the compass at one end of the line segment. Place a pencil at the other end of the line segment. Rotate the pencil tip around the pivot point until a circle is drawn.

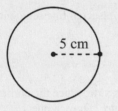

5 cm

2. **Step 1**
Determine the sum of the known angles.
$120° + 90° + 60° = 270°$

Step 2
Determine the total measure of degrees that are unknown.

The total measure of degrees in a circle is 360°. Subtract the known total of degrees from 360°.
$360° - 270° = 90°$

Step 3
Determine the measure of each individual angle.

The three angles are equal, so divide 90° by 3.
$90° \div 3 = 30°$

Each angle measures 30°.

3. **Step 1**
Choose the appropriate formula.
Use the formula $C = \pi d$ to find the circumference.

Step 2
Substitute in the known values.
The diameter is 3 cm, and π is 3.14.

Step 3
Solve for the unknown.
$C = \pi d$
$\quad = 3.14 \times 3$
$\quad = 9.42$ cm

The circumference of the circle is 9.42 cm.

4. **Step 1**
Choose the appropriate formula using the given values.

Use the formula $r = \dfrac{C}{2\pi}$ to find the radius.

Step 2
Substitute in the known values.
The circumference is 188.4 cm, and π is 3.14.

Step 3
Solve for the unknown.
$r = \dfrac{C}{2\pi}$
$\quad = \dfrac{188.4}{2 \times 3.14}$
$\quad = \dfrac{188.4}{6.28}$
$\quad = 30.144$ cm

The radius of the wheel is 30 cm.

PRACTICE EXERCISES
ANSWERS AND SOLUTIONS

1. **Step 1**
Determine the value of r.

The radius is 2.5 cm.

Step 2
Draw a line segment 2.5 cm long using a ruler.

Step 3
Draw the circle using a compass.
Place the pointed end of the compass at one end of

the line segment. Place a pencil at the other end of the line segment. Rotate the pencil tip around the pivot point until a circle is drawn.

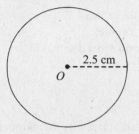

3. **Step 1**
    Calculate the total of the known angles.
    $90° + 110° + 70° = 270°$

    Step 2
    Subtract the total from 360° since the total measure of degrees in a circle is 360°.
    $360° - 270° = 90°$

    Step 3
    Determine the angle measures.
    Angle A and angle B equal 90°. Because angle B is twice the measure of angle A you can divide 90° by 3 to get the measure of angle B.
    $90° \div 3 = 30°$

    Since angle A is twice the measure of angle B, angle A equals 60° ($30° \times 2 = 60°$). Angle B is 30°.

5. **Step 1**
    Choose the appropriate formula using the given values.

    Use $r = \dfrac{C}{2\pi}$ to find the radius.

    Step 2
    Substitute in the known values.

    In this case, the circumference C is 28.26 cm and the value of π is 3.14.

    Step 3
    Solve for the unknown.
    $$r = \frac{C}{2\pi}$$
    $$= \frac{28.26}{6.28}$$
    $$= 4.5 \text{ cm}$$

    The radius of the circle is about 4.5 cm.

7. **Step 1**
    Choose the appropriate formula using the given values.

    Use the formula $C = \pi d$ to calculate the circumference.

    Step 2
    Substitute in the known values.

    In this case, the diameter d is 25 dm and the value of π is 3.14.

    Step 3
    Solve for the unknown.
    $$C = \pi d$$
    $$= (3.14)(25)$$
    $$= 78.5 \text{ dm}$$

    The circumference of the circle is about 78.5 dm.

9. **B**
    The value of π is a constant equal to the circumference of a circle divided by its diameter
    $$\pi = \frac{C}{d}.$$

    Therefore, if the circumference is divided by π, the result is the diameter of the circle.

Lesson 2—Constructing Circle Graphs

YOUR TURN
ANSWERS AND SOLUTIONS

1. **Step 1**
    Convert the data into decimal numbers.

    Divide each part of the data by the total data.

    The total pay cheque for the month is $1000.
    $$\text{Food} = 150 \div 1000$$
    $$= 0.15$$
    $$\text{Clothes} = 400 \div 1000$$
    $$= 0.4$$
    $$\text{Entertainment} = 100 \div 1000$$
    $$= 0.1$$
    $$\text{Savings} = 350 \div 1000$$
    $$= 0.35$$

    The total decimal numbers should add up to 1.
    $$0.15 + 0.4 + 0.1 + 0.35 = 1$$

Step 2
Calculate each percentage as an angle in degrees.

Divide the percentage by 100. Multiply each decimal number by 360°.

$$\text{Food} = 0.15 \times 360°$$
$$= 54°$$
$$\text{Clothes} = 0.4 \times 360°$$
$$= 144°$$
$$\text{Entertainment} = 0.1 \times 360°$$
$$= 36°$$
$$\text{Savings} = 0.35 \times 360°$$
$$= 126°$$

Step 3
Draw a circle.

Use a compass to make a circle large enough to label the sectors.

Use a protractor to draw each of the angles or sectors. Start at the top of the circle graph, using the largest angle. Move in a clockwise direction until the smallest angle is drawn.

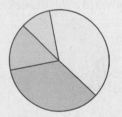

Step 4
Label the circle graph.

Include the category and percentage for each sector. Give the graph a title.

How Andre Used His Paycheque

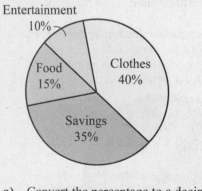

2. **a)** Convert the percentage to a decimal by dividing by 100.
$$56\% = 56 \div 100$$
$$= 0.56$$

Multiply the decimal number by the number of games played.

$$0.56 \times 50 = 28$$
The Cougars won 28 games.

b) Convert the percentage to a decimal by dividing by 100.
$$28\% = 28 \div 100$$
$$= 0.28$$

Multiply the decimal number by the number of games played.

$$0.28 \times 50 = 14$$
The Cougars lost 14 games.

c) Convert the percentage to a decimal by dividing by 100.
$$16\% = 16 \div 100$$
$$= 0.16$$

Multiply the decimal number by the number of games played.

$$0.16 \times 50 = 8$$
The Cougars had 8 tie games.

d) They won 28 games and tied 8 games. In total, 36 games were either won or tied.
or
Subtract the number of games lost from the total number of games played.
$$50 - 14 = 36$$

PRACTICE EXERCISES
ANSWERS AND SOLUTIONS

---

1. **Step 1**
Convert the percentage of money spent on clothes and food to decimal numbers.

Divide the percentage of money spent in each category by 100.
Clothes : $50 \div 100 = 0.50$
Food : $20 \div 100 = 0.20$

Step 2
Multiply the money spent on clothes and food by the total money spent.
Clothes: $0.50 \times 40 = \$20$
Food: $0.20 \times 40 = \$8$

Step 3
Add the money spent on clothes and food to determine the total money spent on food and clothes.
$20 + 8 = 28$

The money she spent on clothes and food altogether is $28.

3. Science was the subject that the most students liked the best.

5. **Step 1**
Convert the data into percentages.

Divide each part of the data by the total data. Then, multiply by 100 to get the percentage for each artist.
$5000 + 7500 + 6000 + 1150 + 4500$
$= 34\ 500$

The total number of people is 34 500.

Jennifer Lopez: $\dfrac{5\ 000}{34\ 500} \times 100\% \doteq 15\%$

Snoop Dog: $\dfrac{7\ 500}{34\ 500} \times 100\% \doteq 22\%$

50 Cent: $\dfrac{6\ 000}{34\ 500} \times 100\% \doteq 17\%$

Usher: $\dfrac{11\ 500}{34\ 500} \times 100\% \doteq 33\%$

Eminem: $\dfrac{4\ 500}{34\ 500} \times 100\% \doteq 13\%$

The total percentages should add up to 100.
$15 + 22 + 17 + 33 + 13 = 100$

Step 2
Calculate each percentage as an angle in degrees. Divide the percentage by 100. Then, multiply by 360°.

Jennifer Lopez: $\dfrac{15}{100} \times 360° = 54°$

Snoop Dog: $\dfrac{22}{100} \times 360° \doteq 79°$

50 Cent: $\dfrac{17}{100} \times 360° \doteq 61°$

Usher: $\dfrac{33}{100} \times 360° \doteq 119°$

Eminem: $\dfrac{13}{100} \times 360° \doteq 47°$

Step 3
Draw a circle. Use a compass to make a circle large enough to label the sectors.

Use a protractor to draw each of the angles or sectors. Start at the top of the circle graph, using the largest angle. Move in a clockwise direction until the smallest angle is drawn.

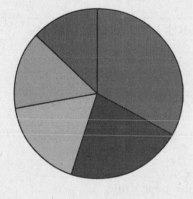

Step 4
Label the circle graph.

Include the category and percentage for each sector. Give the graph a title.

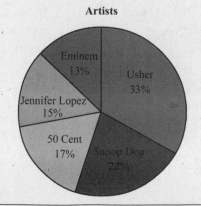

Artists

7. The sum of the percentages for dogs and cats is 65%. Find the percentage of 20 students by converting 65% to a decimal.

$$65 \div 100 = 0.65 \ \text{ or } \ \frac{65}{100} = 0.65$$

Multiply the new decimal fraction by 20 students to find the answer.

$0.62 \times 20 \text{ people} = 13 \text{ people}$ with either dogs or cats as pets

9. Cats
$30 \div 100 = 0.3$
$0.3 \times 20 \text{ people} = 6 \text{ people}$ with cats as pets.

Snakes
$5 \div 100 = 0.05$
$0.05 \times 20 \text{ people} = 1 \text{ person}$ with a snake as a pet.
$6 - 5 = 1$
5 more people have cats as pets than people with snakes.

Practice Test

ANSWERS AND SOLUTIONS

1. $C = \pi d$
   $ = 3.14 \times 3$
   $ = 9.42 \text{ mm}$

3. $d = \dfrac{C}{\pi}$
   $ = \dfrac{59.66}{3.14}$
   $ = 19 \text{ cm}$

5. $r = \dfrac{C}{2\pi}$
   $ = \dfrac{100.48}{2 \times 3.14}$
   $ = \dfrac{100.48}{6.28}$
   $ = 16 \text{ dm}$

7. **Step 1**
   Calculate the decimal number for the time Janet spends watching each type of show.

   Calculate the total umber of hours the television is watched.
   $5 + 15 + 5 = 25$

Soap opera: $5 \div 25 = 0.2$
Reality shows: $15 \div 25 = 0.6$
News: $5 \div 25 = 0.2$

Step 2
Calculate the angle of each section.
Soap opera: $0.2 \times 360° = 72°$
Reality shows: $0.6 \times 360° = 216°$
News: $0.2 \times 360° = 72°$

Step 3
Use a protractor to draw the graph.

Janet's Time Spent Watching Television Each Week

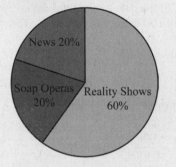

9. Sandals: $\dfrac{36}{184} \times 100\% \doteq 20\%$
   Sandals made up about 20% of the shoe sales.

11. **Step 1**
   Convert the data into percentages.

   Sandals: $\dfrac{36}{184} \times 100\% \doteq 20\%$

   Boots: $\dfrac{28}{184} \times 100\% \doteq 15\%$

   Loafers: $\dfrac{24}{184} \times 100\% \doteq 13\%$

   Sneakers: $\dfrac{48}{184} \times 100\% \doteq 26\%$

   Slippers: $\dfrac{20}{184} \times 100\% \doteq 11\%$

   Pumps: $\dfrac{28}{184} \times 100\% \doteq 15\%$

   Step 2
   Calculate the degrees needed for each section of the circle by converting each percentage into a decimal, and then multiply the result by 360°.
   Sandals : $0.20 \times 360° = 72°$
   Boots : $0.15 \times 360° = 54°$
   Loafers : $0.13 \times 360° \doteq 47°$

Sneakers: $0.26 \times 360° \doteq 94°$

Slippers: $0.11 \times 360° \doteq 40°$

Pumps: $0.15 \times 360° = 54°$

Step 3
Draw a circle using a compass. Use a straight edge to draw a line from the centre of the circle to the top edge. Then, use a protractor to draw each of the angles. Label each section with a percentage and title.

Step 4
Give the graph a title.

Shoe Sales for 1 Week

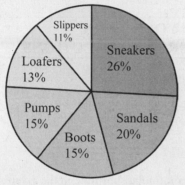

13. **Step 1**
Determine the decimal that represents the portion of sunny days in June.

$$\frac{\text{sunny days}}{\text{total days}} = \frac{12}{30}$$
$$= 12 \div 30$$
$$= 0.40$$

Step 2
Calculate 0.40 of 360°.
$0.40 \times 360° = 144°$

The degrees of the circle used to represent the sunny days is 144°.

AREA

Lesson 1—Area of a Parallelogram

YOUR TURN
ANSWERS AND SOLUTIONS

1. **Step 1**
Determine the given values.
The base is 13.5 cm and the height is 11.0 cm.

Step 2
Apply the area formula, substitute in the given values, and solve.
$$A = b \times h$$
$$= 13.5 \times 11$$
$$= 148.5 \text{ cm}^2$$
The area of the parallelogram is 148.5 cm^2.

2. **Step 1**
Determine the given values.
The height is 27 mm and the area is 2 538 mm^2.

Step 2
Apply the area formula, substitute in the given values, and solve for the base.
$$A = b \times h$$
$$(2\,538) = b \times (27)$$
$$\frac{2\,538}{27} = \frac{27b}{27}$$
$$94 = b$$

The base of the parallelogram is 94 mm.

PRACTICE EXERCISES
ANSWERS AND SOLUTIONS

1. **Step 1**
Determine the given values.
If the base is 5 cm then the height is 5 cm + 2 cm.

The height is 7 cm.

Step 2
Apply the area formula, substitute in the given values, and solve.
$$A = b \times h$$
$$= 5 \times 7$$
$$= 35 \text{ cm}^2$$
The area is 35 cm^2.

3. **Step 1**
Determine the given values.
The base is 1.8 m and the height is 1.4 m.

Step 2
Apply the area formula, substitute in the given values, and solve.
$A = b \times h$
$A = 1.8 \times 1.4$
$A = 2.52 \text{ m}^2$

To cover the floor, 2.52 m^2 of carpet is needed.

5. **Step 1**
Find the area of the parallelogram that has a base of 3 m and a height of 7 m.
$A = b \times h$
$\quad = 3 \times 7$
$\quad = 21 \text{ m}^2$

Step 2
Find the area of the parallelogram that has a base of $3 \text{ m} \times 2$ and the height of $7 \text{ m} \times 2$ is 14 m.
$A = b \times h$
$\quad = 6 \times 14$
$\quad = 84 \text{ m}^2$

Step 3
Calculate how many times bigger the larger parallelogram is than the smaller parallelogram.

Divide the area of the large parallelogram by the area of the smaller. $84 \div 21 = 4$

The larger parallelogram has an area that is four times greater than the smaller parallelogram.

7. **Step 1**
Determine the given values.
The height is 40 m and the area is 400 m^2.

Step 2
Apply the area formula, substitute in the given values, and solve for the base.
$A = b \times h$
$400 = b \times 40$
$\dfrac{400}{40} = \dfrac{40b}{40}$
$\quad 10 = b$

The base of the garden is 10 m.

9. $A = b \times h$
$72 = b \times h$

To find the base and height, try to find multiples of 72 in which one multiple is half of the other multiple.
Multiples of 72:
$1 \times 2, \ 2 \times 36, \ 3 \times 24, \ 4 \times 18, \ 6 \times 12, \ 8 \times 9$

The multiple 6 is half of the multiple 12.
$6 \times 12 = 72$
Therefore, the base is 6 cm and the height is 12 cm.

Lesson 2—Area of a Triangle

YOUR TURN
ANSWERS AND SOLUTIONS

1. **Step 1**
Determine the given values.
The base is 8 square units and the height is 5 square units.

Step 2
Apply the area formula, substitute in the given values, and solve.
$A = \dfrac{1}{2} bh$
$\quad = \dfrac{8 \times 5}{2}$
$\quad = \dfrac{40}{2}$
$\quad = 20 \text{ units}^2$

The area of the triangle is 20 square units.

2. **Step 1**
Determine the given values.
The base is 170 mm, or 1.7 cm, and the height 4 cm.

Step 2
Apply the area formula, substitute in the given values, and solve.
$A = \dfrac{1}{2} bh$
$\quad = \dfrac{1.7 \times 4}{2}$
$\quad = \dfrac{6.8}{2}$
$\quad = 3.4 \text{ cm}^2$

The area of the triangle is 3.4 cm^2.

PRACTICE EXERCISES
ANSWERS AND SOLUTIONS

1. **Step 1**
Determine the given values.
The base is 7.6 m and the height 5 m.

   Step 2
Apply the area formula, substitute in the given values, and solve.

$$A = \frac{1}{2}bh$$
$$= \frac{(7.6) \times (5)}{2}$$
$$= \frac{38}{2}$$
$$= 19 \text{ m}^2$$

   The area of the triangle is 19 m^2.

3. **Step 1**
Determine the given values.
The base is 10.2 cm and the height 7.2 cm.

   Step 2
Apply the area formula, substitute in the given values, and solve.

$$A = \frac{1}{2}bh$$
$$= \frac{10.2 \times 7.2}{2}$$
$$= \frac{73.44}{2}$$
$$= 36.72 \text{ cm}^2$$

   The area of the triangle is 36.72 cm^2.

5. **Step 1**
Determine the given values.
The base is 5 cm and the height 3 cm.

   Step 2
Apply the area formula, substitute in the given values, and solve.

$$A = \frac{1}{2}bh$$
$$= \frac{5 \times 3}{2}$$
$$= 7.5 \text{ cm}^2$$

   The area of the triangle is 7.5 cm^2.

7. **Step 1**
Determine the given values.
If the base is 27 cm then the height is $27 \div 3$.

   The base is 27 cm and the height is 9 cm.

   Step 2
Apply the area formula, substitute in the given values, and solve.

$$A = \frac{1}{2}bh$$
$$= \frac{27 \times 9}{2}$$
$$= \frac{243}{2}$$
$$= 121.5 \text{ cm}^2$$

   The area of the triangle is 121.5 cm^2.

9. **Step 1**
Determine the given values.
The base is BC and the height is AB. The base is 16 cm and the height is 12 cm.

   Step 2
Apply the area formula, substitute in the given values, and solve.

$$A = \frac{1}{2}bh$$
$$= \frac{16 \times 12}{2}$$
$$= \frac{192}{2}$$
$$= 96 \text{ cm}^2$$

   The area of the triangle is 96 cm^2.

Lesson 3—Area of a Circle

YOUR TURN
ANSWERS AND SOLUTIONS

1. **Step 1**
Determine the given values.
The diameter is 6 mm, so the radius is
$6 \div 2 = 3$ mm.

   Step 2
Apply the area formula, substitute in the given values, and solve.

$A = \pi r^2$

$\qquad = (3.14)(3)^2$

$\qquad = (3.14)(9)$

$\qquad = 28.26 \text{ mm}^2$

The area of the circle is about 28.26 mm².

2. **Step 1**

Determine the given values.
The area is 69.08 m².

Step 2

Apply the area formula, substitute in the given values, and solve for the radius.

$A = \pi r^2$

$69.08 = (3.14)r^2$

$\dfrac{69.08}{3.14} = \dfrac{3.14r^2}{3.14}$

$\qquad 22 = r^2$

Take the square root of both sides to solve for r.

$\sqrt{22} = \sqrt{r^2}$

$4.69 \doteq r$

Step 3

Calculate the diameter of the circle.
The diameter of a circle is twice the radius, so the diameter can be found by multiplying the radius by 2.
$4.69 \times 2 = 9.38$

The diameter of the circle is about 9.38 m.

PRACTICE EXERCISES
ANSWERS AND SOLUTIONS

1. **Step 1**

Determine the given values.
The radius is 8.5 mm.

Step 2

Apply the area formula, substitute in the given values, and solve.

$A = \pi r^2$

$\qquad = (3.14)(8.5)^2$

$\qquad = (3.14)(72.25)$

$\qquad = 226.865 \text{ mm}^2$

The area of the circle is about 226.87 mm².

3. **Step 1**

Determine the given values. The radius is 4.2 cm.

Step 2

Apply the area formula, substitute in the given values, and solve.

$A = \pi r^2$

$\qquad = (3.14)(4.2)^2$

$\qquad = (3.14)(17.64)$

$\qquad = 55.39 \text{ cm}^2$

The area of the circle is about 55.39 cm².

5. **Step 1**

Calculate the area of a circle if its radius is 1 m.

$A = \pi r^2$

$\qquad = (3.14)(1)^2$

$\qquad = 3.14 \text{ m}^2$

Step 2

Calculate the area of a circle if its radius is 2 m.

$A = \pi r^2$

$\qquad = (3.14)(2)^2$

$\qquad = (3.14)(4)$

$\qquad = 12.56 \text{ m}^2$

Step 3

Determine how many times bigger the larger circle is than the smaller circle.
$12.56 \div 3.14 = 4$

Each time the radius doubles, the area gets four times larger.

7. **Step 1**

Calculate the area of a triangular garden. The base is 4 m and the height is 5 m.

Apply the area formula for a triangle, substitute in the given values, and solve.

$A = \dfrac{1}{2}bh$

$\qquad = \dfrac{(4) \times (5)}{2}$

$\qquad = \dfrac{20}{2}$

$\qquad = 10 \text{ m}^2$

Step 2

Calculate the area of a circular garden.

The diameter is 4 m and the radius is $4 \div 2 = 2$ m.

Apply the area formula for a circle, substitute in the given values, and solve.

$A = \pi r^2$

$= (3.14)(2)^2$

$= (3.14)(4)$

$= 12.56 \text{ m}^2$

According to these calculations, Jackie will make better use of her backyard if she plants a circular garden.

9. **Step 1**

Calculate the radius of the circle.
To find the radius, divide the diameter by 2.

$r = \dfrac{d}{2}$

$= \dfrac{2.5}{2}$

$= 1.25$

Step 2

Apply the area formula, substitute in the given values, and solve.

$A = \pi r^2$

$= (3.14)(1.25)^2$

$= (3.14)(1.5625)$

$= 4.90625 \text{ m}^2$

The area of the circular base is about 4.9 m².

Practice Test

ANSWERS AND SOLUTIONS

1. **Step 1**

Determine the given values.
The base is $13.5 \text{ cm} \div 2 = 6.75 \text{ cm}$ and the height is $11 \text{ cm} \div 2 = 5.5 \text{ cm}$. The base is 6.75 cm and the height is 5.5 cm.

Step 2

Apply the area formula for a parallelogram, substitute in the given values, and solve.

$A = bh$

$= 6.75 \times 5.5$

$= 37.125 \text{ cm}^2$

The area of the parallelogram is 37.125 cm².

3. **Step 1**

Determine the given values.
The base is 4.5 cm and the height is 3 cm.

Step 2

Apply the area formula for a parallelogram, substitute in the given values, and solve.

$A = bh$

$= 4.5 \times 3$

$= 13.5 \text{ cm}^2$

The area of the parallelogram is 13.5 cm².

5. **Step 1**

Determine the given values.
The base is 4.6 cm and the height is 1.7 cm.

Step 2

Apply the area formula for a parallelogram, substitute in the given values, and solve.

$A = bh$

$= 4.6 \times 1.7$

$= 7.82 \text{ cm}^2$

The area of the parallelogram is 7.82 cm².

7. **Step 1**

Determine the given values.
The radius is 2.8 cm.

Step 2

Apply the area formula for a circle, substitute in the given values, and solve.

$A = \pi r^2$

$= (3.14)(2.8)^2$

$= (3.14)(7.84)$

$= 24.6176 \text{ cm}^2$

The area of the circle is about 24.62 cm².

9. **Step 1**

Determine the given values.
The base of triangle 1 is 10 cm and its height is 40 cm.

The base of triangle 2 is 20 cm and its height is 20 cm.

Step 2

Use the area formula for a triangle, substituting the values.

$A_{\text{triangle 1}} = \dfrac{1}{2} bh \qquad A_{\text{triangle 2}} = \dfrac{1}{2} bh$

$A = \dfrac{10 \times 40}{2} \qquad\qquad A = \dfrac{20 \times 20}{2}$

$A = 200 \text{ cm}^2 \qquad\qquad A = 200 \text{ cm}^2$

The area of both triangles is 200 cm², so they do have the same area.

11. Step 1
Determine the given values. The base of the rectangle is 10 cm and its height is 4 cm.
The diameter of the circle is 3 cm and the radius is $3 \div 2 = 1.5$ cm.

Step 2
Apply the area formula for a rectangle and a circle, substituting the values, and solve.

$A_{\text{rectangle}} = bh$
$A = 10 \times 4$
$A = 40$ cm^2

$A_{\text{circle}} = \pi r^2$
$A = 3.14 \times 1.5^2$
$A = 3.14 \times 2.25$
$A = 7.065$ cm^2

Step 3
To calculate the area of the shaded region subtract the area of the circle from the area of the rectangle.
40 cm$^2 - 7.065$ cm$^2 = 32.935$ cm^2

The area of the shaded region in the rectangle is 32.9 cm^2 (to the nearest centimeter).

13. The area of the parallelogram is twice the area of each triangle.

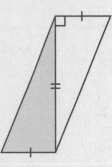

The area of the parallelogram is 50 cm^2.
50 cm$^2 = 2 \times$ area of each triangle
$\dfrac{50 \text{ cm}^2}{2} = \dfrac{2 \times \text{area of each triangle}}{2}$
25 cm$^2 =$ area of each triangle

Therefore, the area of each triangle is 25 cm^2.

PROBABILITY

Lesson 1—Introduction to Probability

YOUR TURN
ANSWERS AND SOLUTIONS

1. a) None of the items that Hank purchased are a pair of shoelaces. Therefore, the probability of Hank picking a pair of shoelaces from the bag is 0.

b) All of the items that Hank purchased are socks. Therefore, the probability of Hank picking a pair of shoes from the bag is 1.

2. Step 1
Calculate the probability.
Substitute the known values into the probability formula and evaluate.

$$P = \frac{\text{favourable outcomes}}{\text{total possible outcomes}}$$

$$P(\text{green marble}) = \frac{2}{6}$$
$$= \frac{1}{3}$$

Step 2
Express the probability as a fraction, ratio, and percentage.

Expressed as a fraction, the probability is $\dfrac{1}{3}$.

Expressed as a ratio, the probability is 1:3.

To express the probability as a percentage, use the probability fraction. Divide the numerator by the denominator, and multiply the result by 100.
$1 \div 3 = 0.\overline{3}$
$0.\overline{3} \times 100 = 33.\overline{3}\%$
The probability of pulling out a green marble is 33%.

PRACTICE EXERCISES
ANSWERS AND SOLUTIONS

Apply the probability formula to determine the probability of each event in questions #1-5.

$$P = \frac{\text{favourable outcomes}}{\text{total possible outcomes}}$$

1. $P(4) = \dfrac{1}{8}$

3. $P(\text{multiple of } 2) = \dfrac{4}{8}$

    $= \dfrac{1}{2}$

5. $P(1 \text{ or } 3) = \dfrac{2}{8}$

    $= \dfrac{1}{4}$

7. Total possible outcomes: 10 pens in the box.
    Favourable outcomes: 2 red pens.

    Substitute the known values into the probability formula and evaluate for *P*.

    $$P = \frac{\text{favourable outcomes}}{\text{total possible outcomes}}$$

    $P(\text{red}) = \dfrac{2}{10}$

    $= \dfrac{1}{5}$

    Expressed as a ratio, the probability is 1:5.
    Expressed as a percentage, the probability is 20%.

9. Total possible outcomes: 660 students.
    Favourable outcomes: 132 students with a pet cat.

    Substitute the known values into the probability formula and evaluate for *P*.

    $$P = \frac{\text{favourable outcomes}}{\text{total possible outcomes}}$$

    $P(\text{cat}) = \dfrac{132}{660}$

    $= \dfrac{1}{5}$

    Expressed as a ratio, the probability is 1:5.
    Expressed as a percentage, the probability is 20%.

Lesson 2—Independent Events and Sample Space

YOUR TURN
ANSWERS AND SOLUTIONS

1. **Step 1**
    Identify the outcomes of the first event.
    Outcomes of rolling the regular number cube are: 1, 2, 3, 4, 5, 6.

    Step 2
    Identify the outcomes of the second event.
    Outcomes of tossing the coin are: Heads, Tails.

    Step 3
    Display outcomes in a table.
    The table headers are the events in the experiment.
    Combine the outcome on the side of the table with the outcome at the top of the table.

		Coin	
		Heads (H)	**Tails (T)**
Number cube	**1**	1H	1T
	2	2H	2T
	3	3H	3T
	4	4H	4T
	5	5H	5T
	6	6H	6T

    The sample space is {1H, 1T, 2H, 2T, 3H, 3T, 4H, 4T, 5H, 5T, 6H, 6T}.

2. **Step 1**
    Identify the outcomes of the first event.
    Outcomes of spinning the spinner are: Yellow, Blue, Purple, Orange.

    Step 2
    Identify the outcomes of the second event.
    Outcomes of tossing the coin are: Heads, Tails.

    Step 3
    Display outcomes in a tree diagram.
    Start with the first event (spinner), and list the outcomes (Yellow, Blue, Purple and Orange).
    Draw a branch from each of these outcomes to each of the outcomes (H, T) of the second event.

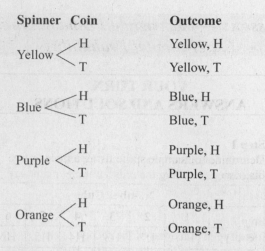

Spinner	Coin	Outcome
Yellow	H	Yellow, H
	T	Yellow, T
Blue	H	Blue, H
	T	Blue, T
Purple	H	Purple, H
	T	Purple, T
Orange	H	Orange, H
	T	Orange, T

The sample space is
{YH, YT, BH, BT, PH, PT, OH, OT}.

PRACTICE EXERCISES
ANSWERS AND SOLUTIONS

1. **Step 1**
Identify the outcomes of the first event.
Outcomes of rolling Cube A are: 1, 2, 3, 4, 5, 6.

Step 2
Identify the outcomes of the second event.
Outcomes of rolling Cube B are: 1, 2, 3, 4, 5, 6.

Step 3
Display outcomes in a table.
The table headers are the events in the experiment.
Combine the outcome on the side of the table with the outcome at the top of the table.

				Cube A			
		1	2	3	4	5	6
Cube B	1	1,1	1,2	1,3	1,4	1,5	1,6
	2	2,1	2,2	2,3	2,4	2,5	2,6
	3	3,1	3,2	3,3	3,4	3,5	3,6
	4	4,1	4,2	4,3	4,4	4,5	4,6
	5	5,1	5,2	5,3	5,4	5,5	5,6
	6	6,1	6,2	6,3	6,4	6,5	6,6

The sample space is {(1, 1), (1, 2), (1, 3), (1, 4), (1, 5), (1, 6), (2, 1), (2, 2), (2, 3), (2, 4), (2, 5), (2, 6), (3, 1), (3, 2), (3, 3), (3, 4), (3, 5), (3, 6), (4, 1), (4, 2), (4, 3), (4, 4), (4, 5), (4, 6), (5, 1), (5, 2), (5, 3), (5, 4), (5, 5), (5, 6), (6, 1), (6, 2), (6, 3), (6, 4), (6, 5), (6, 6)}.

---

3. **Step 1**
Identify the outcomes of the first event.
Outcomes of tossing the coin are: Heads, Tails.

Step 2
Identify the outcomes of the second event.
Outcomes of picking the marbles are: Red, Orange, Blue, Green.

Step 3
Display outcomes in a table.
The table headers are the events in the experiment.
Combine the outcome on the side of the table with the outcome at the top of the table.

		Marble			
		Red (R)	Orange (O)	Blue (B)	Green (G)
Coin	Heads (H)	HR	HO	HB	HG
	Tails (T)	TR	TO	TB	TG

The sample space is
{HR, TR, HO, TO, HB, TB, HG, TG}.

5. **Step 1**
Identify the outcomes of the first event.
Outcomes of tossing the coin are: Heads, Tails.

Step 2
Identify the outcomes of the second event.
Outcomes of tossing the coin are: Heads, Tails.

Step 3
Display outcomes in a tree diagram.
Start with the first event (toss) and list the outcomes (H, T). Draw a branch from each of these outcomes to each of the outcomes (H,T) of the second event.

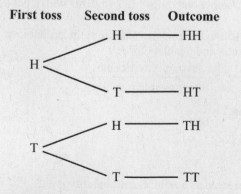

First toss	Second toss	Outcome
H	H	HH
	T	HT
T	H	TH
	T	TT

The sample space is {HH, HT, TH, TT}.

---

7. Step 1
Identify the outcomes of the first event.
Outcomes of spinning the spinner are: Red, Blue, Green, Black, Yellow, Pink.

Step 2
Identify the outcomes of the second event.
Outcomes of tossing the coin are: Heads, Tails.

Step 3
Display outcomes in a tree diagram.
Start with the first event (spinner) and list the outcomes (Red, Blue, Green, Black, Yellow, Pink). Draw a branch from each of these outcomes to each of the outcomes (H,T) of the second event.

Colour	Coin	Outcome

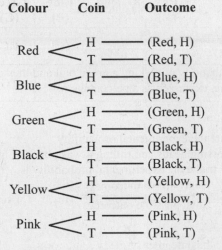

By counting all the possible outcomes, the number of outcomes in the sample space is 12.

9. C
There is no relation between the appearance of a certain number on one regular number cube and the occurrence of a similar event on the other regular number cube. Each is an independent event.

Lesson 3—*Theoretical Probability vs. Experimental Probability*

YOUR TURN
ANSWERS AND SOLUTIONS

1. Step 1
Determine the sample space using a table or tree diagram.

		Number Cube					
		1	**2**	**3**	**4**	**5**	**6**
Coin	**H**	H1	H2	H3	H4	H5	H6
	T	T1	T2	T3	T4	T5	T6

Step 2
Calculate the probability.
There are 12 possible outcomes and 3 favourable outcomes: H1, H3, H5.

$$P = \frac{\text{favourable outcomes}}{\text{total possible outcomes}}$$

$$P(\text{prime, H}) = \frac{3}{12}$$
$$= \frac{1}{4}$$

The probability of rolling a prime number and tossing heads is $\frac{1}{4}$.

2. Step 1
Calculate the theoretical probability.
There are 24 possible outcomes and 2 favourable outcomes.

$$P = \frac{\text{favourable outcomes}}{\text{total possible outcomes}}$$

$$P(\text{Y1, Y3}) = \frac{2}{24}$$
$$= \frac{1}{12}$$
$$= 8\%$$

Step 2
Calculate the experimental probability.
There are 12 possible outcomes and 2 favourable outcomes.

$$P = \frac{\text{favourable outcomes}}{\text{total possible outcomes}}$$

$$P(\text{odd, Y}) = \frac{2}{12}$$
$$= \frac{1}{6}$$
$$\doteq 17\%$$

The experimental probability of rolling an odd number and spinning yellow is much higher than its theoretical probability.

PRACTICE EXERCISES
ANSWERS AND SOLUTIONS

1. **C**
   At first, there may be a large difference between the experimental and theoretical probability; however, the more the experiment is performed, the closer the experimental probability will get to the theoretical probability.

3. The probability of tossing heads on two separate coins is based on the frequencies obtained in an experiment.
   Therefore, it is an example of experimental probability.

5. There are two outcomes when playing a game. Either you will win or you will lose. Therefore, the probability of winning a game + probability of losing a game = 1.

   If the probability of winning a game is $\frac{6}{10}$, then the probability of losing the game can be calculated as follows:
   $$P(\text{winning}) + P(\text{losing}) = 1$$
   $$\frac{6}{10} + P(\text{losing}) = 1$$
   $$\frac{6}{10} - \frac{6}{10} + P(\text{losing}) = 1 - \frac{6}{10}$$
   $$P(\text{losing}) = \frac{4}{10}$$

   The probability of losing the game is $\frac{4}{10}$.

7. **Step 1**
   Determine the sample space using a table or tree diagram.

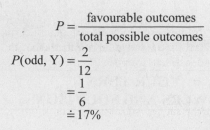

		First Pick				
		Black	Black	Pink	Red	Green
Second Pick	Black	BB	BB	PB	RB	GB
	Black	BB	BB	PB	RB	GB
	Pink	BP	BP	PP	RP	GP
	Red	BR	BR	PR	RR	GR
	Green	BG	BG	PG	RG	GG

Step 2
Calculate the probability.
There are 25 possible outcomes and 1 favourable outcome.

$$P = \frac{\text{favourable outcomes}}{\text{total possible outcomes}}$$

$$P(\text{G, P}) = \frac{1}{25}$$
$$= 4\%$$

The probability of picking a green ball and then a pink one, expressed as a percentage is 4%.

9. **Step 1**
Calculate the experimental probability.
Since tossing heads and rolling 4 was obtained in 3 of the 5 trials, the experimental probability is

$$P = \frac{\text{favourable outcomes}}{\text{total possible outcomes}}$$

$$P(\text{H},4) = \frac{3}{5}$$

Step 2
Calculate the theoretical probability.
There are 8 possible outcomes for this experiment: (H, 1), (H, 2), (H, 3), (H, 4), (T, 1), (T, 2), (T, 3), and (T, 4). Of these outcomes, only (H, 4) is favourable.

$$P = \frac{\text{favourable outcomes}}{\text{total possible outcomes}}$$

$$P(\text{H},4) = \frac{1}{8}$$

Step 3
Calculate the difference between experimental and theoretical probability.
$$\frac{3}{5} - \frac{1}{8} = \frac{24}{40} - \frac{5}{40}$$
$$= \frac{19}{40}$$

The difference between the experimental and theoretical probability expressed as a ratio is 19:40.

Practice Test

ANSWERS AND SOLUTIONS

1. **Step 1**
Determine the sample space using a table or tree diagram.

		First Spin									
		1	**2**	**3**	**4**	**5**	**6**	**7**	**8**	**9**	**10**
Second Spin	**1**	1, 1	2, 1	3, 1	4, 1	5, 1	6, 1	7, 1	8, 1	9, 1	10, 1
	2	1, 2	2, 2	3, 2	4, 2	5, 2	6, 2	7, 2	8, 2	9, 2	10, 2
	3	1, 3	2, 3	3, 3	4, 3	5, 3	6, 3	7, 3	8, 3	9, 3	10, 3
	4	1, 4	2, 4	3, 4	4, 4	5, 4	6, 4	7, 4	8, 4	9, 4	10, 4
	5	1, 5	2, 5	3, 5	4, 5	5, 5	6, 5	7, 5	8, 5	9, 5	10, 5
	6	1, 6	2, 6	3, 6	4, 6	5, 6	6, 6	7, 6	8, 6	9, 6	10, 6
	7	1, 7	2, 7	3, 7	4, 7	5, 7	6, 7	7, 7	8, 7	9, 7	10, 7
	8	1, 8	2, 8	3, 8	4, 8	5, 8	6, 8	7, 8	8, 8	9, 8	10, 8
	9	1, 9	2, 9	3, 9	4, 9	5, 9	6, 9	7, 9	8, 9	9, 9	10, 9
	10	1, 10	2, 10	3, 10	4, 10	5, 10	6, 10	7, 10	8, 10	9, 10	10, 10

Step 2
Calculate the probability.
There are 100 possible outcomes and 20 favourable outcomes.

$$P = \frac{\text{favourable outcomes}}{\text{total possible outcomes}}$$

$$P(\text{prime,even}) = \frac{20}{100}$$
$$= \frac{1}{5}$$

The probability of landing on a prime number and then an even number is $\frac{1}{5}$.

3. **A**
The probability of an event happening is between 0 and 1. The closer the probability is to 1, the more likely it is to happen. If probability is equal to 1, then the event is certain to happen. Since the probability that it will rain on Monday is 1, it will definitely rain on Monday.

5. **D**
The result from tossing the coin has no effect on the result of rolling the regular number cube, so they are independent events.

7. **Step 1**
Determine the sample space using a table or tree diagram.

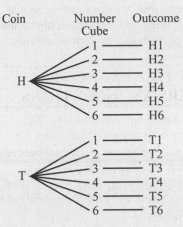

Step 2
Calculate the probability.
There are 12 possible outcomes and 1 favourable outcome.

$$P = \frac{\text{favourable outcomes}}{\text{total possible outcomes}}$$

$$P(\text{T4}) = \frac{1}{12}$$

The probability of Jack winning on his turn is $\frac{1}{12}$.

9. **Step 1**
Determine the sample space using a table or tree diagram.

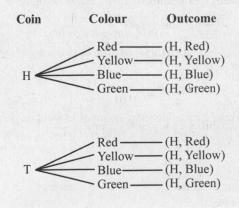

Step 2
Calculate the probability.
There are 8 possible outcomes and 1 favourable outcome.

$$P = \frac{\text{favourable outcome}}{\text{total possible outcomes}}$$

$$P(\text{H, green}) = \frac{1}{8}$$
$$= 12.5\%$$

The probability of tossing heads and spinning green is 12.5%.

11. Step 1
Determine the sample space using a table or tree diagram. Let A represent the angelfish, W represent the wrasses, and C represent the clownfish.

				First Fish				
		A	A	A	W	W	C	C	C
Second Fish	A	A A	A A	A A	W A	W A	C A	C A	C A
	A	A A	A A	A A	W A	W A	C A	C A	C A
	A	A A	A A	A A	W A	W A	C A	C A	C A
	W	A W	A W	A W	W W	W W	C W	C W	C W
	W	A W	A W	A W	W W	W W	C W	C W	C W
	C	A C	A C	A C	W C	W C	CC	CC	CC
	C	A C	A C	A C	W C	W C	CC	CC	CC
	C	A C	A C	A C	W C	W C	CC	CC	CC

Step 2
Calculate the probability.
There are 64 possible outcomes and 9 favourable outcomes.

$$P = \frac{\text{favourable outcomes}}{\text{total possible outcomes}}$$

$$P(\text{angel, clown}) = \frac{9}{64}$$

The probability of picking an angelfish and then a clown fish, expressed as a ratio is 9:64.

13. Total possible outcomes: 6 marbles
Favourable outcomes: 2 marbles

Substitute the known values into the probability formula and evaluate for P.

$$P = \frac{\text{favourable outcomes}}{\text{toal possible outcomes}}$$

$$P(\text{yellow}) = \frac{2}{6}$$
$$= \frac{1}{3}$$

Expressed as a fraction, the probability is $\frac{1}{3}$.

Expressed as a ratio, the probability is 1:3.
Expressed as a percentage, the probability is 33%.

15. Step 1
Determine the sample space using a table or tree diagram.

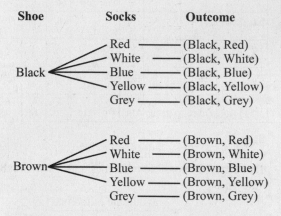

Step 2
Calculate the probability.
There are 10 possible outcomes, and the number of favourable outcomes is 3.

$$P = \frac{\text{favourable outcomes}}{\text{total possible outcomes}}$$

$$P(\text{BG, BW, BR}) = \frac{3}{10}$$

The probability that the man wears brown shoes with either grey, white, or red socks is $\frac{3}{10}$.

DATA ANALYSIS

Lesson 1—Measures of Central Tendency

YOUR TURN
ANSWERS AND SOLUTIONS

1. **Step 1**
   Find the sum of the values.
   $6+3+8+12+6+2+5 = 42$

   Step 2
   Divide the total sum by the number of values.
   There are seven values, so divide the sum by 7.
   $42 \div 7 = 6$

   The mean of the data set is 6.

2. **Step 1**
   Place the values in ascending order.
   12, 15, 16, 20, 24, 26

   Step 2
   Determine the middle numbers.
   12, 15, $\boxed{16, 20}$, 24, 26

   There are an even number of values. Calculate the average of the two middle numbers.
   $16 + 20 = 36$
   $36 \div 2 = 18$

   The median is 18.

3. **Step 1**
   Place the numbers in ascending order.
   3, 3, 4, 4, 5, 6, 7, 8

   Step 2
   Determine the most common numbers.
   The 3 and 4 occur more than the other numbers.

   Therefore, the modes are 3 and 4.

4. **Step 1**
   Place the numbers in ascending order.
   18, 21, 23, 24, 25, 31, 31, 33, 35, 43, 44, 45

   Step 2
   Subtract the lowest value from the greatest value.
   The smallest value is the lower extreme, and the largest value is the upper extreme.

18, 21, 23, 24, 25, 31, 31, 33, 35, 43, 44, 45
↑   ↑
Lower extreme   Upper extreme

The range is the difference between the upper and lower extremes.
range = upper extreme − lower extreme
$= 45 - 18$
$= 27$

The upper extreme is 45, the lower extreme is 18, and the range is 27.

PRACTICE EXERCISES
ANSWERS AND SOLUTIONS

1. $\dfrac{6+3+8+12+7+5+2+5}{8} = 6$

3. $\dfrac{6+13+40+23+35+27+31}{7} = 25$

5. **Step 1**
   Place the values in ascending order.
   114, 135, 187, 196, 249

   Step 2
   Determine the middle number.
   Since there are an odd number of values, the median is the middle value.
   114, 135, $\boxed{187}$, 196, 249

   The median is 187.

7. Place the values in ascending order.
   24, 25, 25, 31, 31, 32, 54, 65

   The modes are 25 and 31.
   The range is $65 - 24 = 41$.

9. Place the values in ascending order.
   237, 252, 256, 323, 342, 345

   There is no mode.
   The range is $345 - 237 = 108$.

Lesson 2—Using Measures of Central Tendency and the Effects of Outliers

YOUR TURN
ANSWERS AND SOLUTIONS

1. **Step 1**
    Place the values in ascending order.
    7, 8, 9, 9, 10, 10, 10, 12, 12, 23

    Step 2
    Determine the outlier.
    The outlier in this set of data is 23 since the difference between it and 12 is the greatest.

    Step 3
    Calculate the mean, median, and mode with the outlier.

    $$7+8+9+9+10+10+10+12+12+23 = 110$$
    $$110 \div 10 = 11$$
    The mean is 11.

    The value 10 occurs three times, so the mode is 10.

    There is an even number of values.
    7, 8, 9, 9, $\boxed{10, 10}$, 10, 12, 12, 23
    $10 + 10 = 20$
    $20 \div 2 = 10$
    The average of the two middle values is 10, so the median is 10.

    Step 4
    Calculate the mean, median, and mode without the outlier.

    $$7+8+9+9+10+10+10+12+12 = 87$$
    $$87 \div 9 = 9.\overline{6}$$
    The mean changes from 11 to $9.\overline{6}$.

    There are an odd number of values.
    7, 8, 9, 9, $\boxed{10}$, 10, 10, 12, 12
    The median is still 10.

    7, 8, 9, 9, 10, 10, 10, 12, 12
    The value 10 occurs three times, so the mode is still 10.

    Step 5
    Compare the results of the calculations.
    After removing the outlier, the mode and the median are still 10, and the mean changes from 11 to $9.\overline{6}$.

    Removing the outlier most significantly affected the mean.

2. **Step 1**
    Assess the data.

    Look for outliers and type of data.
    The data has outliers, so the data is not categorical.

    Step 2
    Choose the best measure of tendency.

    Median is the best measure of tendency when the middle most value is required with an outlier in the data.
    5%, 75%, 75%, 76%, $\boxed{77\%, 79\%}$, 81%, 82%, 83%, 84%
    $$\frac{77+79}{2} = 78$$

    The average was approximately 78%.

    Median is the best representation of the class's performance. One unusually low test score does not influence the middle values.

3. **Step 1**
    Assess the data.
    Look for outliers and type of data.
    The data has no outliers.
    Since the shakes can be grouped into flavours, the data is categorical.

    Step 2
    Choose the best measure of central tendency.
    Mode is the best measure of central tendency for categorical data.
    Therefore, mode is the best representation of the flavours that run out most often because the data can be categorized.

    Step 3
    Determine which flavours occur most frequently.
    Banana occurs four times, grape occurs twice, cherry occurs five times, and the rest of the flavours occur once.

    Cherry is the flavour that runs out most often in her store.

PRACTICE EXERCISES
ANSWERS AND SOLUTIONS

1. **Step 1**
Assess the data.

Place the values in ascending order.
149, 158, 169, 175, 187, 196, 225

Look for outliers and type of data.
There are no major outliers, and the data is not categorical.

Therefore, mean will be the best measure of central tendency for Shane's bowling average.

Step 2
Calculate the mean:
$$\frac{149+158+169+175+187+196+225}{7} \doteq 179.8571$$

Step 3
Round the value to the nearest integer.
$179.8571 \doteq 180$

Shane's bowling average for the last seven games is 180.

The mean is the best measure of central tendency to use.

3. **Step 1**
Place the values in ascending order.
55%, 57%, 60%, 62%, 64%, 65%, 78%

Step 2
Choose the best measure of tendency.
The best measure of central tendency is the mean because Micah wants to find her average test score.

Determine the mean.
$55+57+60+62+64+65+78 = 441$
$441 \div 7 = 63$

Micah's test scores average to 63%.

Mean is the best measure of central tendency in this case because the average of the data is needed.

5. **Step 1**
Place the values in order from least to greatest, and assess the data set for outliers.
2, 8, 18, 22, 24, 24, 26, 26, 30

The outlier in this set of data is 2 because it is the value that is the most numerically distant from the other values.

Step 2
Calculate the mean, median, and mode with the outlier.

The mean is the average of all the values. It is determined by dividing the sum of all the values by the total number of values.
$$\frac{2+8+18+22+24+24+26+26+30}{9} = \frac{180}{9}$$
$$= 20$$

There are an odd number of values. The median is the value in the middle of the data set.
2, 8, 18, 22, $\boxed{24}$, 24, 26, 26, 30
The median of this data set is 24.

The mode is the value that occurs most often in a data set.

The modes are 24 and 26 because they occur twice and the rest of the numbers occur once each.

Step 3
Calculate the mean, median, and mode without the outlier.
$$\frac{8+18+22+24+24+26+26+30}{8} = \frac{178}{8}$$
$$= 22.25$$

There is an even number of values.
8, 18, 22, $\boxed{24, 24}$, 26, 26, 30
$$\frac{24+24}{2} = \frac{48}{2}$$
$$= 24$$

The modes are 24 and 26 because they occur twice and the rest of the numbers occur once.

Step 4
Compare the results of the calculations.

After removing the outlier, the mean changes to 22.25, the median is still 24, and the modes are still 24 and 26.

Removing the outlier affected only the mean.

7. **Step 1**
Arrange the values in ascending order.
4, 14, 14, 16, 19, 20, 24, 25, 25, 30, 35

Step 2
Assess the data set for outliers.

The outlier in the data set is 4, since it is the value that is the farthest away from any other value.

9. **C**

Step 1
Arrange the values in ascending order, and assess the data set for outliers.
4, 14, 14, 16, 19, 20, 24, 25, 25, 30, 35

The outlier in this set of data is 4 since the distance between it and the next number (14) is 10.

Step 2
Determine which measure of central tendency the outlier affects the most.
Calculate the mean, median, and mode with and without the outliers.

Mean with outliers:
$$4 + 14 + 14 + 16 + 19 + 20 + 24$$
$$+ 25 + 25 + 30 + 35 = 226$$
$$226 \div 11 \doteq 20.\overline{54}$$

Mean without outliers:
$$14 + 14 + 16 + 19 + 20 + 24 + 25 + 25 + 30 + 35 = 222$$
$$222 \div 10 \doteq 22.2$$

Median with outliers:
There are an odd number of values. The middle value is the median.
4, 14, 14, 16, 19, $\boxed{20}$, 24, 25, 25, 30, 35

Median without outliers:

There is an even number of values. The average of the middle two values is the median.
14, 14, 16, 19, $\boxed{20, 24}$, 25, 25, 30, 35
$$20 + 24 = 44$$
$$44 \div 2 = 22$$

The modes are 14 and 25 (with or without the outliers). They both occur two times.

Step 3
Compare the results.
The measures of central tendency for this set of data with the outlier and then without the outlier are displayed in the table.

Central Tendency Measures	With Outlier	Without Outlier
Mode	14 and 25	14 and 25
Median	20	22
Mean	20.55	22.2

The two measures of central tendency that are influenced when the outlier is removed are the mean and the median.

Practice Test

ANSWERS AND SOLUTIONS

1. **Step 1**
Place the given values in ascending order.
16, 21, 23, 26, 54

Step 2
Determine the mean.
The mean is the average of all the values.
Calculate by dividing the sum of all the values by the total number of values.
$$16 + 21 + 23 + 26 + 54 = 140$$
$$140 \div 5 = 28$$

The mean is 28.

3. **Step 1**
Place the values in ascending order.
45, 63, 73, 76, 78, 81, 87, 91

Step 2
Determine the middle numbers.
There are an even number of values.
45, 63, 73, $\boxed{76, 78}$, 81, 87, 91
Calculate the average of the two middle numbers.
$$76 + 78 = 154$$
$$154 \div 2 = 77$$

The median is 77.

5. **Step 1**
Place the values in ascending order.
237, 252, 256, 323, 342, 345

Step 2
Determine which numbers occur most frequently.
Each number occurs once in the data set.

There is no mode, since no number occurs more than any of the others.

7. Step 1
Place the values in ascending order.
7, 8, 8, 12, 12, 15, 19, 21

Step 2
Determine the mean, median, and mode.

The mean is the average of the data.
$$\frac{7+8+8+12+12+15+19+21}{8} = \frac{102}{8}$$
$$= 12.75$$

Round the value to the nearest integer.
$12.75 \doteq 13$

The mean is 13.

The modes are 8 and 12. Determine which numbers occur most frequently. 8 and 12 both occur twice while the other numbers each occur only once.

Determine the middle values.
Since there are an even number of values, the median is the average of the middle values.
7, 8, 8, $\boxed{12, 12}$, 15, 19, 21
$$\frac{12+12}{2} = 12$$
The median is 12.

9. Step 1
Place numbers in ascending order: 23, 24, 34, 45, 52, 62, 63, 66.

Step 2
Subtract the lowest value from the greatest value. The smaller value is the lower extreme, the largest value is the upper extreme.

23, 24, 34, 45, 52, 62, 63, 66
↑   ↑

Lower extreme   Upper extreme

The range is the difference between the upper and lower extremes.

Range = upper extreme – lower extreme
= 66 – 23
= 43

The lower extreme is 23, the upper extreme is 66 and the range is 43.

11. The lower extreme is 24, and the upper extreme is 55.
55 – 24 = 31

The range is 31.

13. Step 1
Determine the outlier.
Place the values in order from least to greatest.
3.3, 3.3, 3.5, 3.6, 3.7, 4.1, 4.2, 6.7

The outlier in this set of data is 6.7, because 6.7 is the value that is the most numerically distant from the other values.

Step 2
Calculate the mean, median, and mode with the outlier.

Mean: The mean is the average of all the values. It is determined by dividing the sum of all the values by the total number of values.

$$\frac{3.3+3.3+3.5+3.6+3.7+4.1+4.2+6.7}{8} = \frac{32.4}{8}$$
$$= 4.1$$

Median: The median is the value in the middle of the data set and in this case, there is an even number of values.
3.3, 3.3, 3.5, <u>3.6</u>, <u>3.7</u>, 4.1, 4.2, 6.7

$$\frac{3.6+3.7}{2} = \frac{7.3}{2}$$
$$= 3.7$$

Mode: The mode is the value that occurs most often in a data set.

The mode is 3.3 because it occurs twice and the rest of the numbers occur once.

Step 3
Calculate the mean, median, and mode without the outlier.

Mean:
$$\frac{3.3+3.3+3.5+3.6+3.7+4.1+4.2}{7} = \frac{25.7}{7}$$
$$= 3.7$$

Median: There are an odd number of values.
3.3, 3.3, 3.5, <u>3.6</u>, 3.7, 4.1, 4.2

Therefore, the median is 3.6.
The mode is 3.3 because it occurs twice and the rest of the numbers occur once each.

Step 4
Compare the results of the calculations.
After removing the outlier, the mean changed to 3.7, the median changed to 3.6, and the mode remained 3.3. Removing the outlier affected the mean and the median.

Credits

Every effort has been made to provide proper acknowledgement of the original source and to comply with copyright law. However, some attempts to establish original copyright ownership may have been unsuccessful. If copyright ownership can be identified, please notify Castle Rock Research Corp so that appropriate corrective action can be taken.

Some images in this document are from www.clipart.com, copyright (c) 2009 Jupiterimages Corporation.

ORDERING INFORMATION

SCHOOL ORDERS

Please contact the Learning Resource Centre (LRC) for school discount and order information.

THE KEY **Study Guides** are specifically designed to assist students in preparing for unit tests, final exams, and provincial examinations.

THE KEY **Study Guides** – $29.95 each plus G.S.T.

SENIOR HIGH		JUNIOR HIGH	ELEMENTARY
Biology 30	Biology 20	English Language Arts 9	English Language Arts 6
Chemistry 30	Chemistry 20	Math 9	Math 6
English 30-1	English 20-1	Science 9	Science 6
English 30-2	Mathematics 20-1	Social Studies 9	Social Studies 6
Applied Math 30	Physics 20	Math 8	Math 4
Pure Math 30	Social Studies 20-1		
Physics 30	English 10-1	Math 7	English Language Arts 3
Social Studies 30-1	Math 10 Combined		Math 3
Social Studies 30-2	Science 10		
	Social Studies 10-1		

Student Notes and Problems (SNAP) Workbooks contain complete explanations of curriculum concepts, examples, and exercise questions.

SNAP Workbooks – $29.95 each plus G.S.T.

SENIOR HIGH		JUNIOR HIGH	ELEMENTARY
Biology 30	Biology 20	Math 9	Math 6
Chemistry 30	Chemistry 20	Science 9	Math 5
Applied Math 30	Mathematics 20-1	Math 8	
Pure Math 30	Physics 20	Science 8	Math 4
Math 31	Math 10 Combined	Math 7	Math 3
Physics 30	Science 10	Science 7	

Visit our website for a tour of resource content and features or order resources online at
www.castlerockresearch.com

#2340, 10180 – 101 Street
Edmonton, AB Canada T5J 3S4
e-mail: learn@castlerockresearch.com

Phone: 780.448.9619
Toll-free: 1.800.840.6224
Fax: 780.426.3917

CASTLE ROCK
RESEARCH CORP

ORDER FORM

THE KEY	QUANTITY
Biology 30	
Chemistry 30	
English 30-1	
English 30-2	
Applied Math 30	
Pure Math 30	
Physics 30	
Social Studies 30-1	
Social Studies 30-2	
Biology 20	
Chemistry 20	
English 20-1	
Mathematics 20-1	
Physics 20	
Social Studies 20-1	
English 10-1	
Math 10 Combined	
Science 10	
Social Studies 10-1	
English Language Arts 9	
Math 9	
Science 9	
Social Studies 9	
Math 8	
Math 7	
English Language Arts 6	
Math 6	
Science 6	
Social Studies 6	
Math 4	
English Language Arts 3	
Math 3	

Student Notes and Problems Workbooks	QUANTITY	
	SNAP Workbooks	Solution Manuals
Math 31		
Biology 30		
Chemistry 30		
Applied Math 30		
Pure Math 30		
Physics 30		
Biology 20		
Chemistry 20		
Mathematics 20-1		
Physics 20		
Math 10 Combined		
Science 10		
Math 9		
Science 9		
Math 8		
Science 8		
Math 7		
Science 7		
Math 6		
Math 5		
Math 4		
Math 3		

TOTALS
KEYS
SNAP WORKBOOKS
SOLUTION MANUALS
SOLUTION MANUALS

Learning Resources Centre

Castle Rock Research is pleased to announce an exclusive distribution arrangement with the Learning Resources Centre (LRC). Under this agreement, schools can now place all their orders with LRC for order fulfillment. As well, these resources are eligible for applying the Learning Resource Credit Allocation (LRCA), which gives schools a 25% discount off LRC's selling price. Call LRC for details.

Orders may be placed with LRC by
Telephone: 780.427.2767
Fax: 780.422.9750
Internet: www.lrc.education.gov.ab.ca
Or mail: 12360 – 142 Street NW
Edmonton, AB T5L 4X9

Learning Resources Centre

PAYMENT AND SHIPPING INFORMATION

Name: _____
School Telephone: _____
SHIP TO
School: _____
Address: _____
City: _____ Postal Code: _____

PAYMENT
☐ by credit card
VISA/MC Number: _____
Expiry Date: _____
Name on card: _____
☐ enclosed cheque
☐ invoice school   P.O. number: _____

#2340, 10180 – 101 Street, Edmonton, AB T5J 3S4   **Phone:** 780.448.9619 Fax: 780.426.3917
Email: learn@castlerockresearch.com   **Toll-free:** 1.800.840.6224
www.castlerockresearch.com

CASTLE ROCK
RESEARCH CORP